NATIONAL CURRICULUM
MATHEMA

8B

L. BOSTOCK, B.Sc.

S. CHANDLER, B.Sc.

A. SHEPHERD, B.Sc.

E. SMITH, M.Sc.

First published in 1996 by:
Stanley Thornes (Publishers) Ltd

Reprinted in 2001 by:
Nelson Thornes Ltd
Delta Place
27 Bath Road
CHELTENHAM
GL53 7TH
United Kingdom

03 04 05 06/ 10 9 8

A catalogue record of this book is available from the British Library.

ISBN 0 7487 2441 9

Artwork by Peters and Zabransky, Mark Dunn, Linda Jeffrey.

Typeset by Tech-Set, Gateshead, Tyne & Wear.
Printed and bound in China by Midas Printing International Ltd.

Acknowledgements
Front cover image produced using material kindly supplied by I LOVE LOVE CO, makers of The Happy Cube © Laureyssens/Creative City Ltd 1986/91.
Distributed in UK by: RIGHTRAC, 119 Sandycombe Road, Richmond Surrey TW9 2ER Tel. 0181 940 3322.
The publishers are grateful to the following for granting permission to reproduce copyright material:
Argos: p. 200
BT: p. 373
Staples – The Office Superstore: p. 201
SWEB: p. 372
The Observer/MediaLab: p. 309
The Office for National Statistics: pp. 308, 310

CONTENTS

INTRODUCTION

To the pupil

This book continues to help you to learn, enjoy and progress through
Mathematics in the National Curriculum. As well as a clear and concise
text the book offers a wide range of practical and investigational work
that is relevant to the mathematics you are learning.

Everyone needs success and satisfaction in getting things right. With this
in mind we have divided many of the exercises into three types.

The first type, identified by plain numbers, e.g. **15**, helps you to see if
you understand the work. These questions are considered necessary for
every chapter.

The second type, identified by an underline, e.g. **15**, are extra, but not
harder, questions for quicker workers, for extra practice or for later
revision.

The third type, identified by a coloured square, e.g. **15** , are for those of
you who like a greater challenge.

Most chapters have a 'mixed exercise' after the main work of the chapter
has been completed. This will help you to revise what you have done,
either when you have finished the chapter or at a later date. All chapters
end with some mathematical puzzles, practical and/or investigational
work. For this work you are encouraged to share your ideas with others,
to use any mathematics you are familiar with, and to try to solve each
problem in different ways, appreciating the advantages and disadvantages
of each method.

The book starts with a summary of the main results from Book 7B. After
every five chapters you will find further summaries. These list the most
important points that have been studied in the previous chapters and
conclude with revision exercises that test the work you have studied up
to that point.

At this stage you will find that you use a calculator more frequently but it
is still unwise to rely on a calculator for work that you should do in your
head. Remember, whether you use a calculator or do the working
yourself, always estimate your answer and always ask yourself the
question, 'Is my answer a sensible one?'

Mathematics is an exciting and enjoyable subject when you understand what is going on. Remember, if you don't understand something, ask someone who can explain it to you. If you still don't understand, ask again. Good luck with your studies.

To the teacher
This is the second book of the STP National Curriculum Mathematics series. It is based on the ST(P) Mathematics series but has been extensively rewritten and is now firmly based on the Programme of Study for Key Stages 3 and 4.

The B series of books aims to prepare pupils for about Level 6 at Key Stage 3 and for the intermediate tier at GCSE.

SUMMARY 1

**WHOLE
NUMBERS**

Multiplication by 10, 100, 1000

To multiply a number by 10, or 100 or 1000, move the figures one, two or three places to the left and fill in the gaps with zeros,

e.g. $25 \times 100 = 2500$

Division

Division is the opposite of multiplication,

e.g. $6 \div 3 = 2$ because $6 = 3 \times 2$

Division by 10, 100, 1000

To divide a number by 10, or 100 or 1000, move the figures one, two or three places to the right,

e.g. $25\,000 \div 10 = 2500$

Rounding whole numbers

To round a number to the nearest 10, look at the units. If there are 5 or more units, round up, i.e. add one to the number of tens. If there are 4 units or less, round down, i.e. leave the number of tens untouched.

To round a number to the nearest hundred, look at the tens. To round a number to the nearest 1000, look at the hundreds. Then use the rule above.

e.g. $13|7 = 140$ to the nearest 10,

         $1|37 = 100$ to the nearest 100

and $2|957 = 3000$ to the nearest 1000.

FRACTIONS

A fraction describes the size of part of a quantity.
A fraction is written in the form $\frac{2}{3}$.
The *denominator* (the bottom number) tells us the number of equal-sized parts that the quantity is divided into.
The *numerator* (the top number) tells us the number of the equal-sized parts that are being considered.

For example, $\frac{2}{3}$ of this square is shaded.

1

Equivalent fractions
Two fractions that describe the same sized part of a quantity are called equivalent fractions.

The shaded part of this square can be described as $\frac{4}{6}$ of the square or as $\frac{2}{3}$ of the square.

We can find a fraction equivalent to a given fraction by multiplying the top and bottom by the same number,

e.g. $\qquad \dfrac{2}{3} = \dfrac{2 \times 2}{3 \times 2} = \dfrac{4}{6}$ and $\dfrac{2}{3} = \dfrac{2 \times 5}{3 \times 5} = \dfrac{10}{15}$

Simplifying fractions
A fraction can be simplified to an equivalent fraction with a smaller numerator and denominator by dividing the top and bottom by the same number,

e.g. $\qquad \dfrac{12}{18} = \dfrac{12 \div 6}{18 \div 6} = \dfrac{2}{3}$ This is sometimes called *cancelling*.

PERCENTAGES

A percentage of a quantity means the number of one hundredths of the quantity, e.g. 20% of an apple means 20 out of 100 equal-sized parts of the apple, i.e. $20\% = \frac{20}{100}$.

Changing percentages to fractions
Any percentage can be written as a fraction whose bottom number is 100. That fraction can often be simplified,

e.g. $\qquad 20\% = \dfrac{20}{100} = \dfrac{20 \div 20}{100 \div 20} = \dfrac{1}{5}$ and conversely $\dfrac{30}{100} = 30\%$.

DECIMALS

In decimal notation, numbers to the right of the decimal point represent tenths, hundredths, ...,

e.g. $\qquad 0.53 = \frac{5}{10} + \frac{3}{100}$

Changing decimals to fractions
A decimal with one figure after the decimal point can be written as a number of tenths and then simplified when possible,

e.g. $\qquad \dfrac{6}{10} = \dfrac{6 \div 2}{10 \div 2} = \dfrac{3}{5}$

A decimal with two figures after the point can be written as a number of hundredths and then simplified when possible,

e.g. $\qquad 0.35 = \dfrac{35}{100} = \dfrac{35 \div 5}{100 \div 5} = \dfrac{7}{20}$

Addition and subtraction of decimals

Decimals can be added or subtracted in the same way as whole numbers. We must remember to place the decimal points in line and, when necessary, to fill in any blank spaces with zeros,

e.g.   to add 12.5 and 7.95, we can write them as

$$\begin{array}{r} 12.50 \\ +\ \ 7.95 \\ \hline 20.45 \end{array}$$

Rounding decimals

To round a decimal to the nearest whole number, look at the tenths, i.e. the first number to the right of the decimal point. If it is 5 or more, round up. If it is 4 or less, round down,

e.g. $1.53 = 2$ to the nearest whole number.

To round a decimal to the nearest tenth, i.e. to one decimal place, look at the number of hundredths. Then use the rule above,

e.g. $1.53 = 1.5$ to the nearest tenth.

TYPES OF NUMBER

A *factor* of a number will divide into the number exactly,

e.g.   3 is a factor of 12 because $12 \div 3 = 4$ exactly.

A *multiple* of a number is the product of that number and any other whole number, e.g. 12 is a multiple of 3 because $3 \times 4 = 12$.

Even numbers divide exactly by 2, e.g. 6, 10, . . .
Odd numbers do not divide exactly by 2, e.g. 3, 7, . . .

A *prime number* has only two different factors, 1 and itself,

e.g. $7 = 7 \times 1$.

(The smallest prime number is 2; 1 is not a prime number because it does not have a factor other than one.)

A *square number* can be drawn as a square grid of dots, e.g. 9:
The smallest square number is 1.

When a quantity can go below a zero level, we can describe where it is by using *negative numbers*.
For example, $2\,°C$ below freezing point ($0\,°C$) is written $-2\,°C$ and is called 'minus' $2\,°C$ or 'negative' $2\,°C$.

UNITS

The *metric* units of length in common use are the *kilometre*, the *metre*, the *centimetre* and the *millimetre*, where

$$1\,km = 1000\,m, \quad 1\,m = 100\,cm, \quad 1\,cm = 10\,mm$$

The metric units of mass (these are the units we use for weighing) are the *tonne*, the *kilogram*, the *gram* and the *milligram*, where

$$1\,t = 1000\,kg, \quad 1\,kg = 1000\,g, \quad 1\,g = 1000\,mg$$

TIME

$$1\,day = 24\,hours, \quad 1\,hour = 60\,minutes,$$
$$1\,minute = 60\,seconds$$

The day starts at midnight.

There are two systems for giving the time of day.

In the a.m., p.m. system, the twelve hours from midnight to midday (noon) are a.m. times,

e.g. 9.15 a.m. mean 9 hours 15 minutes after midnight.

The twelve hours from noon to midnight are p.m. times,

so, 9.15 p.m. means 9 hours 15 minutes after midday.

For the 24-hour system, the time starts at midnight and carries on through 24 hours to the next midnight,

e.g. 13.15 hours means 13 hours 15 minutes after midnight.

So 13.15 hours is equivalent to 1.15 p.m.

COORDINATES

Coordinates give the position of a point on a grid. They are written as a pair of numbers, e.g. (2, 4).

The first number is called the
x-coordinate.
The second number is called the
y-coordinate.

The x-coordinate and/or the
y-coordinate of a point can be
negative.

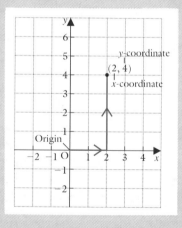

FORMULAS

A formula is an instruction for finding one quantity from other quantities. This instruction is a formula: 'The perimeter of a square is found by multiplying the length of a side by four.'

SHAPES

Perimeter

The perimeter of a shape is the total distance all round its edge.

Area

Area is measured in numbers of standard sized squares.

A square with side 1 cm long is called one square centimetre and written $1 \, cm^2$.

Other standard sized squares are the square millimetre, the square metre and the square kilometre.

Cubes and cuboids

A cube is a solid and all of its faces
are squares.

A cuboid is a rectangular block.

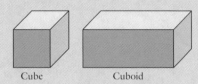

Cube   Cuboid

Volume

Volume is measured as a number of standard sized cubes.

A cube with edges 1 cm long has a volume of 1 cubic centimetre, written $1 \, cm^3$.

Capacity

The capacity of a container is the volume of liquid it could hold.

The main metric units of capacity are the litre (l) and the millilitre (ml), where

$$1 \text{ litre } = 1000 \, ml \quad \text{and} \quad 1 \text{ litre } = 1000 \, cm^3$$

$$(\text{Note:} \quad 1 \, ml = 1 \, cm^3)$$

Line symmetry

A shape has a line of symmetry if, when it is folded along that line, one half of the shape fits exactly over the other half,

e.g. this shape has one line of symmetry.

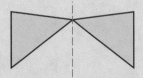

Rotational symmetry

A shape has rotational symmetry if, when it is turned about a centre point to a new position, it looks the same.

e.g. this shape has rotational symmetry.

STATISTICS

Mode

The mode of a list of values is the value that occurs most often, e.g. this list of lengths: 12 cm, 10 cm, 12 cm, 9 cm, 12 cm, 10 cm, has a mode of 12 cm.

Sometimes there is no mode, sometimes there is more than one mode.

Median

The median of a list of values is the middle value when they have been arranged in order of size.

When there are two middle values, the median is half their sum, e.g. the list of lengths given above arranged in order is

9 cm, 10 cm, 10 cm, 12 cm, 12 cm, 12 cm.

There are two middle values, 10 cm and 12 cm.

In this case the median is $(10 + 12) \div 2$ cm, i.e. 11 cm.

PROBABILITY

Probability measures the chance that an event in the future may happen. Probability ranges from impossible, through degrees of likelihood to certainty.

When we try to quantify probability, we need to know all the possibilities for what could happen. This is called the list of all *possible outcomes*.

REVISION EXERCISE 1.1

(Whole numbers)

Do not use a calculator for this exercise.

1 a Write in figures
   i seven hundred and fifty-nine
   ii three thousand four hundred and thirty-two
   iii five thousand four hundred and seven
   iv eight thousand and eleven.

b Write in words **i** 729   **ii** 5982   **iii** 4089   **iv** 7305

c What does the figure 8 mean in each of the following numbers?
   i 48   **ii** 867   **iii** 3829   **iv** 8223

d Put the numbers 583, 538, 584, 854, 458, 845 in order of size with the smallest first.

2 Find

a $47 + 53$	**d** $273 + 827$	**g** $426 + 421$
b $77 + 82$	**e** $421 + 943$	**h** $642 + 883$
c $48 + 85$	**f** $513 + 748$	**i** $693 + 258$

3 Find

    a $59 - 37$ **d** $834 - 312$ **g** $333 - 278$

    b $82 - 49$ **e** $747 - 553$ **h** $478 - 249$

    c $83 - 19$ **f** $638 - 145$ **i** $846 - 378$

4 Find

    a $234 + 678 + 332$ **d** $263 + 713 + 429$

    b $745 - 324 - 145$ **e** $612 - 385$

    c $734 - 592 + 215$ **f** $5210 - 3763 + 2140$

5 Find

    a 45×10 **i** 55×7 **r** $432 \div 6$

    b 45×100 **j** 64×500 **s** $420 \div 70$

    c 45×1000 **k** 38×700 **t** $628 \div 4$

    d $4 \times 5 \times 3$ **l** 36×300 **u** $368 \div 8$

    e $2 \times 3 \times 7$ **m** $3200 \div 10$ **v** $1434 \div 3$

    f $3 \times 5 \times 5$ **n** $65\,000 \div 1000$ **w** $702 \div 9$

    g 72×8 **p** $450\,000 \div 100$ **x** $931 \div 7$

    h 49×6 **q** $435 \div 5$ **y** $568 \div 4$

6 Copy these questions and fill in the missing digits.

    a
```
   6 2 □
  +□ 3 6
  ───────
   8 □ 0
```
    b
```
   6 7 □
  −□ 9 8
  ───────
   2 □ 6
```

    c $\square \times 8 = 56$ **d** $6 \times \square = 54$

    e
```
    1 □ 7
  ×     5
  ───────
    6 3 5
```
    f
```
    3 □ 4
  ×     8
  ───────
  □ 4 3 2
```

7 a Copy and replace each box with the symbol $<$, $>$ or $=$.

    i $9 \div 4 \,\square\, 3$ **ii** $18 \div 6 \,\square\, 3$ **iii** $70 \div 9 \,\square\, 8$ **iv** $36 \div 7 \,\square\, 5$

    b Calculate, giving the remainder if there is one

      i $56 \div 7$ **v** $347 \div 8$ **ix** $285 \div 6$

      ii $44 \div 8$ **vi** $5224 \div 7$ **x** $735 \div 4$

      iii $826 \div 4$ **vii** $2428 \div 7$ **xi** $4286 \div 3$

      iv $675 \div 5$ **viii** $256 \div 5$ **xii** $8462 \div 6$

8 a Copy and place either < or > between each pair of temperatures.

   i −5 °C 7 °C   **iii** −7 °C −8 °C
   ii 4 °C −3 °C   **iv** −5 °C −2 °C

b What temperature is
   i 3 degrees higher than −8 °C
  ii 9 degrees lower than −2 °C
 iii 5 degrees higher than −1 °C
  iv 6 degrees lower than 4 °C ?

9 a Give 759 correct to **i** the nearest 10   **ii** the nearest 100

b Write each number correct to the nearest 100.

   i 3490   **ii** 65 737   **iii** 8567   **iv** 1235

10 By working out rough answers decide which of the following answers are probably wrong and which are likely to be correct.

  a $213 \times 8 = 1704$ **e** $218 + 772 = 1090$
  b $427 \times 4 = 1208$ **f** $3140 - 2674 = 466$
  c $832 \div 8 = 204$ **g** $29 \times 393 = 11\,397$
  d $495 \div 9 = 55$ **h** $79 \times 492 = 48\,868$

11 a Express as the product of two factors in as many different ways as you can

   i 36   **ii** 96   **iii** 28   **iv** 42

b Look at the numbers

   8, 9, 10, 11, 12, 13, 14, 15, 16, 17, 18, 19, 20, 21, 22.

Which of these numbers are

   i prime   **iii** multiples of 6
  ii square   **vi** multiples of both 3 and 4 ?

c The digit sum of the number 462 is $4 + 6 + 2$. Is the digit sum divisible by 3 ? Is the original number divisible by 3 ?

12 a A sequence is formed by starting with 3 and adding 6 each time. Write down the first five terms.

b State the instruction necessary to generate the sequence

   8, 15, 22, 29, 36, . . .

Write down the next three terms.

**REVISION
EXERCISE 1.2
(Fractions,
decimals and
percentages)**

Do not use a calculator for this exercise.

1 a Write each of the following fractions as an equivalent fraction
with denominator 24.

$$\frac{1}{2}, \quad \frac{1}{3}, \quad \frac{1}{6}, \quad \frac{5}{12}, \quad \frac{3}{4}$$

b Write each of the following fractions as an equivalent fraction
with numerator 21.

$$\frac{3}{5}, \quad \frac{7}{10}, \quad \frac{1}{2}, \quad \frac{3}{4}$$

2 Simplify $\frac{21}{24}, \quad \frac{28}{36}, \quad \frac{32}{48}, \quad \frac{21}{49}, \quad \frac{45}{81}, \quad \frac{36}{48}, \quad \frac{40}{55}, \quad \frac{56}{72}$

3 a Write as a percentage   **i** $\frac{34}{100}$ **ii** $\frac{70}{100}$ **iii** $\frac{42}{100}$

b Express as a fraction in its lowest terms
   i 30 out of 60   **iii** 30 out of 50
   ii 20 out of 25   **iv** 5 out of 25

4 Three of the equivalent fractions given below are correct and three
are wrong. Find the wrong ones and explain why they are wrong.

a $\frac{3}{5} = \frac{8}{10}$ **c** $\frac{4}{9} = \frac{20}{45}$ **e** $\frac{3}{7} = \frac{9}{49}$

b $\frac{8}{11} = \frac{88}{100}$ **d** $\frac{5}{12} = \frac{20}{48}$ **f** $\frac{3}{8} = \frac{33}{88}$

5 Copy each shape and shade the fraction asked for.

a   **b**   **c**

Shade $\frac{1}{4}$

Shade $\frac{5}{8}$

Shade $\frac{3}{5}$

6 Write down as a percentage, the part of the circle that is
   i shaded   **ii** unshaded.

a 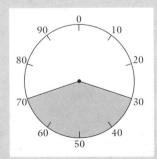   **b**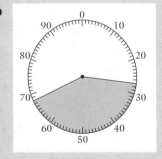

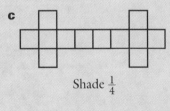

7 a Express as a fraction in its lowest terms

   i 45%   **ii** 88%   **iii** 16%   **iv** 72%

  b Which is the bigger **i** 63% or $\frac{62}{100}$ **ii** $\frac{18}{25}$ or 76%?

  c Which is the smaller **i** 37% or $\frac{19}{50}$ **ii** $\frac{29}{50}$ or 56%?

8 a What is the value of the figure 6 in each of the following numbers?

$$2.6, 64.2, 14.6, 56.2$$

  b Write these numbers in order of size, with the smallest first.

$$7.2, 7.02, 2.07, 2.7, 2.77$$

  c Two of the numbers 3, 0.3, 3.0, 30 are the same. Which are they?

  d Write each decimal as a fraction in its lowest terms.

   i 0.06   **ii** 0.66   **iii** 0.48   **iv** 0.86

9 Give the following readings

  i in decimal form

  ii as a number of hundredths

 iii as a simplified fraction.

a

c

b
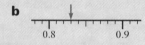

d
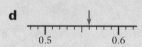

10 Find

a $32.5 + 16.4$	**g** $15.8 - 5.3$	**m** $42.4 - 9.82$
b $16.7 + 13.4$	**h** $7.89 - 4.82$	**n** $72.8 - 16.04$
c $4.04 + 0.63$	**i** $64.82 - 15.64$	**p** $3.68 - 1.9$
d $56.3 + 26.4$	**j** $67.2 - 3.09$	**q** $20 - 7.28 - 2.94$
e $3.67 + 38.44$	**k** $23.4 - 16.8$	**r** $8 - 1.2 + 0.55$
f $73.22 + 38.57$	**l** $48.3 - 26.6$	**s** $4.78 - 3.07 + 0.88$

REVISION EXERCISE 1.3 (Using metric units)

1 Express

  a 5 cm in mm **b** 8 m in cm **c** 4 km in m **d** 12 m in mm

2 a Which length is the longer, and by how much?

   i 80 mm or 6 cm   **ii** 3 m or 330 cm   **iii** 44 mm or 12 cm

  b Which length is the shorter, and by how much?

   i 3 km or 2647 m   **ii** 3345 cm or 2 m   **iii** 869 mm or 90 cm

3 Find, giving your answers in the smaller unit

   a 5 cm + 34 mm   **d** 8490 mm − 242 cm   **g** 4934 g + 3 kg

   b 4 km − 1760 m   **e** 6t − 4260 kg   **h** 8400 g − 5 kg

   c 3 kg − 720 g   **f** 2 m + 537 cm   **i** 5320 m − 2 km

4 In each part of this question choose the answer which is the more likely to be correct.

   a The height of an average domestic door is
     A 20 cm   **B** 2 km   **C** 200 mm   **D** 2 m

   b The weight of a large orange could be
     A 150 mg   **B** 400 g   **C** 35 g   **D** 6 kg

   c The weight of an average man could be
     A 5 kg   **B** 1 tonne   **C** 75 kg   **D** 600 g

5 Find the perimeter of each shape.

   a A square of side 56 mm

   b A rectangle measuring 24 cm by 15 cm

   c
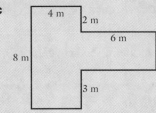
   d
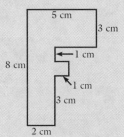

6 a How many one-centimetre cubes are needed to cover the base of this box?

   b How many layers of 1 cm cubes are needed to fill the box?

   c What is the volume of the box?

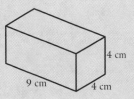

7 This stack is made from loose cubes.

   a How many cubes can you see?

   b How many cubes are needed to make this stack?

   c What is the least number of cubes needed to make this stack if the cubes can be glued together?

8 The sketch shows a cuboid.

   a For this shape write down the number of
      i faces   **ii** edges.

   b How many faces are rectangles measuring
      i 4 cm by 3 cm   **ii** 4 cm by 8 cm?

   c What are the measurements of the remaining rectangles?

9 Put the following areas in order of size, with the smallest first
$$1\,m^2, \ 1\,km^2, \ 1\,mm^2, \ 1\,cm^2$$

10 Express

   a 5 litres in cm^3 **c** 15 g in mg   **e** 750 000 ml in litres

   b 2 litres in ml   **d** 3000 cm^3 in litres   **f** 3 t in kg

**REVISION
EXERCISE 1.4
(Summarising
data and
probability)**

1 The weights of seven sweets are 2.6 g, 2.8 g, 2.7 g, 2.6 g, 2.8 g, 2.9 g and 2.8 g.
Find   **a** the mode   **b** the median.

2 In her last eight tests Jo got the following marks out of 10.
$$5, \ 6, \ 9, \ 5, \ 7, \ 3, \ 9, \ 10$$

   a Find her median mark.

   b What is the mode of this set of marks?

3 The ages of the boys attending a masterclass are
$$10, \ 10, \ 11, \ 11, \ 11, \ 12, \ 12, \ 12, \ 12, \ 13,$$
$$13, \ 13, \ 14, \ 14, \ 14, \ 15, \ 15, \ 15, \ 16$$

   a How many boys attended the class?

   b Find the mode.

   c What is the median age?

4 The table shows the scores when Jeff rolled this dice.

Score	1	2	3	4	5	6
Number of times score was obtained	4	3	4	5	2	4

   a How many times was the dice rolled?

   b How many times did Jeff score more than 3?

   c Which score is the median?

   d Which score is the mode?

5 This bar chart shows the distribution of the number of pets kept by the pupils in Class 8E.

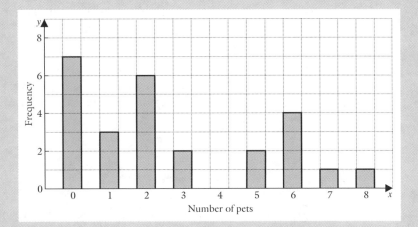

a How many pupils kept 4 pets?

b How many pupils kept more than 4 pets?

c How many pupils are there in the class?

d Use the bar chart to draw up a frequency table.

e What is the modal number of pets kept?

f What is the median?

6 Karl conducted a traffic survey. He counted the number of cars passing the school gate each day between 12.30 p.m. and 1.30 p.m. for the period of the survey. The list shows his results which have been arranged in ascending order.

34, 36, 39, 42, 43, 43, 44, 48, 48, 50, 53,
53, 56, 56, 56, 56, 57, 58, 60, 62, 63, 63,
65, 65, 66, 66, 69, 69, 69, 70, 70, 72, 74

a For how many days did Karl conduct the survey?

b Is there a modal value? If so, what is it?

c What is the median numbers of cars passing the school gate each lunch time?

d Arrange these numbers into the groups

0–14, 15–29, 30–44, 45–59, 60–74

and then illustrate them on a bar chart.

e One day three weeks later Sally counted 57 cars passing the school gate between 12.30 p.m.and 1.30 p.m. Is this more or less than half of the number of cars that Karl counted in his survey?

7 How many possible outcomes are there if

   a an ordinary 50 p coin is tossed

   b one letter is chosen from the word PROVIDE

   c one disc is taken from a bag containing 1 red, 1 white, 1 blue and 1 yellow disc?

8 Copy this scale and on it mark an arrow showing, roughly, the place on the scale that measures the chance of each event happening. The first one is done for you.

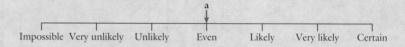

| Impossible | Very unlikely | Unlikely | Even | Likely | Very likely | Certain |

   a Drawing a black card from a pack of 52 playing cards.

   b Opening this book at page 512.

   c Drawing a red disc from a bag that contains 12 red discs and 1 white disc.

   d Choosing a word on this page and finding that it contains a vowel.

9 How many outcomes are there for the following experiments? In each case write down the list of all possible outcomes.

   a Choosing a card from the suit of hearts that have been taken from a pack of ordinary playing cards.

   b Choosing one number from the first 5 multiples of 4.

   c Choosing an odd number from the first twenty positive whole numbers.

   d Choosing one coin from a bag containing one 5 p coin, one 10 p coin, one 20 p coin, one 50 p coin and one £1 coin.

WORKING WITH WHOLE NUMBERS

Sam collected 45 pence from each of the 11 members of the under-fifteen football team and from each of the 7 members of the under-fifteen netball team. He didn't keep the money separate from his own, so he used his calculator to work out the amount he needed to hand over.

The calculator display read 972 so Sam handed over £9.72; this was £1.62 more than he should have handed in.

Sam clearly made a mistake when he used his calculator, but he didn't know that he had. This meant he was unaware that he was losing £1.62.

If Sam could

- work out that he had collected 45 pence from 18 people, and realise that this amounts to less than 50 pence from 18 people, that is, £9, he would know that £9.72 was too much.

- calculate the amount using pen and paper, he could then just use the calculator as a check; any mistakes would then be obvious.

EXERCISE 1A   Discuss what you need to know and be able to do so that you have some control in these situations. Assume that you do not have a calculator with you.

1 Gareth goes into a shop with £4.35 to buy some stationery. He chooses 4 pens costing 35 pence each and 15 rubbers costing 27 pence each. At the cash desk he finds that he does not have enough money to pay for all these things, and has to put some back.

2 Raj has to order coaches to take 317 children on a school outing. Each coach has 54 seats available. The coach company says it will send 6 coaches.

3 Anna needs to work out how much money she took at the tuck shop in the mid-morning break. She knows she sold 67 bars of chocolate at 27 pence each and 115 cans of drink at 24 pence each.

4 Now see if you can spot what Sam had keyed in to get his wrong answer.

THE FOUR RULES   These examples show that there are situations when we can have some control if we can calculate confidently with whole numbers without needing to use a calculator.

Addition, subtraction, multiplication and division are called the four rules of arithmetic. The basic work on the four rules for whole numbers is covered in Book 7B and further practice is given in Revision Exercise 1.1 on page 6 of this book. In this chapter we apply the four rules in less simple situations.

MENTAL ADDITION   You need to know (without having to do any calculation) the sum of any two numbers less than 10,

i.e. $3 + 6$, $5 + 9$, and so on.

These are called the addition facts, and knowing them makes it easy to add larger numbers in your head.

For example, to find $37 + 6$,

we add the units first, then add on 30,

i.e. $37 + 6 = 30 + 7 + 6$

$= 30 + 13$

$= 43$

EXERCISE 1B

Calculate in your head

___ These are
extra questions

1 $24 + 3$	**5** $81 + 7$	**9** $24 + 8$	**13** $47 + 2$
2 $32 + 5$	**6** $36 + 5$	**10** $46 + 4$	**14** $56 + 7$
3 $54 + 4$	**7** $24 + 7$	**11** $57 + 8$	**15** $87 + 9$
4 $62 + 6$	**8** $47 + 8$	**12** $68 + 9$	**16** $17 + 8$

| **17** $125 + 4$ | **19** $378 + 3$ | **21** $444 + 9$ | **23** $505 + 8$ |
| **18** $257 + 2$ | **20** $682 + 8$ | **22** $688 + 5$ | **24** $609 + 3$ |

This method can be extended to adding a two-digit number to another number by adding the units on first, then adding on the tens.

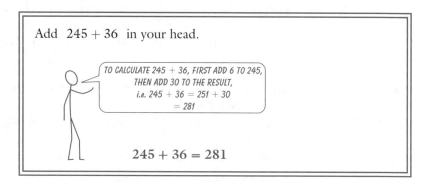

Add $245 + 36$ in your head.

TO CALCULATE 245 + 36, FIRST ADD 6 TO 245, THEN ADD 30 TO THE RESULT, i.e. $245 + 36 = 251 + 30$ $= 281$

$245 + 36 = 281$

Calculate in your head

___ These are
extra questions

25 $154 + 33$	**30** $527 + 45$	**35** $1455 + 21$
26 $288 + 11$	**31** $651 + 29$	**36** $2066 + 26$
27 $504 + 21$	**32** $348 + 55$	**37** $212 + 97$
28 $716 + 73$	**33** $486 + 21$	**38** $5037 + 54$
29 $687 + 12$	**34** $643 + 72$	**39** $1332 + 88$

ADDING LARGER NUMBERS

Some people can add larger numbers in their heads but most of us need to write these numbers down and add them systematically.

EXERCISE 1C

Do not use a calculator.

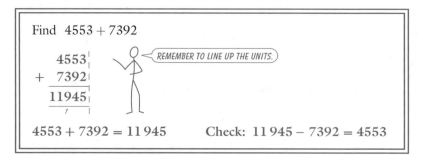

Find $4553 + 7392$

$$\begin{array}{r} 4553 \\ + \ 7392 \\ \hline 11945 \end{array}$$

REMEMBER TO LINE UP THE UNITS.

$4553 + 7392 = 11\,945$ Check: $11\,945 - 7392 = 4553$

Find

___ These are extra questions

1 $2154 + 325$

2 $6553 + 3312$

3 $3155 + 3577$

4 $5182 + 3116$

5 $6233 + 5222$

6 $5231 + 8564$

7 $692 + 7794$

8 $4009 + 5155$

9 $7873 + 5134$

10 $886 + 1050$

11 $4652 + 7520$

12 $5909 + 7342$

MIXED ADDITION AND SUBTRACTION

Helen bought a pen marked at $52\,\mathrm{p}$ with $10\,\mathrm{p}$ off, and a ruler marked at $36\,\mathrm{p}$ (with nothing off).
She can find the total cost by taking $10\,\mathrm{p}$ away from $52\,\mathrm{p}$ and then adding $36\,\mathrm{p}$ to the result.
This calculation can be written in one line as

$$52 - 10 + 36 = 42 + 36 = 78$$

Helen could also work out the cost by adding 52 and 36 first and taking 10 from the result,

i.e. by finding $52 + 36 - 10 = 88 - 10 = 78$

This shows that,

in any calculation with a mixture of addition and subtraction, the sign in front of a number refers to that number *only*; the order in which we add and subtract does not matter.

EXERCISE 1D

Find, in your head

1 $2 + 6 - 3$ **2** $4 + 7 - 5$ **3** $8 - 4 + 9$ **4** $7 - 4 + 6$

___ These are extra questions	**5** $5 - 8 + 7$	**9** $16 - 7 - 5$	**13** $6 - 3 + 2$
	6 $12 - 7 + 9$	**10** $25 - 8 + 11$	**14** $6 + 7 - 8$
	7 $14 - 9 - 2$	**11** $15 + 5 - 9 + 2$	**15** $27 - 29 + 8$
	8 $24 + 15 - 7$	**12** $36 - 12 + 14 - 3$	**16** $36 - 9 + 3 - 7$

MULTIPLYING A STRING OF NUMBERS

To find the value of $2 \times 7 \times 5 \times 3$, we can work from left to right,

i.e.
$$2 \times 7 \times 5 \times 3 = 14 \times 5 \times 3$$
$$= 70 \times 3$$
$$= 210$$

However *the order in which numbers are multiplied does not matter*, so we can multiply these numbers together in any order we choose,

e.g.
$$2 \times 7 \times 5 \times 3 = 10 \times 7 \times 3 \quad (\text{choosing } 2 \times 5 \text{ first})$$
$$= 10 \times 21 \quad (\text{choosing } 7 \times 3 \text{ next})$$
$$= 210$$

or
$$2 \times 7 \times 5 \times 3 = 10 \times 7 \times 3$$
$$= 70 \times 3 \quad (\text{choosing } 10 \times 7 \text{ next})$$
$$= 210$$

EXERCISE 1E

Do not use a calculator.

Find the value of each string of numbers.

1 $3 \times 4 \times 2 \times 2$	**5** $3 \times 2 \times 3 \times 2$	**9** $9 \times 3 \times 5 \times 3$
2 $5 \times 2 \times 3 \times 7$	**6** $5 \times 7 \times 3 \times 4$	**10** $4 \times 3 \times 3 \times 5$
3 $3 \times 4 \times 2 \times 5$	**7** $6 \times 4 \times 2 \times 3$	**11** $8 \times 7 \times 3 \times 6$
4 $7 \times 2 \times 2 \times 2$	**8** $8 \times 2 \times 2 \times 7$	**12** $2 \times 3 \times 4 \times 5 \times 6$

13 Joan gave each of her 5 closest friends 2 boxes of chocolates and each box contained 3 chocolates. How many chocolates did she give?

14 Rene worked out $2 \times 7 \times 4$ as $8 \times 28 = 224$.
This contains a mistake; find it and explain why it is wrong.

15 Find the missing digits in the following products.

a $2 \times \square \times 3 = 24$

c $7 \times 3 \times \square = 4\square$

b $\square \times 5 \times 3 = 30$

d $\square \times 4 \times 3 = \square 0$

16 Decide whether each of these statements is true. Give reasons for your decision.

a $4 \times 20 = 4 \times 5 \times 4$ **c** $4 \times 4 \times 2 = 16 \times 8$

b $12 \times 500 = 12 \times 50 \times 50$ **d** $5 \times 20 \times 20 = 400 \times 10$

Find 24×300

> We use the fact that $300 = 3 \times 100$ to write the calculation as $24 \times 3 \times 100$; we can then find 24×3 first.
> Remember that to multiply by 10, 100, 1000, ... we move the figures 1, 2, 3, ... places to the left and fill in the gaps with zeros.

$$24 \times 300 = 24 \times 3 \times 100$$
$$= 72 \times 100$$
$$= 7200$$

$$\begin{array}{r} 24 \\ \times\ 3 \\ \hline 72 \\ \hline {\scriptstyle 1} \end{array}$$

Find

___ **These are extra questions**

17 24×400 **21** 37×600 **25** 95×30

18 141×500 **22** 71×40 **26** 558×300

19 28×2000 **23** 703×300 **27** 29×7000

20 54×30 **24** 87×60 **28** 2883×40

29 A school orders 24 packs of exercise books. There are 40 books in each pack. How many exercise books did the school order?

30 Which of these answers are obviously wrong and why?

$72 \times 40 \times 100 =$ **A** $28\,800$ **B** $72\,000$ **C** $288\,000$

31 Without calculating the result, write down, with reasons, which of these products gives the largest answer.

A 25×400 **B** $5 \times 10 \times 4000$ **C** $200 \times 25 \times 10$

This is a 'challenge' question

32 Sue ordered 30 boxes of paper. Each box contained 5 reams, and 1 ream of paper is 500 sheets. How many sheets of paper did she order?

USING BRACKETS

Sam collected 45 pence from each of the 11 members of the football team and from each of the 7 members of the netball team.

To find the total amount he has collected, Sam can first add 11 and 7, and then multiply the result by 45.

We can use brackets to show that 11 and 7 have to be added first,

i.e. $(11 + 7) \times 45$ means add 11 and 7 first.

Similarly, $23 \times (5 - 3)$ means work out $5 - 3$ first.

EXERCISE 1F

Find $4 \times (2 + 5)$

$4 \times (2 + 5) = 4 \times 7$
$= 28$

Find, without using a calculator

___ These are extra questions

1 $12 \times (2 + 3)$

2 $8 \times (1 + 4)$

3 $5 \times (12 - 7)$

4 $(1 + 7) \times 8$

5 $(2 - 1) \times 6$

6 $(7 + 3) \times 18$

7 $(3 + 9) \times 20$

8 $42 \times (17 + 13)$

9 $36 \times (27 - 7)$

10 $(46 - 16) \times 24$

LONG MULTIPLICATION

Another way that Sam can find the amount that he collected is to work out how much he received from each team, and then add these amounts together,

i.e. $(45 \times 11) + (45 \times 7)$

This means that $45 \times (11 + 7)$ is the same as $(45 \times 11) + (45 \times 7)$.

Any number can be written as the sum of two or more numbers. To multiply two large numbers together, we write one of the numbers as a sum of units, tens, hundreds,...,

e.g. to multiply 84×26 we use the fact that

$$84 \times 26 = 84 \times (6 + 20)$$
$$= (84 \times 6) + (84 \times 20)$$

This can be set out as

$$
\begin{array}{r}
84 \\
\times \quad 26 \\
\hline
504 \\
+ \; 1680 \\
\hline
2184
\end{array}
$$

(84 × 6)

(84 × 20)

EXERCISE 1G   Do not use a calculator.

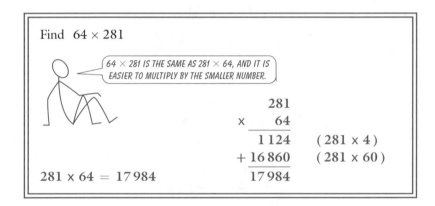

Find 64 × 281

64 × 281 IS THE SAME AS 281 × 64, AND IT IS EASIER TO MULTIPLY BY THE SMALLER NUMBER.

$$
\begin{array}{r}
281 \\
\times \quad 64 \\
\hline
1\,124 \\
+ \; 16\,860 \\
\hline
17\,984
\end{array}
$$

(281 × 4)

(281 × 60)

281 × 64 = 17 984

Find

___ **These are extra questions**

1 32 × 21

2 43 × 13

3 86 × 15

4 27 × 21

5 34 × 42

6 38 × 41

7 107 × 26

8 53 × 82

9 74 × 106

10 36 × 89

11 241 × 32

12 15 × 202

13 43 × 901

14 1251 × 28

15 3421 × 33

Find 402 × 2813

402 × 2813 = 2813 × 402

   = (2813 × 2) + (2813 × 400)

$$
\begin{array}{r}
2\,813 \\
\times \quad 402 \\
\hline
5\,626 \\
+ \; 1\,125\,200 \\
\hline
1\,130\,826
\end{array}
$$

(2813 × 2)

(2813 × 400)

2813 × 402 = 1 130 826

Find

___ These are
extra questions

16 512×210 **21** 2004×43 **26** 385×95

17 487×18 **22** 584×97 **27** 750×450

18 724×98 **23** 187×906 **28** 605×750

19 146×209 **24** 270×709 **29** 1008×908

20 805×703 **25** 3060×470 **30** 1500×802

31 There are three answers given for each calculation. Two of them are obviously wrong. Write down the letter of the answer that *might* be correct.

   a 521×36: **A** 1876   **B** 11886   **C** 18756
   b 63×95:   **A** 6005   **B** 585   **C** 10000

32 Multiply three hundred and fifty-six by twenty-three.

33 One jar of marmalade weighs 450 grams. Find the weight of 124 jars.

34 Find the value of one hundred and fifty multiplied by itself.

35 A car-park has 34 rows and each row has 42 parking spaces. How many cars can be parked?

36 A supermarket takes delivery of 54 crates of soft drink cans. Each crate contains 48 cans. How many cans are delivered?

These are
'challenge'
questions

37 A light bulb was tested by being left on non-stop. It failed after 28 days exactly. For how many hours was it working?

38 Fill in the missing digits in these calculations.

   a $2\square \times 42 = 966$ **c** $157 \times 3\square = 5495$
   b $125 \times \square6 = 7000$ **d** $206 \times 4\square = \square682$

39 How can you tell, without doing the division or using a calculator, that 153918 is not divisible exactly by 4?

DIVISION BY 10, 100, 1000 . . .

Remember that to multiply by 10, 100, 1000, . . . we move the figures 1, 2, 3, . . . places to the left and fill in the gaps with zeros.
As division is the opposite of multiplication,
to divide by ten, we move the figures one place to the right,
to divide by 100, we move the figures two places to the right, and so on.

To divide by 50, we can use the fact that $50 = 10 \times 5$ to divide first by 10 then by 5,

e.g.
$$250 \div 50 = (250 \div 10) \div 5$$
$$= 25 \div 5$$
$$= 5$$

EXERCISE 1H

___ These are extra questions

Find, without using a calculator

1 $3600 \div 200$ **5** $8400 \div 60$ **9** $4200 \div 20$

2 $3090 \div 30$ **6** $72\,000 \div 120$ **10** $81\,600 \div 40$

3 $74\,000 \div 2000$ **7** $550 \div 110$ **11** $505\,000 \div 5000$

4 $2700 \div 90$ **8** $22\,000 \div 220$ **12** $69\,000 \div 300$

13 A greengrocer orders 25 000 paper bags. The bags come in packs of 500. How many packs did the greengrocer order?

14 Envelope labels are supplied in sheets of 20. How many sheets should be ordered if 5000 labels are required?

15 Jenny worked out that 216 divided by 27 is 8. How can she check her answer without dividing?

This is a 'challenge' question

16 Explain why the method used above will not help you to find the answer to $4977 \div 200$.

LONG DIVISION

Long divsion is short division with the working set down more carefully.
To find $2678 \div 21$ we can set the working out as follows:

```
        127
   21 ) 2678
        21
        ‾‾
        57
        42
       ‾‾‾
        158
        147
       ‾‾‾
         11
```

There is 1 twenty-one in 26, r 5 (hundreds).

There are 2 twenty-ones in 57, r 15 (tens).

There are 7 twenty-ones in 158, r 11 (units).

So $2678 \div 21 = 127$, r 11.

EXERCISE 1I

> Find $2606 \div 25$, giving the remainder.
>
> $2606 \div 25 = 104$, r 6
>
> $$\begin{array}{r} 104 \\ 25\overline{)2606} \\ \underline{25} \\ 106 \\ \underline{100} \\ 6 \end{array}$$
>
> Check: $104 \times 25 + 6 = 2606$

Calculate the following divisions, giving the remainders.
(If you do the calculation on a calculator to check your answers, it will
  give the whole number part of the answer but it will not give the
  remainder as a whole number. A better check is to use your calculator
  to reverse the calculation as shown in the example above.)

___ These are
extra questions

1 $254 \div 20$	**5** $394 \div 19$	**9** $389 \div 23$
2 $685 \div 13$	**6** $267 \div 32$	**10** $298 \div 14$
3 $739 \div 41$	**7** $875 \div 25$	**11** $433 \div 15$
4 $862 \div 25$	**8** $269 \div 16$	**12** $614 \div 27$
13 $2804 \div 13$	**17** $2943 \div 23$	**21** $7514 \div 34$
14 $7315 \div 21$	**18** $2694 \div 31$	**22** $5829 \div 43$
15 $8392 \div 34$	**19** $1875 \div 25$	**23** $6372 \div 27$
16 $6841 \div 15$	**20** $3621 \div 30$	**24** $8261 \div 38$
25 $7315 \div 24$	**30** $2694 \div 30$	**35** $8200 \div 250$
26 $8602 \div 15$	**31** $8013 \div 40$	**36** $3606 \div 300$
27 $3004 \div 31$	**32** $829 \div 106$	**37** $8491 \div 150$
28 $1608 \div 25$	**33** $5241 \div 201$	**38** $7625 \div 302$
29 $7092 \div 35$	**34** $3689 \div 151$	**39** $1092 \div 206$

40 4000 apples are packed into boxes, each box holding 75 apples.
How many boxes are required?

41 A vegetable plot is 1000 cm long. Cabbages are planted in a row down the length of the plot.
If the cabbages are planted 30 cm apart and the first cabbage is planted 5 cm from the end, how many cabbages can be planted in one row?

42 A class is told to work out the odd-numbered questions in an exercise containing 29 questions.
How many questions do they have to do?

43 Find the missing digits in the following calculations.

a $256 \div 1\square = 16$

b $86\square \div 24 = 36$

c $105\square \div 25 = 42, \text{r } 2$

44 Explain how you can find the remainder when 216 is divided by 17 without using either a calculator or multiplication or division.

MIXED OPERATIONS OF $+, -, \times, \div$

We have seen how brackets can be used to show which operations are to be done first,

e.g. $2 \times (5 + 1)$ means add 5 and 1 first.

Although we *can* use brackets when multiplication is to be done first, e.g. $(2 \times 5) + 1$, brackets are not usually used;

$2 \times 5 + 1$ is taken to mean 'do the multiplication first'.

When a calculation involves a mixture of the operations $+, -, \times, \div$ we always work out the inside of any brackets first, then we do

multiplication and division before addition and subtraction.

For example,

$$2 \times 4 + 3 \times 6 = 8 + 18$$

$$= 26$$

Do the multiplication first, i.e. 2×4 and 3×6, before adding.

EXERCISE 1J   Do not use a calculator.

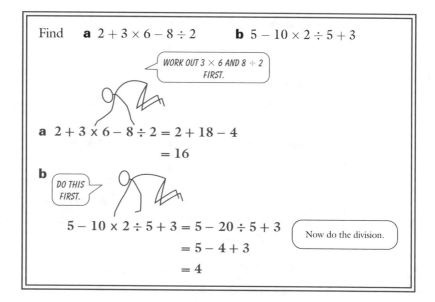

Find **a** $2 + 3 \times 6 - 8 \div 2$ **b** $5 - 10 \times 2 \div 5 + 3$

WORK OUT 3×6 AND $8 \div 2$ FIRST.

a $2 + 3 \times 6 - 8 \div 2 = 2 + 18 - 4$
$$= 16$$

b

DO THIS FIRST.

$5 - 10 \times 2 \div 5 + 3 = 5 - 20 \div 5 + 3$ Now do the division.
$$= 5 - 4 + 3$$
$$= 4$$

Find

1 $2 + 4 \times 6 - 8$

2 $24 \div 8 - 3$

3 $6 + 3 \times 2$

4 $7 \times 2 + 6 - 1$

5 $18 \div 3 - 3 \times 2$

6 $7 + 4 - 3 \times 2$

7 $8 \div 2 + 6 \times 3$

8 $14 \times 2 \div 7 - 3 + 6$

9 $6 - 2 \times 3 + 7$

10 $5 + 4 \times 3 + 8 \div 2$

11 $24 \div 6 + 12 \div 4$

12 $8 - 15 \div 3 + 2$

13 $7 + 3 \times 2 - 8 \div 2$

14 $5 \times 4 \div 2 + 7 \times 2$

15 $6 \times 3 - 8 \times 2$

16 $9 \div 3 + 12 \div 6$

17 $12 \div 3 - 15 \div 5$

18 $9 + 3 - 6 \div 2 + 1$

19 $6 - 3 \times 2 + 9 \div 3$

20 $7 + 2 \times 4 - 8 \div 4$

21 $7 \times 2 + 8 \times 3 - 2 \times 6$

22 $5 \times 3 \times 2 - 4 \times 3 \div 2$

23 $5 \times 4 \times 3 - 6 \times 2 \times 2$

24 $20 \div 5 \times 2 - 3 \times 4 \div 6$

___ These are
extra questions

25 $19 + 3 \times 2 - 8 \div 2$

30 $5 \times 3 \times 4 \div 12 + 6 - 2$

26 $7 \times 2 - 3 + 6 \div 2$

31 $5 + 6 \times 2 - 8 \div 2 + 9 \div 3$

27 $8 + 3 \times 2 - 4 \div 2$

32 $7 - 9 \div 3 + 6 \times 2 - 4 \div 2$

28 $7 \times 2 - 4 \div 2 + 1$

33 $9 \div 3 - 2 + 1 + 6 \times 2$

29 $6 + 8 \div 4 + 6 \times 3 \div 2$

34 $4 \times 2 - 6 \div 3 + 3 \times 2 \times 4$

In the greengrocer's I bought three oranges that cost 12 p each
and one cabbage that cost 36 p. I paid with a £1 coin. How much
change did I get?

Cost of the oranges	$= 36\,\text{p}$
Cost of the cabbage	$= 36\,\text{p}$
Total cost	$= 72\,\text{p}$
Change from £1	$= 100\,\text{p} - 72\,\text{p}$
	$= 28\,\text{p}$

---

35 I bought five oranges that cost 10 p each and two lemons that cost 9 p
each.
How much did I spend?

36 Three children went into a sweet shop. The first child bought three
sweets costing 2 p each, the second child bought three sweets costing
1 p each and the third child bought three sweets costing 3 p each.
How much money did they spend altogether?

37 A club started the year with 82 members. During the year 36
people left and 28 people joined.
How many people belonged to the club at the end of the year?

38 One money box has five 5 p pieces and four 10 p pieces in it.
Another money box has six 10 p pieces and ten 2 p pieces in it.

a What is the total sum of money in the two money boxes?

b Which box has more money in it? How much more is there in
this box than the other box?

39 At a school election one candidate got 26 votes, and the other candidate got 35 votes. 10 voting papers were spoiled and 5 pupils did not vote.
How many children altogether could have voted?

40 An extension ladder is made of three separate parts, each 300 cm long. When it is fully extended, there is an overlap of 30 cm at each junction.
How long is the extended ladder?

41 Jane, Sarah and Claire come to school with 20 p each. Jane owes Sarah 10 p and she also owes Claire 5 p. Sarah owes Jane 4 p and she also owes Claire 8 p.
When all their debts are settled, how much money does each girl have?

42 The total number of children in the first year of a school is 500. There are 50 more girls than boys. How many of each are there?

43 In a book of street plans of a town, the street plans start on page 6 and end on page 72. How many pages of street plans are there?

44 Sam said that $25 + 5 \times 5$ was equal to 150.
Explain his mistake and give the correct answer.

45 A mountaineer starts from a point which is 150 m above sea level. He climbs 200 m and then descends 50 m before climbing another 300 m. How far is he now above sea level?

46 The calculation needed for the worked example above question **35** can be set out *using only the numbers given in the question*, as $100 - 3 \times 12 - 36$.
Set out the calculations for questions **35** to **40** in the same way using only the numbers given in the questions.

These are 'challenge' questions

47 My great-grandmother died in 1894, aged 62.
In which year was she born?

48 An oak tree was planted in the year in which Lord Swell was born. He died in 1940, aged 80. How old was the oak tree in 1984?

This is
a 'challenge'
question

49 A bus leaves the bus station at 9.30 a.m. It reaches the Town Hall
at 9.40 a.m. and gets to the railway station at 9.52 a.m.

a How long does it take to go from the Town Hall to the railway
station?

b Which piece of information given in the question is not needed
to answer part **a**?

**NUMBER
PUZZLES**

1 Copy the following sets of numbers. Put $+$, $-$, $\times$ or $\div$ in each
space so that the calculations are correct.

a $9 \square 4 = 5$ **e** $5 \square 4 \square 6 = 3$

b $7 \square 3 = 21$ **f** $8 \square 3 \square 4 = 1$

c $28 \square 4 = 7$ **g** $3 \square 4 \square 2 = 9$

d $8 \square 2 = 4$ **h** $2 \square 2 \square 3 = 8$

2 Solve the following cross-number puzzle.

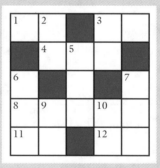

Across	Down
1 $127 - 64$	2 $3 \times 13 - 6$
3 $44 + 73 - 58$	3 $464 \div 8$
4 6×53	5 $625 \div 5$
8 330×41	6 74×7
11 $9 \times 10 - 9$	7 9×89
12 The next number	9 $5 \times 8 - 27 \div 3$
after 40	10 $2 \times 19 - 4$

3 My calculator has an odd fault. The + button multiplies and the × button adds.

  a When I press 7 + 5, what number shows on the display?

  b Before I realised what the fault was, I got 21 when I tried to add two numbers. What were the two numbers?

  c I pressed 2 + 8 × 5. What number showed in the display?

  d Find a calculation using three or four numbers for which my calculator will give the correct answer.

INVESTIGATION

(You will need to use a calculator.)

A pandigital number contains each of the digits 0, 1, 2, 3, 4, 5, 6, 7, 8, 9 just once. (An example is 3 278 016 945.)

  a Try to find a pandigital that, when multiplied by one of the numbers from 2 to 9, remains pandigital.

  b Try to find a pandigital that is divisible by every number from 2 to 18.

  Explain the strategy that you use in your search.

ANGLES

You have arrived in a strange town and wish to visit the castle. There are two things you need to know.
In which direction is the castle?
How far is it?

- The directions you are given could well be: Go to the end of the street, take the first right and then the second left.

For an aeroplane flying from London to Los Angeles the directions would not be given in this crude way. Very sensitive instruments give accurate directions which are checked and rechecked at regular intervals.

When the Channel Tunnel was built it was necessary to measure direction very accurately. Discuss the consequences of poor measurements.

Can you think of other situations where we have to measure directions accurately?
The examples above show that we need to give and measure directions accurately.

- To describe a direction we measure the amount of turning from some fixed direction. This fixed direction could be the main street in a town, the direction of true north or the position of the minute hand of a clock at a particular time. Having decided on the fixed direction we measure the amount of turn needed to give the direction we seek.

FRACTIONS OF A REVOLUTION

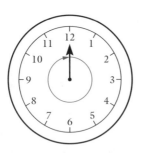

When the seconds hand of a clock starts at 12 and moves round until it stops at 12 again it has gone through one complete turn.

One complete turn is called a revolution.

When the seconds hand starts at 12 and stops at 3 it has turned through $\frac{1}{4}$ of a revolution.

EXERCISE 2A

What fraction of a revolution does the seconds hand of a clock turn through when

a it starts at 3 and stops at 12

b it starts at 4 and stops at 8 ?

A sketch of a clockface shows the angle clearly.

a $\frac{3}{4}$ of a revolution.

b $\frac{1}{3}$ of a revolution.

What fraction of a revolution does the seconds hand of a clock turn through when it

1 starts at 12 and stops at 9

8 starts at 10 and stops at 4

2 starts at 12 and stops at 6

9 starts at 8 and stops at 8

3 starts at 6 and stops at 9

10 starts at 8 and stops at 11

4 starts at 3 and stops at 9

11 starts at 10 and stops at 2

5 starts at 9 and stops at 12

12 starts at 12 and stops at 4

6 starts at 1 and stops at 7

13 starts at 8 and stops at 5

7 starts at 5 and stops at 11

14 starts at 5 and stops at 2 ?

Where does the hand stop if it starts at 12 and turns through $\frac{1}{4}$ of a revolution?

It stops at 3.

Where does the hand stop if

15 it starts at 12 and turns through $\frac{1}{2}$ a turn

16 it starts at 12 and turns through $\frac{3}{4}$ of a turn

17 it starts at 6 and turns through $\frac{1}{4}$ of a turn

18 it starts at 9 and turns through $\frac{1}{2}$ a turn

19 it starts at 6 and turns through a complete revolution

20 it starts at 9 and turns through $\frac{3}{4}$ of a revolution

21 it starts at 12 and turns through $\frac{1}{3}$ of a revolution

22 it starts at 12 and turns through $\frac{2}{3}$ of a revolution

23 it starts at 9 and turns through a complete revolution?

COMPASS DIRECTIONS

The four main compass directions are north, south, east and west.

If you stand facing north and turn clockwise through $\frac{1}{2}$ a revolution you are then facing south.

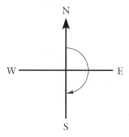

EXERCISE 2B

1 If you stand facing west and turn anticlockwise through $\frac{3}{4}$ of a revolution, in which direction are you facing?

2 If you stand facing south and turn clockwise through $\frac{1}{4}$ of a revolution, in which direction are you facing?

3 If you stand facing north and turn, in either direction, through a complete revolution, in which direction are you facing?

4 If you stand facing west and turn through $\frac{1}{2}$ a revolution, in which direction are you facing? Does it matter if you turn clockwise or anticlockwise?

5 If you stand facing south and turn through $1\frac{1}{2}$ revolutions, in which direction are you facing?

6 If you stand facing west and turn clockwise to face south what part of a revolution have you turned through?

7 If you stand facing east and turn to face west what part of a revolution have you turned through?

ANGLES

When the hand of a clock moves from one position to another it has turned through an angle.

RIGHT ANGLES

A quarter of a revolution is called a *right angle*.

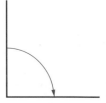

Half a revolution is two right angles.

EXERCISE 2C

How many right angles does the seconds hand of a clock turn through when it starts at 3 and stops at 12 ?

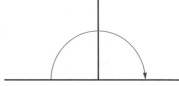

It turns through three right angles.

How many right angles does the seconds hand of a clock turn through when it

1 starts at 6 and stops at 9   **5** starts at 12 and stops at 12

2 starts at 3 and stops at 9   **6** starts at 8 and stops at 2

3 starts at 12 and stops at 9   **7** starts at 9 and stops at 6

4 starts at 3 and stops at 6   **8** starts at 7 and stops at 7 ?

How many right angles do you turn through if you

9 face north and turn clockwise to face south

10 face west and turn clockwise to face north

11 face south and turn clockwise to face west

12 face north and turn anticlockwise to face east

13 face north and turn to face north again ?

**ACUTE, OBTUSE
AND REFLEX
ANGLES**

Any angle that is smaller than a right
angle is called an *acute angle*.

Any angle that is greater than one
right angle and less than two right
angles is called an *obtuse angle*.

Any angle that is greater than two
right angles is called a *reflex angle*.

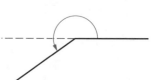

EXERCISE 2D   What type is each of the following angles?

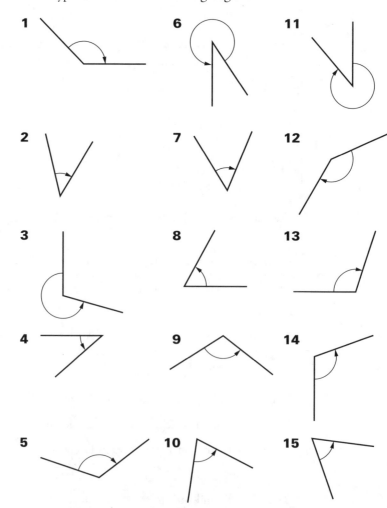

DEGREES

One complete revolution is divided into 360 parts. Each part is called a *degree*. 360 degrees is written 360°.

360 seems a strange number of parts to have in a revolution but it is a good number because so many whole numbers divide into it exactly. This means that there are many fractions of a revolution that can be expressed as an exact number of degrees.

It is possible that the number 360 was chosen because thousands of years ago they believed that the sun took 360 days to make one complete cycle of the earth, that is, to make a complete turn.

EXERCISE 2E

1 How many degrees are there in half a revolution?

2 How many degrees are there in one-third of a revolution?

3 How many degrees are there in one right angle?

4 How many degrees are there in three right angles?

5 How many degrees are there in one-and-a-half right angles?

How many degrees has the seconds hand of a clock turned through when it moves from 6 to 9?

It has turned through 90°.

How many degrees has the seconds hand of a clock turned through when it moves from

6 12 to 6	**10** 9 to 6	**14** 8 to 5
7 3 to 6	**11** 2 to 5	**15** 4 to 10
8 6 to 3	**12** 7 to 10	**16** 5 to 8
9 9 to 3	**13** 1 to 10	**17** 6 to 12?

How many degrees has the seconds hand of a clock turned through when it moves from 6 to 8?

> When the hand moves from
> 6 to 8 it turns through $\frac{2}{12}$ of a
> revolution.
> From 6 to 8 is $\frac{2}{12}$ of 360°
> and $\frac{1}{12}$ of 360° = 360° ÷ 12
> = 30°

The hand turns through $\frac{2}{12}$ of 360°, i.e. 2 × 30° = 60°

How many degrees has the seconds hand of a clock turned through when it moves from

18 8 to 9

23 4 to 5

19 10 to halfway between 11 and 12

24 7 to 11

20 6 to 10

25 5 to 6

21 1 to 3

26 7 to 9

22 3 to halfway between 4 and 5

27 11 to 3

28 3 to 10

32 9 to 2

36 11 to 4

29 2 to 8

33 8 to 3

37 2 to 9

30 10 to 8

34 7 to 5

38 2 to 10

31 12 to 11

35 10 to 5

39 6 to 3?

40 You wish to divide a complete turn into an exact number of parts.
Is 360 a good number?
Try dividing 360 by each of the whole numbers from 1 to 12.
Now do the same for 100.
Which is the better number of degrees to have in one complete turn, 100 or 360?
Give reasons for your choice.

USING A PROTRACTOR TO MEASURE ANGLES

A protractor looks like this:

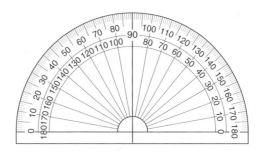

It has a straight line at or near the straight edge. This line is called the *base line*. The *centre* of the base line is marked.

The protractor has two scales, an inside one and an outside one.

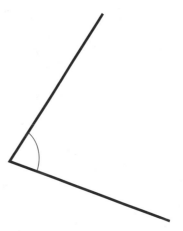

To measure the size of this angle, first decide whether it is acute or obtuse.

This is an acute angle because it is *less* than 90°.

Next place the protractor on the angle as shown.

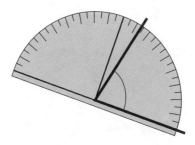

One arm of the angle is on the base line.

The vertex (point) of the angle is at the centre of the base line.

Choose the scale that starts at 0° on the arm on the base line. Read off the number where the other arm cuts this scale.

Check with the earlier decision about the size of the angle to make sure that you have chosen the right scale.

EXERCISE 2F   Measure the following angles (if necessary, turn the page to a convenient position).

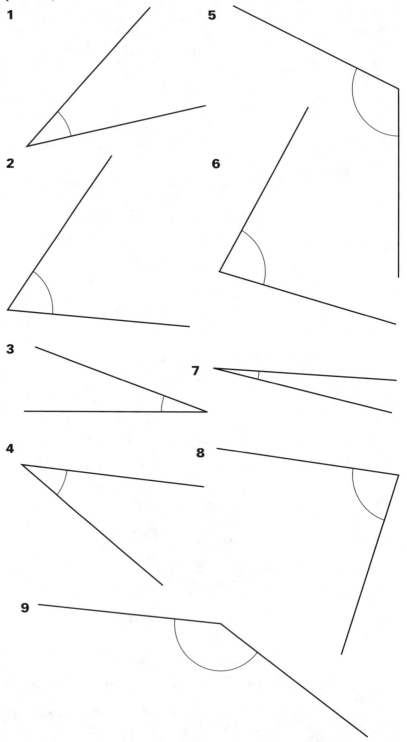

1

5

2

6

3

7

4

8

9

Find the size of the angle marked $p°$.

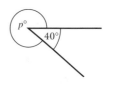

Angle $p°$ and 40° together make 360°

So angle $p°$ is 360° − 40° = 320°.

In questions **10** to **14** write down the size of the marked angle.

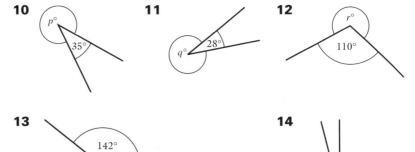

10

11

12

13

14

Measure the following angle.

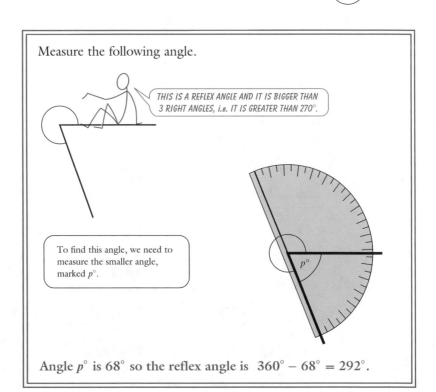

THIS IS A REFLEX ANGLE AND IT IS BIGGER THAN 3 RIGHT ANGLES, i.e. IT IS GREATER THAN 270°.

To find this angle, we need to measure the smaller angle, marked $p°$.

Angle $p°$ is 68° so the reflex angle is 360° − 68° = 292°.

Measure the following angles.

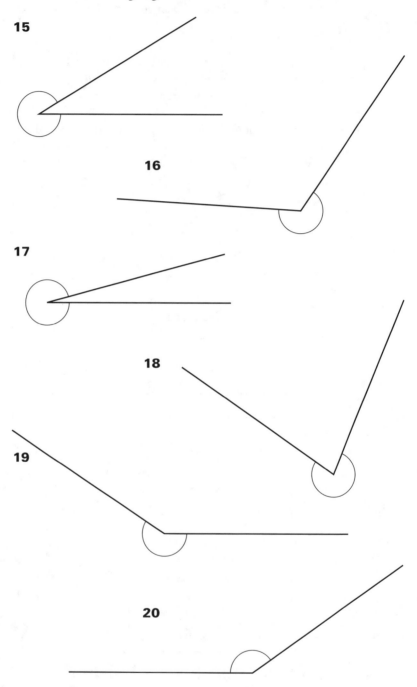

15

16

17

18

19

20

21 Draw a reflex angle. Now find its size.
Change books with your neighbour and each check the other's
measurement.

EXERCISE 2G   This exercise contains mixed questions on angles. Use a clock diagram to draw the angle that the *minute* hand of a clock turns through in the following times. In each question write down the size of the angle in degrees.

1 5 minutes   **3** 15 minutes   **5** 25 minutes

2 10 minutes   **4** 20 minutes   **6** 30 minutes

The seconds hand of a clock starts at 12. Which number is it pointing to when it has turned through an angle of

7 90°   **11** 150°   **15** 420°   **19** 540°

8 60°   **12** 270°   **16** 180°   **20** 240°

9 120°   **13** 30°   **17** 450°   **21** 390°

10 360°   **14** 300°   **18** 210°   **22** 720° ?

If you stand facing north and turn clockwise, draw a sketch to show roughly the direction in which you are facing if you turn through 60°.

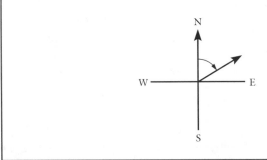

If you start by facing north and turn clockwise, draw a sketch to show roughly the direction in which you are facing if you turn through the following angles.

23 45°   **26** 50°   **29** 20°   **32** 10°

24 70°   **27** 200°   **30** 100°   **33** 80°

25 120°   **28** 300°   **31** 270°   **34** 250°

Estimate the size, in degrees, of each of the following angles.

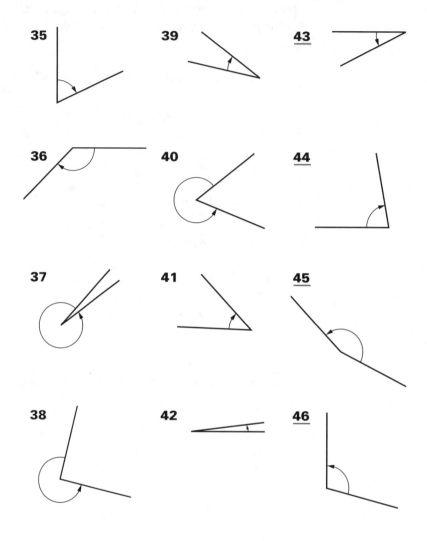

Draw the following angles as well as you can by estimating, i.e. without using a protractor. Use a clockface if it helps. Then measure your angles with a protractor.

47 45°	**50** 30°	**53** 150°	**56** 20°	**59** 330°
48 90°	**51** 60°	**54** 200°	**57** 5°	**60** 95°
49 120°	**52** 10°	**55** 290°	**58** 170°	**61** 250°

DRAWING ANGLES USING A PROTRACTOR

To draw an angle of 120° start by drawing one arm and mark the corner.

The corner, or point of an angle, is called the *vertex*.

Place your protractor as shown in the diagram. Make sure that the vertex is at the centre of the base line.

Choose the scale that starts at 0° on your drawn line and mark the paper next to the 120° mark on the scale.

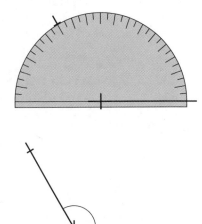

Remove the protractor and join your mark to the vertex.

Now look at your angle: does it look the right size?

EXERCISE 2H

Use your protractor to draw the following angles accurately.

1 25°	**4** 160°	**7** 110°	**10** 125°	**13** 105°
2 37°	**5** 83°	**8** 49°	**11** 175°	**14** 136°
3 55°	**6** 15°	**9** 65°	**12** 72°	**15** 85°

Change books with your neighbour and measure each other's angles as a check on accuracy.

EXERCISE 2I

In questions **1** and **2** first measure the angle marked $r°$. Then estimate the size of the angle marked $s°$. Check your estimate by measuring angle $s°$.

1

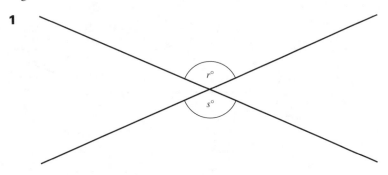

2

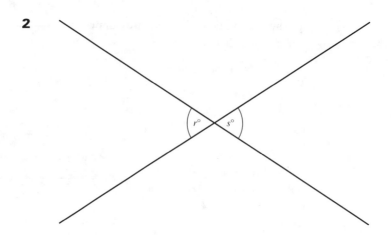

3 Draw some more similar diagrams and repeat questions **1** and **2**.

In each of the following questions, write down the size of the angle marked $t°$, without measuring it.

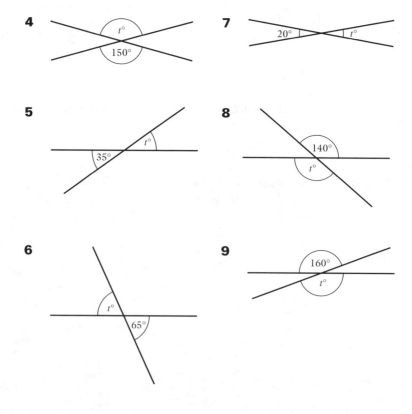

VERTICALLY OPPOSITE ANGLES

When two straight lines cross, four angles are formed.

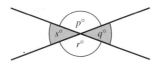

The two angles that are opposite each other are called *vertically opposite angles*. After working through the last exercise you should now be convinced that

vertically opposite angles are equal

i.e. $p° = r°$ and $s° = q°$

ANGLES ON A STRAIGHT LINE

The seconds hand of a clock starts at 9 and stops at 11 and then starts again and finally stops at 3.

Altogether the seconds hand has turned through half a revolution, so $p° + q° = 180°$.

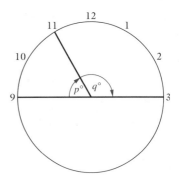

EXERCISE 2J

1 Draw a diagram showing the two angles that you turn through if you start by facing north and then turn clockwise through 60°, stop for a moment and then continue turning until you are facing south. What is the sum of these two angles?

2 Draw a clock diagram to show the two angles turned through by the seconds hand if it is started at 2, stopped at 6, started again and finally stopped at 8. What is the sum of these two angles?

3 Draw an angle of 180°, without using your protractor.

4 Darren asks you what an angle of 180° is.
Write down how you would answer Darren.

SUPPLEMENTARY
ANGLES

Angles on a straight line add up to 180°.

Two angles that add up to 180° are called supplementary angles.

EXERCISE 2K

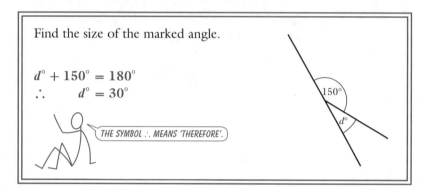

Find the size of the marked angle.

$$d° + 150° = 180°$$
$$\therefore \qquad d° = 30°$$

THE SYMBOL ∴ MEANS 'THEREFORE'.

In questions **1** to **12** calculate the size of the marked angle .

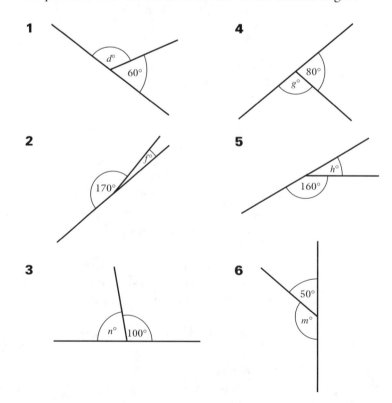

1

$d°$

$60°$

4

$80°$

$g°$

2

$f°$

$170°$

5

$h°$

$160°$

3

$n°$ $100°$

6

$50°$

$m°$

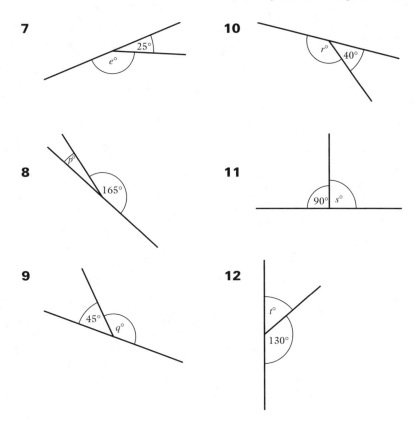

7

10

8

11

9

12

In questions **13** to **18** write down the pairs of angles that are supplementary.

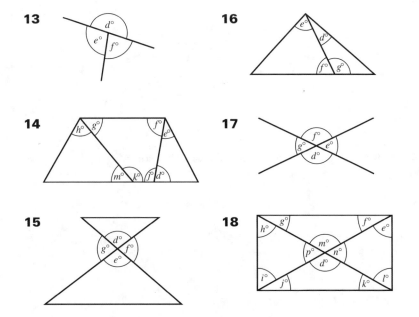

13

16

14

17

15

18

Calculate the size of each marked angle.

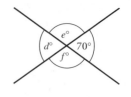

$d°$ and $70°$ are equal
(they are vertically opposite)
∴ $d° = 70°$
$e°$ and $70°$ add up $180°$
(they are angles on a straight line)
∴ $e° = 110°$
$f°$ and $e°$ are equal
(they are vertically opposite)
∴ $f° = 110°$

> Notice that reasons are given for statements made about angles.

In questions **19** to **24** calculate, giving reasons, the sizes of the marked angles.

19
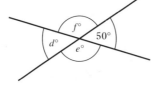

22
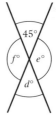

20
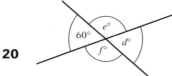

23
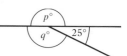

21
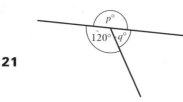

24
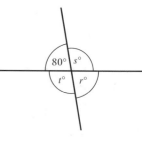

ANGLES AT A POINT

When several angles make a complete revolution they are called *angles at a point*.

> Angles at a point add up to 360°.

EXERCISE 2L

Calculate the size of the marked angle.

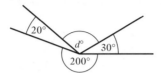

The three given angles add up to 250°.

$\therefore \quad d° = 360° - 250°$

$\qquad d° = 110°$

$$\begin{array}{r} 30 \\ 200 \\ + \underline{20} \\ \underline{250} \end{array}$$

Find the size of each marked angle. Show your working and give reasons.

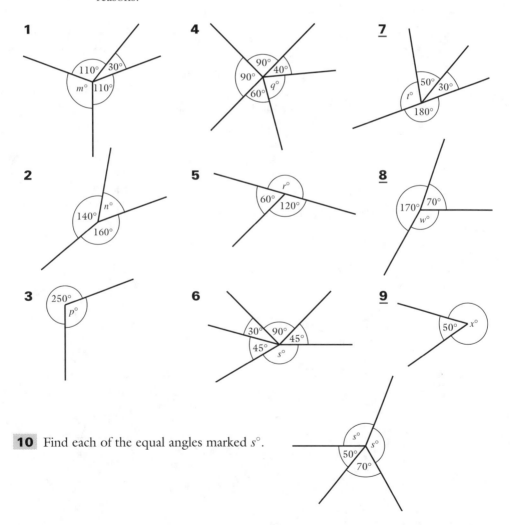

10 Find each of the equal angles marked $s°$.

11 Find each of the equal angles marked $d°$.

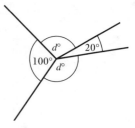

12 Each of the equal angles marked $p°$ is 25°.
Find the reflex angle $q°$.

13 The angle marked $f°$ is twice the
angle marked $g°$.
Find angles $f°$ and $g°$.

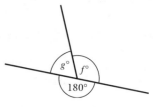

14 Each of the equal angles marked $d°$ is
30°. Angle $d°$ and angle $e°$ are
supplementary.
Find angles $e°$ and $f°$. (An angle
marked with a square is a right angle.)

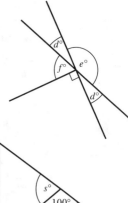

15 Angle $s°$ is twice angle $t°$.
Find angle $r°$.

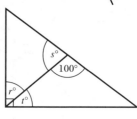

16 The angle marked $d°$ is 70°.
Find angle $e°$.

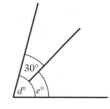

17 Find the angles marked $p°$, $q°$, $r°$ and $s°$.

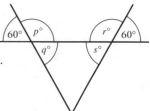

MIXED EXERCISE

EXERCISE 2M

1 What angle does the minute hand of a clock turn through when it moves from 1 to 9 ?

2 Draw an angle of 50°.

3 Estimate the size of this angle.

4 Write down the size of the angle marked $p°$.

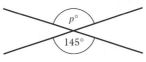

5 Write down the size of the angle marked $s°$.

6 Find each of the equal angles marked $e°$.

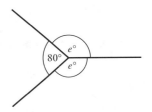

PRACTICAL WORK

This is an exercise for two people. You need a good map and a protractor.

Toss a coin to see who takes the first turn.

One player finds two places on the map. This player shows the other player the position of one place on the map and gives the direction of the second place from the first by estimating the angle that must be turned through clockwise from north. If the second player finds this place within 10 seconds, he has won and it is his turn. Otherwise the first player has won and gets another turn. Play as many times as you wish.

The winner is the player with the most successes.

Any disputes about the direction given are solved by measuring the actual angle with a protractor. Directions within 10° are acceptable.

If 10 seconds is not long enough, increase the time allowed to 15 seconds.

NUMBER AND PATTERN

A manufacturer has three customers who want large weekly deliveries of his packs of paper cups. The first customer wants 80 packs a week, the second 120 and the third 60. The manufacturer would like to make up sealed cartons, each with the same number of packs, so that these orders can each be fulfilled by delivering a whole number of sealed packs.

- The number of packs needed for each order, that is, 80, 120 and 60, is an even number, so sealed cartons with two packs would be all right but it would be far more convenient to have more packs in each carton. To supply 80 packs, the number of packs in each sealed carton must divide exactly into 80, so the number of packs must be a factor of 80. This factor must also divide exactly into 120 and 60 if the other two orders are also to be delivered in the same sealed cartons. To make the best use of the sealed cartons, this number has to be as large as possible.

The church at Hicksome has a peel of three bells. No. 1 bell rings every 6 seconds, No. 2 bell every 8 seconds and No. 3 bell every 9 seconds. They start by all tolling together. How can we find out how long it will take before they ring together again?

- One way of doing this is to keep a running total of the times when each bell tolls,

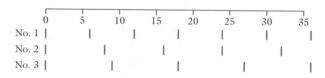

and keep on extending these lines until the three match up.
We can see that we are looking for the smallest number that 6, 8 and 9 will divide into exactly. This is the smallest number that is a multiple of 6, 8 and 9.

These and similar problems can be solved quite easily if we understand the properties of different types of numbers.

54

EXERCISE 3A Discuss how you might solve the following problems.

1

Sandra wants to choose a group of people for a cheerleader's competition. At certain times in the competition she wants them to march in equal rows of 5, and at other times in equal rows of 6. What is the smallest number of people she should choose? What is the largest number she can use?

2 A plant breeding station wishes to divide a rectangular field measuring 525 m by 450 m into squares so that different varieties of plants can be grown under different conditions.
Assuming that the whole of the field is used, how can they decide on the size of the largest possible square?

FACTORS AND MULTIPLES

The exercise above illustrates that the problems involve finding factors or multiples of numbers. Simple work on factors and multiples was covered in Chapter 14 of Book 7B. If you need to revise this work try question 11 in Revision Exercise 1.1.

PRIME NUMBERS

Some numbers can be expressed as the product of two different factors in one way only. For example, the only factors of 3 are 1 and 3 and the only factors of 5 are 1 and 5. Any number bigger than 1 that is of this type is called a *prime number*. Note that 1 is not a prime number because it does not have two different factors.

EXERCISE 3B

1 Express these numbers as the product of two factors in as many different ways as possible.

a 48   **b** 72   **c** 84

2 Write down all the multiples of 7 between 50 and 100.

3 Write down all the prime numbers between 30 and 40.

4 a Write all the numbers from 1 to 100 in a table as shown below.

1	2	3	4	5	6	7	8	9	10
11	12	13	14	15	16	17	18	19	20
21	22	23	24	25	26	27	28	29	30
31	32	33	34	35	36	37	38	39	40
41	42	43	44	45	46	47	48	49	50
51	52	53	54	55	56	57	58	59	60
61	62	63	64	65	66	67	68	69	70
71	72	73	74	75	76	77	78	79	80
81	82	83	84	85	86	87	88	89	90
91	92	93	94	95	69	79	98	99	100

b Cross out 1, which is not a prime number.

c Do not cross out 2 because it is a prime number, but cross out all the multiples of 2.

d Do not cross out 3 because it is a prime number but cross out all the multiples of 3.

e Do the same for 5 and 7. Does it make any difference if you repeat what you have been doing for 11? Why?

f List the numbers that have not been crossed out. These are the prime numbers less than 100.

5 Which of the following numbers are prime numbers?

$$41, \quad 57, \quad 91, \quad 101, \quad 127$$

6 Find as many prime numbers as you can between 100 and 150.

7 Write each even number from 8 to 20 as the sum of two odd prime numbers.

8 Write each odd number between 10 and 24 as the sum of three odd prime numbers.

9 Are the following statements true or false? Give reasons for your answers.

a All the prime numbers are odd numbers.

b All odd numbers are prime numbers.

c All prime numbers between 10 and 20 are odd numbers.

d The only even prime number is 2.

e There are six prime numbers less than 10.

INDEX NUMBERS
The accepted shorthand way of writing $2 \times 2 \times 2 \times 2$ is 2^4.
We read this as '2 to the power 4' or '2 to the four'. The 4 is called the *index* or *power*.
Hence $16 = 2 \times 2 \times 2 \times 2 = 2^4$ and similarly $3^3 = 3 \times 3 \times 3 = 27$
The powers 2 and 3 have special names. Any number to the power 2 is said to be 'squared' and any number to the power 3 is said to be 'cubed', e.g. 5^2 is called '5 squared' and 4^3 is called '4 cubed'.

EXERCISE 3C
Write the following products in index form.

1 2×2

2 3×3

3 $2 \times 2 \times 2 \times 2$

4 $5 \times 5 \times 5 \times 5 \times 5$

5 $2 \times 2 \times 2 \times 2 \times 2 \times 2$

6 $7 \times 7 \times 7$

7 $3 \times 3 \times 3 \times 3$

8 $7 \times 7 \times 7 \times 7$

9 11×11

10 $3 \times 3 \times 3 \times 3 \times 3 \times 3 \times 3$

11 17×17

12 $2 \times 2 \times 2 \times 2 \times 2 \times 2 \times 2$

Find the value of 3^5.

$3^5 = 3 \times 3 \times 3 \times 3 \times 3$
$\quad = 243$

$3 \times 3 \times 3 \times 3 \times 3 = 9 \times 3 \times 3 \times 3$
$\qquad\qquad\qquad\quad = 27 \times 3 \times 3$
$\qquad\qquad\qquad\quad = 81 \times 3$
$\qquad\qquad\qquad\quad = 243$

Without using a calculator, find the value of

13 2^3

14 3^2

15 5^2

16 2^4

17 10^3

18 3^4

19 5^3

20 2^5

21 six squared

22 four cubed

23 eight squared

24 three cubed

Express 125 in index form.

$$125 = 5 \times 25$$
$$= 5 \times 5 \times 5$$
$$= 5^3$$

Express in index form using prime factors

25 4   **28** 8   **31** 16   **34** 81

26 9   **29** 49   **32** 32   **35** 169

27 27   **30** 25   **33** 64   **36** 125

PRODUCTS OF   Sometimes we have products involving more than one prime number.
PRIME NUMBERS For example, consider $2 \times 2 \times 2 \times 7 \times 7$
                   Since $2 \times 2 \times 2 = 2^3$ and $7 \times 7 = 7^2$
                   we can write $2 \times 2 \times 2 \times 7 \times 7$ as $2^3 \times 7^2$

EXERCISE 3D

Write these products in index form.

a $2 \times 2 \times 2 \times 5 \times 5$ **b** $2 \times 3 \times 3 \times 3 \times 2$

a $2 \times 2 \times 2 \times 5 \times 5 = 2^3 \times 5^2$

b

> Remember that we can arrange the product of a string of numbers in any order so we can rearrange these to bring the 2s together.

$2 \times 3 \times 3 \times 3 \times 2 = 2 \times 2 \times 3 \times 3 \times 3$
$$= 2^2 \times 3^3$$

Write the following products in index form.

1 $2 \times 2 \times 7 \times 7$ **5** $2 \times 3 \times 2 \times 3 \times 2 \times 3 \times 2$

2 $3 \times 3 \times 3 \times 5 \times 5$ **6** $5 \times 3 \times 3 \times 5 \times 5$

3 $5 \times 5 \times 5 \times 13 \times 13 \times 5$ **7** $3 \times 2 \times 3 \times 2 \times 2$

4 $3 \times 3 \times 3 \times 3 \times 5 \times 5$ **8** $5 \times 11 \times 5 \times 11 \times 11$

> Write the product $3 \times 2 \times 7 \times 3 \times 7 \times 2 \times 3$ in index form.
>
> $3 \times 2 \times 7 \times 3 \times 7 \times 2 \times 3 = 2 \times 2 \times 3 \times 3 \times 3 \times 7 \times 7$
> $$= 2^2 \times 3^3 \times 7^2$$

Write the following products in index form.

9 $2 \times 2 \times 3 \times 3 \times 5 \times 5$ **15** $3 \times 5 \times 2 \times 5 \times 3 \times 2 \times 2$

10 $3 \times 2 \times 7 \times 3 \times 3 \times 2 \times 7$ **16** $2 \times 2 \times 2 \times 7 \times 7$

11 $2 \times 3 \times 2 \times 3 \times 5 \times 2$ **17** $5 \times 7 \times 7 \times 5 \times 5$

12 $7 \times 7 \times 7 \times 3 \times 5 \times 7 \times 3$ **18** $3 \times 5 \times 3 \times 5 \times 3 \times 5$

13 $2 \times 5 \times 3 \times 5 \times 2 \times 3$ **19** $2 \times 3 \times 3 \times 3 \times 2$

14 $3 \times 5 \times 5 \times 3 \times 7 \times 3 \times 7$ **20** $7 \times 3 \times 3 \times 7 \times 2 \times 7$

> Find the value of $2^3 \times 3^2$
>
> $2^3 \times 3^2 = 2 \times 2 \times 2 \times 3 \times 3 = 72$

Without using a calculator, find the value of

21 $2^2 \times 3^3$ **24** $2^2 \times 3^2 \times 5$ **27** $5^2 \times 7$

22 $3^2 \times 5^2$ **25** $3^2 \times 5$ **28** $2^3 \times 3^2$

23 $2^4 \times 7$ **26** $2 \times 3^2 \times 7$ **29** $3^2 \times 7^2$

30 a Find, without using a calculator, the value of
    i $2^3 \times 2^4$ **ii** $2^2 \times 2^5$ **iii** 2×2^6 **iii** $2^2 \times 2^2 \times 2^3$
   b Comment on your answers to part **a**.

FINDING PRIME FACTORS

The following rules may help us to decide whether a given number has certain prime numbers as factors.
A number is divisible

       by 2 if the last figure is even
       by 3 if the sum of the digits is divisible by 3
       by 5 if the last figure is 0 or 5.

EXERCISE 3E

Is **a** 126 divisible by 2 **b** 252 divisible by 3 **c** 745 divisible by 5?

a Since the last figure is even, 126 is divisible by 2.

b The sum of the digits is $2 + 5 + 2 = 9$, which is divisible by 3. Therefore 252 is divisible by 3.

c Since the last digit is 5, 745 is divisible by 5.

---

1 Which of the following numbers are divisible by 3?

 a 47   **b** 138   **c** 627

2 Which of the following numbers are divisible by 5?

 a 34   **b** 135   **c** 247

3 Which of the following numbers are divisible by 2?

 a 68   **b** 226   **c** 349

4 Is 525 divisible by 3?   **7** Is 1424 divisible by 2?

5 Is 747 divisible by 5?   **8** Is 9471 divisible by 3?

6 Is 543 divisible by 5?   **9** Is 740 divisible by 5?

Is 1860 divisible by 15?

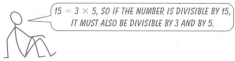
15 = 3 × 5, SO IF THE NUMBER IS DIVISIBLE BY 15, IT MUST ALSO BE DIVISIBLE BY 3 AND BY 5.

1860 is divisible by 5 since it ends in 0.

1860 is divisible by 3 since $1 + 8 + 6 = 15$ which is divisible by 3.

1860 is therefore divisible by both 5 and 3,
∴ it is divisible by 5 × 3, i.e. 15.

---

10 Is 466 divisible by   **14** Is 22 212 divisible by 6?

 a 2   **b** 3   **c** 6?

11 Is 930 divisible by   **15** Is 5645 divisible by 15?

 a 2   **b** 3   **c** 6?

12 Is 2988 divisible by 6?   **16** Is 6540 divisible by 20?

13 Is 2925 divisible by 15?   **17** Is 6540 divisible by 30?

EXPRESSING A NUMBER IN PRIME FACTORS

We can now write any number as the product of prime numbers in index form. Consider the number 36.

$$36 = 4 \times 9$$
$$= 2 \times 2 \times 3 \times 3$$
$$= 2^2 \times 3^2$$

i.e. $36 = 2^2 \times 3^2$

Therefore 36 expressed as the product of prime numbers or factors in index form is $2^2 \times 3^2$.

Similarly $108 = 4 \times 27$
$$= 2 \times 2 \times 3 \times 3 \times 3$$
$$= 2^2 \times 3^3$$

We can use a more organised method to express a number in prime factors: start by trying to divide by 2 and keep on until you can no longer divide exactly by 2. Next try 3 in the same way, then 5 and so on for each prime number until you are left with 1.

EXERCISE 3F

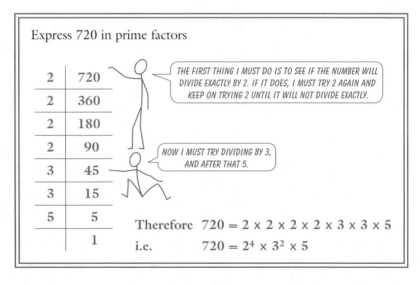

Express 720 in prime factors

2	720
2	360
2	180
2	90
3	45
3	15
5	5
	1

THE FIRST THING I MUST DO IS TO SEE IF THE NUMBER WILL DIVIDE EXACTLY BY 2. IF IT DOES, I MUST TRY 2 AGAIN AND KEEP ON TRYING 2 UNTIL IT WILL NOT DIVIDE EXACTLY.

NOW I MUST TRY DIVIDING BY 3, AND AFTER THAT 5.

Therefore $720 = 2 \times 2 \times 2 \times 2 \times 3 \times 3 \times 5$

i.e. $720 = 2^4 \times 3^2 \times 5$

Express each of the following numbers in prime factors in index form.

1 24   **4** 63   **7** 136   **10** 216   **13** 52

2 28   **5** 72   **8** 84   **11** 528   **14** 784

3 44   **6** 405   **9** 96   **12** 198   **15** 507

COMMON FACTORS

The manufacturer referred to at the beginning of this chapter can solve his problem if he can find the largest number that will divide exactly into 80, 120 and 60.

Two or more numbers may have the same factor. This is called a common factor.

For example, 7 is a common factor of 14, 28 and 42. Sometimes it is useful to find the highest factor that is common to a set of numbers. In this case the highest factor that will divide exactly into 14, 28 and 42 is 14.

EXERCISE 3G

Find the largest whole number that will divide exactly into all the given numbers.

1 9, 12	**6** 6, 8, 16	**11** 36, 52, 56
2 8, 16	**7** 30, 40, 50	**12** 9, 14, 42
3 12, 24	**8** 25, 50, 75	**13** 8, 24, 32
4 3, 9, 12	**9** 22, 33, 44	**14** 30, 45, 60
5 4, 8, 12	**10** 21, 42, 84	**15** 108, 162, 270

16 Solve the manufacturer's problem at the beginning of the chapter.

COMMON MULTIPLES

The bell ringing problem discussed at the beginning of the chapter can be solved if we find the smallest number that 6, 8 and 9 will all divide into exactly.

The smallest number that two or more numbers divide into exactly is called the smallest common multiple of the numbers. The smallest number that 5 and 8 will divide into exactly is 40 and the smallest number that 3, 5 and 6 will divide into is 30. (Notice that 3 divides exactly into 6 so we need not worry about the 3.)

EXERCISE 3H

Find the smallest number that can be divided exactly by 7 and by 9.

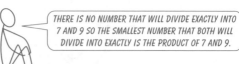

THERE IS NO NUMBER THAT WILL DIVIDE EXACTLY INTO 7 AND 9 SO THE SMALLEST NUMBER THAT BOTH WILL DIVIDE INTO EXACTLY IS THE PRODUCT OF 7 AND 9.

63 is the smallest number that 7 and 9 will divide into exactly.

Find the smallest number that both the given numbers will divide into exactly.

1 3, 5   **3** 3, 7   **5** 4, 5   **7** 7, 11

2 8, 5   **4** 12, 5   **6** 10, 11   **8** 5, 19

Find the smallest common multiple of 15 and 20.

WHEN THE REQUIRED NUMBER IS NOT OBVIOUS, WE TRY MULTIPLES OF THE SMALLER NUMBER (15) UNTIL WE FIND ONE THAT THE LARGER NUMBER (20) DIVIDES INTO EXACTLY; i.e. 15, 30, 45, 60.

60 is the smallest number that 15 and 20 divide into exactly.

Find the smallest common multiple of the given numbers.

9 6, 8   **12** 8, 12   **15** 25, 15   **18** 32, 8

10 5, 15   **13** 9, 12   **16** 12, 18   **19** 12, 48

11 6, 9   **14** 8, 24   **17** 26, 39   **20** 27, 36

21 Now solve the bell-ringing problem.

EXERCISE 3I

Some problems in this exercise can be solved by finding factors, others by finding multiples.

1 What is the smallest sum of money that can be made up of an exact number of 20 p pieces or 50 p pieces?

2 Find the least sum of money that 12 p and 27 p will divide into exactly.

3 Find the shortest length of wire that can be divided into equal sections of length 8 m or of length 12 m.

4 The light at one lighthouse flashes every 12 seconds while the light at another lighthouse flashes every 15 seconds. They flash together at midnight.
What is the time when they next flash together?

5 If I go up a flight of stairs three at a time I get to the top without any stairs being left over. If I then try five at a time I still get to the top without any being left over.

   a Find the shortest flight of stairs for which this is possible.

   b How many would remain if I went up
     i 2 at a time   **ii** 4 at a time?

6 A room measures 450 cm by 350 cm.
Find the side of the largest square tile that can be used to tile the floor without cutting.

7 Two cars travel around a Scalextric track, one completing the circuit in 8 seconds and the other in 10 seconds.
If they leave the starting line together how long will it be before they are side by side again?

8 Find the largest number of children who can share equally 42 oranges and 63 bananas.

9 A gear wheel with 30 teeth drives another wheel with 65 teeth.
A certain pair of teeth are touching when the wheels start.
How many times must each wheel turn before the same two teeth touch each other again?

10 In the first year of a large comprehensive school it is possible to divide the pupils into equal-sized registration classes of either 28 or 32 and have no pupils left over.

   a Find the size of the smallest entry that makes this possible.

   b The headteacher would like to have registration classes that are less than 28. If the entry is the value found in part **a**
     i can she have equal-sized registration classes of 20?
     ii what is the largest number of pupils in each registration class if the classes are to be all the same size but with fewer than 28 pupils?

RECTANGULAR NUMBERS

Any number that can be shown as a rectangular pattern of dots is called a rectangular number.
24 is a rectangular number,

e.g.   24 dots can be arranged as

or

5 is not a rectangular number since a line of dots is not a rectangle,
i.e.   ● ● ● ● ●

EXERCISE 3J

In questions **1–5** draw dot patterns for any of the following numbers that are rectangular numbers.

1 8   **2** 15   **3** 6   **4** 11   **5** 14

6 Show in two different ways that 12 is a rectangular number.

7 Show in at least two different ways that the following numbers are rectangular.

a 18   **b** 24   **c** 36

8 a Which of the numbers between 2 and 20 are not rectangular numbers? What special name do we give to these numbers?

b Which of the numbers between 2 and 20 are rectangular numbers?

c Which of the rectangular numbers between 2 and 20 are also square numbers?

9 Look at the pattern.

$$
\begin{array}{c}
1 \\
1\ 2\ 1 \\
1\ 2\ 3\ 2\ 1 \\
1\ 2\ 3\ 4\ 3\ 2\ 1
\end{array}
$$

What total do you get for each line in this pattern?
Are all these totals rectangular numbers and/or square numbers?

10

$$
\begin{array}{l}
1 \\
1 + 3 \\
1 + 3 + 5 \\
1 + 3 + 5 + 7
\end{array}
$$

Repeat question **9** for the pattern formed by adding the odd numbers.

TRIANGULAR NUMBERS

If the dots are arranged in rows so that each row is one dot longer than the row above, we have a pattern of triangular numbers.

$$1: \bullet \qquad 3: \overset{\bullet}{\bullet\,\bullet} \qquad 6: \overset{\bullet}{\underset{\bullet\,\bullet\,\bullet}{\bullet\,\bullet}} \qquad 10: \overset{\bullet}{\underset{\bullet\,\bullet\,\bullet\,\bullet}{\overset{\bullet\,\bullet}{\bullet\,\bullet\,\bullet}}}$$

EXERCISE 3K

1 Draw a dot pattern for the next three triangular numbers after 10.

2 Without drawing a dot pattern write down the next three triangular numbers after 28.

3 What pattern do you get if you sum the numbers in each line of this pattern?

$$1$$
$$1 + 2$$
$$1 + 2 + 3$$
$$1 + 2 + 3 + 4$$
$$1 + 2 + 3 + 4 + 5$$

MIXED EXERCISE

EXERCISE 3L

1 Write in index form **a** $5 \times 5 \times 5$ **b** $3 \times 3 \times 3 \times 3 \times 3$

2 Find the value of **a** 4^3 **b** $3^2 \times 4^3$

3 Express as the product of prime numbers in index form

   a 48   **b** 216.

4 Is 245 divisible by **a** 5 **b** 3?

5 Find the largest whole number that will divide exactly into 42 and 70.

6 Find the smallest whole number that 8 and 12 will divide into exactly.

7 Find the largest number of children that can share equally 72 sweets and 54 chocolates.

8 Which of the numbers between 24 and 40 are

   a rectangular numbers

   b square numbers

   c prime numbers?

PUZZLE

a List all the prime numbers less than 50.

b

```
                    1
                 2     5
              8    9    19
           11   5   17   12
         7    3    9    13   14
      38   13   33   7    28   36
   15   10   19   5    9    11   18
 5   47   8    23   14   11   26   13
```

Begin at the top and move down through the pyramid until you get to the bottom. You must go through one number in each row but, apart from 1, this number must be a prime number and must be next to the number you have just passed through. For example, if you are at 5 in the second row from the top the only choice you have next is 9 or 19.

Is there more than one route?

INVESTIGATIONS

1 Write down the first 10 triangular numbers in order. Now follow these instructions.

Step 1 Choose any triangular number other than 1.

Step 2 Multiply your chosen number by the next but one triangular number. Note your answer.

Step 3 Write down the triangular number that was between the two numbers you chose.

Step 4 Multiply this number by the number that is 1 smaller.

Step 5 Compare your Step 2 and Step 4 answers.

Step 6 Repeat the previous steps for a different number.

Will the same thing happen for any triangular number?
Give reasons for your answer.

2 a If the digits of a number are added together we have a reduced number. For example 26 reduces to 8, 167 reduces to 14 which further reduces to 5.

Investigate the reduced numbers for the numbers in the pattern of square numbers

$$1, 4, 9, 16, 25, 36, 49, \ldots$$

Add more numbers to the original pattern. If you go far enough the pattern of reduced numbers starts to repeat itself. Why does this happen?

Can you be certain that it will continue to happen as you add more numbers to the pattern?

b Investigate the pattern of reduced numbers for the cube numbers

$$1, 8, 27, 64, 125, \ldots$$

What happens when you write down alternate numbers from the pattern of reduced numbers?

c Try making up some patterns of your own. Find the reduced numbers for your pattern.

Do the reduced numbers have a pattern?

3 Suppose that we multiply a 3-figure number by a 2-figure number, e.g. $243 \times 27 = 6561$

Now check the answer using the following method.

a Add together the digits of the two numbers we multiplied together,

i.e. $2 + 4 + 3 = 9$ and $2 + 7 = 9$

b Multiply these two numbers together

i.e. $9 \times 9 = 81$

and add the digits in your answer together

i.e. $8 + 1 = 9$

c Add together the digits in the answer you got by multiplying 243×27

i.e. add the digits in 6561

$$6 + 5 + 6 + 1 = 18 \quad \text{and} \quad 1 + 8 = 9$$

Notice that your answers to parts **b** and **c** are both 9.

Investigate whether or not it is true to say that if you multiply any two numbers together correctly the corresponding answers to parts **b** and **c** are always the same.

ADDING AND SUBTRACTING FRACTIONS

The members of a Youth Club decide to raise some money for charity. When they have finished collecting they have to decide how they will divide it between their three chosen charities. After long discussions they decide to give $\frac{1}{4}$ of the sum collected to the NSPCC, $\frac{1}{3}$ to the local hospice and the remainder to OXFAM.

Anna commented 'That leaves more than half to give to OXFAM!' Hasib quickly replied 'No, it doesn't.'

Do you know who is right?

Sam joined in the argument with 'But $\frac{1}{3}$ is more than $\frac{1}{4}$, so $\frac{1}{4}$ and $\frac{1}{3}$ together must be more than $\frac{1}{2}$.'

Is this a sensible statement?

- To solve this problem we must be able to add two fractions together and subtract their total from 1.

EXERCISE 4A

1 In an audience $\frac{1}{15}$ are men, $\frac{7}{15}$ are women, $\frac{1}{5}$ are boys and the rest are girls.
Discuss what you need to be able to do to work out the fraction that are

a males **b** girls.

2 Think of problems where fractions are involved.

3 Discuss what you need to be able to do with fractions to solve the problems you thought of in question **2**.

Your discussions arising from the examples in **Exercise 4A** should convince you of the need to be able to add and subtract fractions, and to have an idea whether your answers are roughly correct.

EQUIVALENT
FRACTIONS

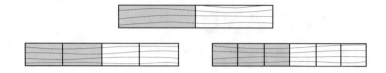

We know that $\frac{1}{2}$ of a length of wood is exactly the same as $\frac{2}{4}$ of the length and also exactly the same as $\frac{3}{6}$ of it.

$\frac{1}{2}$, $\frac{2}{4}$ and $\frac{3}{6}$ are *equivalent fractions*.

We also know that we can find an equivalent fraction by multiplying the top and the bottom of a given fraction by the same number. In the next exercise we extend this work a little further.

EXERCISE 4B

Fill in the missing numbers to make equivalent fractions.

a $\dfrac{4}{5} = \dfrac{8}{\rule{1em}{0.4pt}}$
    b $\dfrac{2}{9} = \dfrac{\rule{1em}{0.4pt}}{36}$

a $\dfrac{4}{5} = \dfrac{8}{10}$
    If $\frac{4}{5} = \frac{8}{\ }$ the top has been multiplied by 2 so the bottom must also be multiplied by 2.

b $\dfrac{2}{9} = \dfrac{8}{36}$
    If $\frac{2}{9} = \frac{\ }{36}$ the bottom has been multiplied by 4 so the top must also be multiplied by 4.

In questions **1** to **15** copy the fractions and make equivalent fractions by filling in the missing numbers.

1 $\dfrac{3}{7} = \dfrac{9}{\rule{1em}{0.4pt}}$

6 $\dfrac{2}{3} = \dfrac{\rule{1em}{0.4pt}}{12}$

11 $\dfrac{5}{7} = \dfrac{35}{\rule{1em}{0.4pt}}$

2 $\dfrac{1}{10} = \dfrac{10}{\rule{1em}{0.4pt}}$

7 $\dfrac{2}{9} = \dfrac{20}{\rule{1em}{0.4pt}}$

12 $\dfrac{8}{11} = \dfrac{40}{\rule{1em}{0.4pt}}$

3 $\dfrac{4}{5} = \dfrac{16}{\rule{1em}{0.4pt}}$

8 $\dfrac{3}{8} = \dfrac{\rule{1em}{0.4pt}}{800}$

13 $\dfrac{2}{9} = \dfrac{\rule{1em}{0.4pt}}{54}$

4 $\dfrac{3}{7} = \dfrac{\rule{1em}{0.4pt}}{28}$

9 $\dfrac{9}{10} = \dfrac{90}{\rule{1em}{0.4pt}}$

14 $\dfrac{6}{7} = \dfrac{\rule{1em}{0.4pt}}{49}$

5 $\dfrac{5}{9} = \dfrac{\rule{1em}{0.4pt}}{36}$

10 $\dfrac{4}{5} = \dfrac{\rule{1em}{0.4pt}}{50}$

15 $\dfrac{3}{8} = \dfrac{3000}{\rule{1em}{0.4pt}}$

Write $\frac{2}{3}$ as an equivalent fraction with denominator 36.

$$\frac{2}{3} = \frac{2 \times 12}{3 \times 12} = \frac{24}{36}$$

To change 3 to 36, we need to multiply 3 by 12, but if we multiply the denominator by 12 we must also multiply the numerator by 12.

16 Write each of the following fractions as an equivalent fraction with denominator 24.

a $\frac{3}{4}$ **b** $\frac{5}{6}$ **c** $\frac{11}{12}$ **d** $\frac{7}{8}$ **e** $\frac{2}{3}$ **f** $\frac{1}{2}$

17 Write each of the following fractions in equivalent form with denominator 45.

a $\frac{2}{15}$ **b** $\frac{4}{9}$ **c** $\frac{3}{5}$ **d** $\frac{1}{3}$ **e** $\frac{14}{15}$ **f** $\frac{1}{5}$

18 Find an equivalent fraction with denominator 36 for each of the following fractions.

a $\frac{3}{4}$ **b** $\frac{5}{9}$ **c** $\frac{1}{6}$ **d** $\frac{5}{18}$ **e** $\frac{7}{12}$ **f** $\frac{2}{3}$

19 Change each of the following fractions into an equivalent fraction with numerator 12.

a $\frac{1}{6}$ **b** $\frac{3}{4}$ **c** $\frac{6}{7}$ **d** $\frac{4}{5}$ **e** $\frac{2}{3}$ **f** $\frac{1}{2}$

20 Some of the following equivalent fractions are correct but two of them are wrong.
Find the wrong ones and explain why they are wrong.

a $\frac{2}{5} = \frac{6}{15}$ **c** $\frac{3}{7} = \frac{6}{14}$ **e** $\frac{7}{10} = \frac{77}{100}$

b $\frac{2}{3} = \frac{4}{9}$ **d** $\frac{4}{9} = \frac{12}{27}$ **f** $\frac{9}{13} = \frac{18}{26}$

21 a Change each fraction into an equivalent fraction with a denominator of 24. Hence put the fractions in order, with the smallest first.

$$\frac{7}{12}, \quad \frac{3}{4}, \quad \frac{17}{24}, \quad \frac{5}{6}, \quad \frac{7}{8}$$

b Put the following fractions in order with the largest first.

$$\frac{7}{9}, \quad \frac{2}{3}, \quad \frac{7}{12}, \quad \frac{13}{18}, \quad \frac{3}{4}$$

**SIMPLIFYING
FRACTIONS**

We can also find equivalent fractions by dividing the top and the bottom of a fraction by the same number. This is called simplifying a fraction.

For example, $\dfrac{24}{27} = \dfrac{8}{9}$ Dividing top and bottom by 3.

Similarly, $\dfrac{9}{27} = \dfrac{1}{3}$ Dividing top and bottom by 9. and $\dfrac{8}{28} = \dfrac{2}{7}$ Dividing top and bottom by 4.

EXERCISE 4C

Simplify $\dfrac{66}{176}$.

$\dfrac{66}{176} = \dfrac{3}{8}$ We divided the top and the bottom by 2 and then by 11.

Simplify the following fractions.

1 $\dfrac{9}{27}$ **6** $\dfrac{14}{70}$ **11** $\dfrac{60}{100}$ **16** $\dfrac{24}{72}$

2 $\dfrac{30}{50}$ **7** $\dfrac{36}{72}$ **12** $\dfrac{36}{90}$ **17** $\dfrac{54}{126}$

3 $\dfrac{12}{18}$ **8** $\dfrac{16}{56}$ **13** $\dfrac{24}{60}$ **18** $\dfrac{45}{81}$

4 $\dfrac{30}{36}$ **9** $\dfrac{15}{75}$ **14** $\dfrac{176}{192}$ **19** $\dfrac{45}{85}$

5 $\dfrac{9}{36}$ **10** $\dfrac{27}{90}$ **15** $\dfrac{84}{144}$ **20** $\dfrac{168}{216}$

21 There are times when a fraction looks unfamiliar and it is difficult to get an idea of its size. When this is so it is useful to approximate the fraction to a fraction that is more familiar. Familiar fractions include those fractions less than 1 which have denominators of 2, 3, 4, 5, 6, 8 or 10 such as $\dfrac{3}{4}$, $\dfrac{5}{8}$ and $\dfrac{7}{10}$.

For example $\dfrac{6}{17}$ is very close to $\dfrac{6}{18}$ which simplifies to $\dfrac{1}{3}$

i.e. $\dfrac{6}{17} \approx \dfrac{1}{3}$

and $\dfrac{37}{48} \approx \dfrac{36}{48} = \dfrac{3}{4}$ i.e. $\dfrac{37}{48} \approx \dfrac{3}{4}$

Approximate each of the following fractions to a fraction, simplified if possible, with a denominator chosen from the numbers given opposite.

a $\frac{7}{15}$ **c** $\frac{10}{33}$ **e** $\frac{20}{39}$ **g** $\frac{11}{20}$ **i** $\frac{9}{28}$

b $\frac{19}{25}$ **d** $\frac{11}{47}$ **f** $\frac{8}{23}$ **h** $\frac{19}{30}$ **j** $\frac{23}{44}$

ADDING FRACTIONS

Suppose there is a bowl of oranges and apples. First you take three oranges and then two more oranges. You then have five oranges; we can add the 3 and the 2 together because they are the same kind of fruit. However, three oranges and two apples cannot be added together because they are different kinds of fruit.

For fractions it is the denominator, the number on the bottom, that tells us the kind of fraction, so we can add fractions together if they have the same denominator but not while their denominators are different.

EXERCISE 4D

Add these fractions, simplifying the answers where you can

a $\frac{2}{7}+\frac{3}{7}$ **b** $\frac{9}{22}+\frac{5}{22}$

a $\frac{2}{7}+\frac{3}{7}=\frac{2+3}{7}$

The denominators are the same so we can add the numerators straight away.

$=\frac{5}{7}$

b $\frac{9}{22}+\frac{5}{22}=\frac{9+5}{22}$

$=\frac{14^{7}}{_{11}22}$

We divide the top and bottom by 2 to get a simpler fraction.

$=\frac{7}{11}$

Add the fractions given in questions **1** to **18**, simplifying the answers where you can.

1 $\frac{1}{4}+\frac{2}{4}$ **3** $\frac{3}{11}+\frac{2}{11}$ **5** $\frac{2}{7}+\frac{4}{7}$

2 $\frac{1}{8}+\frac{3}{8}$ **4** $\frac{3}{13}+\frac{7}{13}$ **6** $\frac{8}{30}+\frac{19}{30}$

7 $\dfrac{11}{23} + \dfrac{8}{23}$ **11** $\dfrac{5}{16} + \dfrac{7}{16}$ **15** $\dfrac{6}{13} + \dfrac{5}{13}$

8 $\dfrac{1}{7} + \dfrac{2}{7}$ **12** $\dfrac{21}{100} + \dfrac{19}{100}$ **16** $\dfrac{1}{10} + \dfrac{7}{10}$

9 $\dfrac{2}{5} + \dfrac{1}{5}$ **13** $\dfrac{2}{21} + \dfrac{9}{21}$ **17** $\dfrac{4}{11} + \dfrac{2}{11}$

10 $\dfrac{3}{10} + \dfrac{1}{10}$ **14** $\dfrac{7}{30} + \dfrac{8}{30}$ **18** $\dfrac{7}{15} + \dfrac{3}{15}$

We can add more than two fractions in the same way.

Add the fractions $\dfrac{3}{17} + \dfrac{5}{17} + \dfrac{8}{17}$

$$\dfrac{3}{17} + \dfrac{5}{17} + \dfrac{8}{17} = \dfrac{3+5+8}{17}$$

$$= \dfrac{16}{17}$$

Add the fractions given in questions **19** to **24**.

19 $\dfrac{2}{15} + \dfrac{4}{15} + \dfrac{6}{15}$ **22** $\dfrac{1}{14} + \dfrac{3}{14} + \dfrac{5}{14}$

20 $\dfrac{8}{100} + \dfrac{21}{100} + \dfrac{11}{100}$ **23** $\dfrac{2}{51} + \dfrac{4}{51} + \dfrac{6}{51}$

21 $\dfrac{4}{45} + \dfrac{11}{45} + \dfrac{8}{45} + \dfrac{2}{45}$ **24** $\dfrac{3}{99} + \dfrac{11}{99} + \dfrac{4}{99} + \dfrac{7}{99}$

25 If $\frac{5}{8}$ of the spectators at a match are men and $\frac{1}{8}$ are women, what fraction of the spectators are adults?

26 In a shop $\frac{1}{10}$ of the videos are films, $\frac{3}{10}$ sport and $\frac{3}{10}$ are documentaries.
What fraction of the videos are either films or sport or documentaries?

27 In a bag $\frac{5}{24}$ of the discs are red, $\frac{11}{24}$ are white and $\frac{7}{24}$ are blue.
What fraction of the discs in the bag are coloured red or white or blue?

ADDING FRACTIONS WITH DIFFERENT DENOMINATORS

To add two fractions with different denominators we must first change the fractions into equivalent fractions with the same denominator. This new denominator must be a number that both original denominators divide into.

For instance, if we want to add $\frac{2}{5}$ and $\frac{3}{7}$ we choose 35 for our new denominator because 35 can be divided by both 5 and 7:

$$\frac{2}{5} = \frac{14}{35}$$

$$\frac{3}{7} = \frac{15}{35}$$

So

$$\frac{2}{5} + \frac{3}{7} = \frac{14}{35} + \frac{15}{35} = \frac{29}{35}$$

EXERCISE 4E

Find $\dfrac{2}{7} + \dfrac{3}{8}$

$$\frac{2}{7} + \frac{3}{8} = \frac{16}{56} + \frac{21}{56}$$

7 and 8 both divide into 56, so we use 56 as the new denominator.

$$= \frac{16 + 21}{56}$$

$$= \frac{37}{56}$$

Find

1 $\dfrac{2}{3} + \dfrac{1}{5}$

2 $\dfrac{1}{5} + \dfrac{3}{8}$

3 $\dfrac{1}{5} + \dfrac{1}{6}$

4 $\dfrac{2}{5} + \dfrac{3}{7}$

5 $\dfrac{3}{10} + \dfrac{2}{3}$

6 $\dfrac{4}{7} + \dfrac{1}{8}$

7 $\dfrac{3}{7} + \dfrac{1}{6}$

8 $\dfrac{2}{3} + \dfrac{2}{7}$

9 $\dfrac{1}{6} + \dfrac{2}{7}$

10 $\dfrac{5}{6} + \dfrac{1}{7}$

11 $\dfrac{3}{11} + \dfrac{5}{9}$

12 $\dfrac{2}{9} + \dfrac{3}{10}$

13 $\dfrac{2}{3} + \dfrac{2}{7}$

14 $\dfrac{4}{9} + \dfrac{2}{5}$

15 $\dfrac{3}{5} + \dfrac{3}{11}$

The new denominator, which is called the *common denominator*, is not always as big as you might first think. For instance, if we want to add $\frac{3}{4}$ and $\frac{1}{12}$, the common denominator is 12 because 12 can be divided exactly by 4 and by 12.

Find $\frac{3}{4} + \frac{1}{12}$

$$\frac{3}{4} + \frac{1}{12} = \frac{9}{12} + \frac{1}{12}$$

$$= \frac{9+1}{12}$$

$$= \frac{10^5}{{}_6 12}$$

Divide top and bottom by 2

$$= \frac{5}{6}$$

Find

16 $\frac{2}{5} + \frac{3}{10}$ **20** $\frac{1}{5} + \frac{7}{10}$ **24** $\frac{1}{20} + \frac{3}{5}$

17 $\frac{3}{8} + \frac{7}{16}$ **21** $\frac{1}{4} + \frac{3}{8}$ **25** $\frac{4}{11} + \frac{5}{22}$

18 $\frac{3}{7} + \frac{8}{21}$ **22** $\frac{2}{3} + \frac{2}{9}$ **26** $\frac{2}{5} + \frac{7}{15}$

19 $\frac{3}{10} + \frac{3}{100}$ **23** $\frac{4}{9} + \frac{5}{18}$ **27** $\frac{7}{12} + \frac{1}{6}$

More than two fractions can be added in this way. The common denominator must be divisible by *all* of the original denominators.

Find $\frac{1}{8} + \frac{1}{2} + \frac{1}{3}$

$$\frac{1}{8} + \frac{1}{2} + \frac{1}{3} = \frac{3}{24} + \frac{12}{24} + \frac{8}{24}$$

8, 2 and 3 all divide into 24 so 24 is the new denominator.

$$= \frac{3 + 12 + 8}{24}$$

$$= \frac{23}{24}$$

Find

28 $\frac{1}{5} + \frac{1}{4} + \frac{1}{2}$

31 $\frac{5}{12} + \frac{1}{6} + \frac{1}{3}$

34 $\frac{1}{3} + \frac{2}{9} + \frac{1}{6}$

29 $\frac{1}{8} + \frac{1}{4} + \frac{1}{3}$

32 $\frac{1}{3} + \frac{1}{6} + \frac{1}{2}$

35 $\frac{2}{15} + \frac{1}{10} + \frac{2}{5}$

30 $\frac{3}{10} + \frac{2}{5} + \frac{1}{4}$

33 $\frac{1}{2} + \frac{3}{8} + \frac{1}{10}$

36 $\frac{1}{4} + \frac{1}{12} + \frac{1}{3}$

37 In a class $\frac{1}{5}$ of the pupils are less than 120 cm in height and $\frac{3}{10}$ are between 120 cm and 130 cm. No pupil is exactly 120 cm or 130 cm.
What fraction of the class is less than 130 cm?

38 When Kirsty comes home from shopping $\frac{1}{12}$ of the weight in her basket is green vegetables, $\frac{1}{3}$ is fruit and $\frac{1}{4}$ is other root vegetables.
What fraction of the weight she carries is fruit and vegetables?

39 In a car-park $\frac{3}{7}$ of the cars were manufactured in the UK and $\frac{5}{14}$ in mainland Europe.
What fraction were made in Europe?
(The UK is part of Europe but does not belong to mainland Europe.)

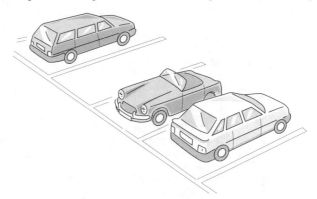

40 Decide, without adding the fractions, whether $\frac{1}{4} + \frac{1}{5}$ is more or less than $\frac{1}{2}$.
Give reasons for your answer.

41 Three possible answers are given for each 'sum'. Two of them are obviously wrong. Without working out the sum, decide which answer is most likely to be correct.

a $\dfrac{1}{5} + \dfrac{1}{7} = \ldots$ **A** $\dfrac{1}{4}$ **B** $\dfrac{1}{35}$ **C** $\dfrac{12}{35}$

b $\dfrac{2}{7} + \dfrac{1}{3} = \ldots$ **A** $\dfrac{3}{10}$ **B** $\dfrac{13}{21}$ **C** $\dfrac{2}{21}$

c $\dfrac{5}{18} + \dfrac{2}{9} = \ldots$ **A** $\dfrac{1}{2}$ **B** $\dfrac{10}{27}$ **C** $\dfrac{7}{27}$

42 Lyn adds two fractions and writes down

$$\frac{1}{4} + \frac{2}{5} = \frac{5}{20} + \frac{4}{20} = \frac{9}{40}$$

How many mistakes are there? Explain why they are mistakes.

SUBTRACTING FRACTIONS

Exactly the same method is used for subtracting fractions as for adding them. To work out the value of $\frac{7}{8} - \frac{3}{8}$ we notice that the denominators are the same, so

$$\frac{7}{8} - \frac{3}{8} = \frac{7 - 3}{8}$$
$$= \frac{4}{8}$$
$$= \frac{1}{2}$$

EXERCISE 4F

Find $\dfrac{11}{14} - \dfrac{3}{14}$

$$\frac{11}{14} - \frac{3}{14} = \frac{11 - 3}{14}$$

The denominators are the same so we can subtract the numerators straight away.

$$= \frac{\overset{4}{8}}{\underset{7}{14}}$$

$$= \frac{4}{7}$$

Find

1 $\dfrac{8}{9} - \dfrac{2}{9}$

2 $\dfrac{7}{10} - \dfrac{2}{10}$

3 $\dfrac{7}{12} - \dfrac{1}{12}$

4 $\dfrac{5}{8} - \dfrac{3}{8}$

5 $\dfrac{5}{7} - \dfrac{2}{7}$

6 $\dfrac{11}{12} - \dfrac{5}{12}$

Find $\dfrac{7}{9} - \dfrac{1}{4}$

$$\dfrac{7}{9} - \dfrac{1}{4} = \dfrac{28}{36} - \dfrac{9}{36}$$

The denominators are not the same so we use equivalent fractions with denominator 36.

$$= \dfrac{28 - 9}{36}$$

$$= \dfrac{19}{36}$$

Find

7 $\dfrac{5}{12} - \dfrac{1}{6}$

8 $\dfrac{3}{4} - \dfrac{1}{5}$

9 $\dfrac{9}{10} - \dfrac{1}{2}$

10 $\dfrac{2}{3} - \dfrac{4}{9}$

11 $\dfrac{2}{3} - \dfrac{3}{7}$

12 $\dfrac{4}{5} - \dfrac{11}{15}$

13 $\dfrac{7}{10} - \dfrac{3}{8}$

14 $\dfrac{11}{15} - \dfrac{3}{5}$

15 $\dfrac{17}{20} - \dfrac{7}{10}$

16 $\dfrac{7}{9} - \dfrac{2}{3}$

17 $\dfrac{8}{13} - \dfrac{1}{2}$

18 $\dfrac{11}{12} - \dfrac{5}{6}$

19 $\dfrac{5}{8} - \dfrac{2}{7}$

20 $\dfrac{15}{16} - \dfrac{3}{4}$

21 $\dfrac{7}{15} - \dfrac{1}{5}$

22 $\dfrac{7}{12} - \dfrac{1}{3}$

23 $\dfrac{13}{18} - \dfrac{5}{9}$

24 $\dfrac{13}{15} - \dfrac{3}{5}$

25 In the supermarket $\dfrac{7}{12}$ of Paula's bill is for fruit and vegetables. If $\dfrac{1}{8}$ is for fruit, what fraction is for vegetables?

26 Decide, without subtracting the fractions, if $\dfrac{3}{4} - \dfrac{1}{3}$ is less than or more than $\dfrac{1}{2}$.
Give reasons for your answer.

27   In a class $\frac{2}{5}$ of the pupils are less than $115\,cm$ in height and $\frac{7}{10}$ are less than $130\,cm$. No pupil is exactly $115\,cm$.
What fraction of the class is more than $115\,cm$ but less than $130\,cm$ in height?

28   Three possible answers are given for each of the following subtractions. Without working them out, choose the answer you think is most likely to be correct.

a $\dfrac{5}{9} - \dfrac{1}{3} = \ldots$ **A** $\dfrac{2}{9}$ **B** $\dfrac{5}{6}$ **C** $\dfrac{2}{3}$

b $\dfrac{14}{15} - \dfrac{4}{5} = \ldots$ **A** 1 **B** $\dfrac{2}{3}$ **C** $\dfrac{2}{15}$

c $\dfrac{19}{21} - \dfrac{3}{7} = \ldots$ **A** $\dfrac{16}{21}$ **B** $\dfrac{10}{21}$ **C** $\dfrac{4}{7}$

29   The following calculation contains at least one mistake.
Point out any mistake and give a reason why you think it is a mistake.
$$\frac{11}{12} - \frac{7}{9} = \frac{33}{36} - \frac{27}{36} = \frac{6}{36} = \frac{1}{3}$$

ADDING AND SUBTRACTING FRACTIONS

Fractions can be added and subtracted in one problem in a similar way.

For example
$$\frac{7}{12} - \frac{2}{12} + \frac{5}{12} = \frac{7 - 2 + 5}{12}$$
$$= \frac{10}{12}$$
$$= \frac{5}{6}$$

and
$$\frac{7}{9} + \frac{1}{18} - \frac{1}{6} = \frac{14}{18} + \frac{1}{18} - \frac{3}{18}$$
$$= \frac{14 + 1 - 3}{18}$$
$$= \frac{12}{18}$$
$$= \frac{2}{3}$$

It is not always possible to work from left to right in order because we have to subtract too much too soon. In this case we can do the adding first. Remember that it is the sign *in front* of a number that tells you what to do with that number.

EXERCISE 4G

Find $\dfrac{1}{8} - \dfrac{3}{4} + \dfrac{11}{16}$

$$\dfrac{1}{8} - \dfrac{3}{4} + \dfrac{11}{16} = \dfrac{2}{16} - \dfrac{12}{16} + \dfrac{11}{16}$$

Find $2 + 11$ first.

$$= \dfrac{13 - 12}{16}$$

$$= \dfrac{1}{16}$$

Find

1 $\dfrac{3}{4} + \dfrac{1}{2} - \dfrac{7}{8}$

4 $\dfrac{3}{5} + \dfrac{3}{25} - \dfrac{27}{50}$

7 $\dfrac{7}{10} - \dfrac{41}{100} + \dfrac{1}{20}$

2 $\dfrac{6}{7} - \dfrac{9}{14} + \dfrac{1}{2}$

5 $\dfrac{2}{3} + \dfrac{1}{6} - \dfrac{5}{12}$

8 $\dfrac{5}{8} - \dfrac{21}{40} + \dfrac{2}{5}$

3 $\dfrac{3}{8} + \dfrac{7}{16} - \dfrac{3}{4}$

6 $\dfrac{4}{5} - \dfrac{7}{10} + \dfrac{1}{2}$

9 $\dfrac{7}{12} - \dfrac{1}{6} + \dfrac{1}{3}$

10 $\dfrac{2}{9} - \dfrac{1}{3} + \dfrac{1}{6}$

13 $\dfrac{1}{6} - \dfrac{5}{18} + \dfrac{1}{3}$

16 $\dfrac{3}{10} - \dfrac{61}{100} + \dfrac{1}{2}$

11 $\dfrac{1}{6} - \dfrac{2}{3} + \dfrac{7}{12}$

14 $\dfrac{1}{5} - \dfrac{7}{10} + \dfrac{17}{20}$

17 $\dfrac{1}{8} - \dfrac{7}{24} + \dfrac{5}{12}$

12 $\dfrac{1}{8} - \dfrac{13}{16} + \dfrac{3}{4}$

15 $\dfrac{2}{3} - \dfrac{5}{6} + \dfrac{1}{2}$

18 $\dfrac{3}{10} + \dfrac{2}{15} - \dfrac{2}{5}$

19 Some scientific calculators will work with fractions.

Using a Casio, $\frac{1}{2} + \frac{1}{3}$ can be found as a fraction by pressing

The display then reads $5\_\!\rfloor 6$; i.e. $\frac{1}{2} + \frac{1}{3} = \frac{5}{6}$

Use your calculator, if it will work in fractions, to check your answers to questions **1** to **18**.

In a class of school children, $\frac{1}{3}$ of the children come to school by bus, $\frac{1}{4}$ come to school on bicycles and the rest walk to school.
What fraction of the children ride to school?
What fraction do not use a bus?

The fraction who ride to school on bicycle

$$\text{or bus} = \frac{1}{3} + \frac{1}{4}$$

$$= \frac{4+3}{12} = \frac{7}{12}$$

Therefore $\frac{7}{12}$ of the children ride to school.

The complete class of children is a whole unit, i.e. 1.

The fraction of children who do not use a bus is found by taking the bus users from the complete class,

i.e.
$$\frac{1}{1} - \frac{1}{3} = \frac{3}{3} - \frac{1}{3}$$

$$= \frac{3-1}{3} = \frac{2}{3}$$

Do not use your calculator for these questions.

20 A girl spends $\frac{1}{5}$ of her pocket money on sweets and $\frac{2}{3}$ on records.
What fraction has she spent?
What fraction has she left?

21 A group of friends went to a hamburger bar; $\frac{2}{5}$ of them bought a hamburger, $\frac{1}{3}$ of them just bought chips. The rest bought cola.
What fraction of the group bought food?
What fraction bought a drink?

22 At a pop festival, $\frac{2}{3}$ of the groups were all male, $\frac{1}{4}$ of the groups included one girl and the rest included more than one girl.
What fraction of the groups
  a were not all male   **b** contained more than one girl?

23 At a Youth Club, $\frac{1}{2}$ of the meetings are for playing table tennis, $\frac{1}{8}$ of the meetings are discussions and the rest are record sessions.
What fraction of the meetings are
  a record sessions   **b** not for discussions?

24 Jim can dig a plot of ground in 5 hours and Ray can dig it in 6 hours.

What fraction of the plot can each of them dig in 1 hour?

If they work together, what fraction can they dig in 1 hour?

What fraction remains to be dug after 2 hours?

MIXED NUMBERS AND IMPROPER FRACTIONS

Most of the fractions we have met so far have been less than a whole unit. These are called *proper* fractions. But we often have more than a whole unit. Suppose, for instance, that we have one and a quarter bars of chocolate:

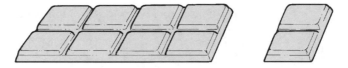

We have $1\frac{1}{4}$ bars, and $1\frac{1}{4}$ is called a mixed number.

Another way of describing the amount of chocolate is to say that we have five quarter bars.

We have $\frac{5}{4}$ bars and $\frac{5}{4}$ is called an *improper* fraction because the numerator is bigger than the denominator.

But the amount of chocolate in the two examples is the same, so

$$\frac{5}{4} = 1\frac{1}{4}$$

Improper fractions can be changed into mixed numbers by finding out how many whole units there are. For instance, to change $\frac{8}{3}$ into a mixed number we look for the biggest number below 8 that divides by 3, i.e. 6. Then

$$\frac{8}{3} = \frac{6+2}{3} = \frac{6}{3} + \frac{2}{3} = 2 + \frac{2}{3} = 2\frac{2}{3}$$

We can also change mixed numbers into improper fractions. For instance, in $2\frac{4}{5}$ we have two whole units and $\frac{4}{5}$. In each whole unit there are five fifths, so in $2\frac{4}{5}$ we have ten fifths and four fifths, i.e.

$$2\frac{4}{5} = \frac{10}{5} + \frac{4}{5} = \frac{14}{5}$$

Change $\frac{15}{4}$ into a mixed number.

$\frac{15}{4} = \frac{12+3}{4}$

12 is the biggest number below 15 that divides exactly by 4.

$= \frac{12}{4} + \frac{3}{4}$

$= 3\frac{3}{4}$

Do not use a calculator in this exercise.

In questions **1** to **16** change the improper fractions into mixed numbers.

1 $\frac{9}{4}$ **5** $\frac{88}{9}$ **9** $\frac{127}{5}$ **13** $\frac{41}{3}$

2 $\frac{19}{4}$ **6** $\frac{7}{2}$ **10** $\frac{114}{11}$ **14** $\frac{67}{5}$

3 $\frac{37}{6}$ **7** $\frac{27}{4}$ **11** $\frac{83}{7}$ **15** $\frac{49}{10}$

4 $\frac{53}{10}$ **8** $\frac{41}{8}$ **12** $\frac{91}{6}$ **16** $\frac{53}{7}$

Change $3\frac{1}{7}$ into an improper fraction.

$3\frac{1}{7} = 3 + \frac{1}{7}$

There are 7 sevenths in 1, so there are 7×3, i.e. 21 sevenths in 3.

$= \frac{21}{7} + \frac{1}{7}$

$= \frac{22}{7}$

In questions **17** to **32** change the mixed numbers into improper fractions.

17 $4\frac{1}{3}$ **21** $8\frac{1}{7}$ **25** $3\frac{2}{3}$ **29** $8\frac{3}{4}$

18 $8\frac{1}{4}$ **22** $6\frac{3}{5}$ **26** $5\frac{1}{2}$ **30** $1\frac{9}{10}$

19 $1\frac{7}{10}$ **23** $2\frac{6}{7}$ **27** $7\frac{2}{5}$ **31** $7\frac{3}{8}$

20 $10\frac{8}{9}$ **24** $4\frac{1}{6}$ **28** $3\frac{4}{5}$ **32** $4\frac{5}{12}$

THE MEANING OF
15 ÷ 4

$15 \div 4$ means 'how many fours are there in 15?'

There are 3 fours in 15 with 3 left over, so $15 \div 4 = 3$, remainder 3.

Now that remainder, 3, is $\frac{3}{4}$ of 4.

Thus we can say that there are $3\frac{3}{4}$ fours in 15

i.e.
$$15 \div 4 = 3\frac{3}{4}$$

But
$$\frac{15}{4} = 3\frac{3}{4}$$

Therefore $\boxed{15 \div 4 \text{ and } \frac{15}{4} \text{ mean the same thing}}$

EXERCISE 4I

> Calculate $27 \div 8$, giving your answer as a mixed number.
>
> $27 \div 8 = \frac{27}{8}$
>
> $\qquad = 3\frac{3}{8}$

Calculate the following divisions, giving your answers as mixed numbers.

1 $36 \div 7$	**5** $82 \div 5$	**9** $98 \div 12$
2 $59 \div 6$	**6** $29 \div 4$	**10** $107 \div 10$
3 $52 \div 11$	**7** $41 \div 3$	**11** $37 \div 5$
4 $20 \div 8$	**8** $64 \div 9$	**12** $52 \div 8$

ADDING MIXED
NUMBERS

If we want to find the value of $2\frac{1}{3} + 3\frac{1}{4}$ we add the whole numbers and then the fractions, i.e.

$$2\frac{1}{3} + 3\frac{1}{4} = 2 + 3 + \frac{1}{3} + \frac{1}{4}$$

$$= 5 + \frac{4+3}{12}$$

$$= 5 + \frac{7}{12}$$

$$= 5\frac{7}{12}$$

Sometimes there is an extra step in the calculation. For example

$$3\tfrac{1}{2} + 2\tfrac{3}{8} + 5\tfrac{1}{4} = 3 + 2 + 5 + \tfrac{1}{2} + \tfrac{3}{8} + \tfrac{1}{4}$$

$$= 10 + \tfrac{4}{8} + \tfrac{3}{8} + \tfrac{2}{8}$$

$$= 10 + \tfrac{4+3+2}{8} = 10 + \tfrac{9}{8}$$

But $\tfrac{9}{8}$ is an improper fraction, so we change it into a mixed number

i.e.
$$3\tfrac{1}{2} + 2\tfrac{3}{8} + 5\tfrac{1}{4} = 10 + \tfrac{8+1}{8}$$

$$= 10 + 1 + \tfrac{1}{8}$$

$$= 11\tfrac{1}{8}$$

EXERCISE 4J

Find $3\tfrac{1}{3} + 4\tfrac{1}{5}$

$$3\tfrac{1}{3} + 4\tfrac{1}{5} = 7 + \tfrac{1}{3} + \tfrac{1}{5}$$

$$= 7\tfrac{5+3}{15}$$

$$= 7\tfrac{8}{15}$$

Find

1 $2\tfrac{1}{4} + 3\tfrac{1}{2}$ **4** $5\tfrac{1}{9} + 4\tfrac{1}{3}$ **7** $2\tfrac{1}{7} + 1\tfrac{1}{14}$

2 $1\tfrac{1}{2} + 2\tfrac{1}{3}$ **5** $1\tfrac{7}{10} + 2\tfrac{1}{5}$ **8** $6\tfrac{3}{10} + 1\tfrac{2}{5}$

3 $4\tfrac{1}{5} + 1\tfrac{3}{8}$ **6** $3\tfrac{1}{4} + 1\tfrac{1}{5}$ **9** $3\tfrac{5}{12} + 2\tfrac{1}{6}$

Find $2\tfrac{1}{2} + 4\tfrac{3}{4} + 1\tfrac{1}{6}$

$$2\tfrac{1}{2} + 4\tfrac{3}{4} + 1\tfrac{1}{6} = 7\tfrac{6+9+2}{12}$$ Add whole numbers.

$$= 7\tfrac{17}{12}$$ Add fractions.

$$= 7 + 1 + \tfrac{5}{12}$$ Split $\tfrac{17}{12}$ into $1 + \tfrac{5}{12}$.

$$= 8\tfrac{5}{12}$$

Find

10 $3\frac{1}{2} + 2\frac{5}{9}$

15 $8\frac{4}{7} + 5\frac{2}{3}$

11 $7\frac{5}{8} + 3\frac{7}{16}$

16 $2\frac{7}{10} + 9\frac{3}{5}$

12 $1\frac{3}{4} + 4\frac{7}{12}$

17 $5\frac{9}{10} + 2\frac{2}{5}$

13 $3\frac{5}{7} + 7\frac{1}{2}$

18 $9\frac{2}{3} + 8\frac{5}{6}$

14 $6\frac{1}{2} + 1\frac{9}{16}$

19 $2\frac{4}{5} + 7\frac{3}{10}$

20 $4\frac{2}{5} + 2\frac{1}{4}$

25 $3\frac{3}{4} + 4\frac{2}{5}$

21 $7\frac{11}{12} + 1\frac{3}{8}$

26 $5\frac{2}{7} + 3\frac{1}{4}$

22 $8\frac{7}{8} + 3\frac{3}{16}$

27 $6\frac{3}{10} + 4\frac{4}{5}$

23 $1\frac{1}{4} + 3\frac{2}{3} + 6\frac{7}{12}$

28 $3\frac{3}{4} + 5\frac{1}{8} + 8\frac{5}{16}$

24 $5\frac{1}{7} + 4\frac{1}{2} + 7\frac{11}{14}$

29 $10\frac{2}{3} + 3\frac{1}{6} + 7\frac{2}{9}$

30 Sid wanted to raise his front gate because it was dragging on the ground when it opened. He put three washers on each support: one $\frac{1}{8}$ inch thick, one $\frac{3}{16}$ inch thick and one $\frac{1}{16}$ inch thick. How much higher did this make the gate?

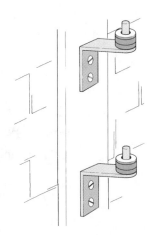

31 George has three pieces of wood. One is $10\frac{1}{8}$ ft long, another is $6\frac{1}{2}$ ft long and the third is $5\frac{7}{8}$ ft long. How far do they stretch if they are laid end to end?

32 A recipe for sugar crisps requires

$\frac{1}{2}$ cup fat, $\frac{3}{4}$ cup sugar, $\frac{2}{3}$ cup syrup and $2\frac{1}{2}$ cups flour.

How many cups of ingredients is this altogether?

33 Is $6\frac{1}{4}$ bigger or smaller than the sum of $3\frac{1}{3}$ and $2\frac{7}{8}$?

34 Hank has a length of timber that is $9\frac{1}{2}$ ft long. He wants to cut off three pieces, one $1\frac{5}{8}$ ft long, a second twice as long, and a third three times as long as the first.
Does he have enough wood?

SUBTRACTING MIXED NUMBERS

If we want to find the value of $5\frac{3}{4} - 2\frac{2}{5}$ we can use the same method as for adding, that is, deal with the whole numbers and fractions separately.

$$5\frac{3}{4} - 2\frac{2}{5} = 5 - 2 + \frac{3}{4} - \frac{2}{5}$$
$$= 3 + \frac{15-8}{20}$$
$$= 3 + \frac{7}{20}$$
$$= 3\frac{7}{20}$$

But when we find the value of $6\frac{1}{4} - 2\frac{4}{5}$ we get

$$6\frac{1}{4} - 2\frac{4}{5} = 6 - 2 + \frac{1}{4} - \frac{4}{5}$$
$$= 4 + \frac{1}{4} - \frac{4}{5}$$

This time it is not so easy to deal with the fractions because $\frac{4}{5}$ is bigger than $\frac{1}{4}$. We can get over this difficulty by taking one of the whole units and changing it into a fraction. This gives

$$3 + 1 + \frac{1}{4} - \frac{4}{5} = 3 + \frac{20}{20} + \frac{5}{20} - \frac{16}{20}$$
$$= 3 + \frac{20+5-16}{20}$$
$$= 3 + \frac{9}{20}$$
$$= 3\frac{9}{20}$$

EXERCISE 4K

> Find $5\frac{5}{8} - 3\frac{1}{4}$
>
> $$5\frac{5}{8} - 3\frac{1}{4} = 2 + \frac{5}{8} - \frac{2}{8}$$
> $$= 2 + \frac{5-2}{8}$$
> $$= 2\frac{3}{8}$$

Find

1 $2\frac{3}{4} - 1\frac{1}{8}$ **5** $7\frac{3}{4} - 2\frac{1}{3}$ **9** $4\frac{4}{5} - 3\frac{1}{10}$

2 $3\frac{2}{3} - 1\frac{2}{5}$ **6** $3\frac{5}{6} - 2\frac{1}{3}$ **10** $6\frac{5}{7} - 3\frac{2}{5}$

3 $1\frac{5}{6} - \frac{2}{3}$ **7** $2\frac{6}{7} - 1\frac{1}{2}$ **11** $3\frac{1}{3} - 1\frac{1}{5}$

4 $3\frac{1}{4} - 2\frac{1}{8}$ **8** $4\frac{1}{2} - 2\frac{1}{5}$ **12** $5\frac{3}{4} - 2\frac{1}{2}$

> Find $8\frac{1}{3} - 4\frac{3}{4}$
>
> $$8\frac{1}{3} - 4\frac{3}{4} = 4 + \frac{1}{3} - \frac{3}{4}$$
> $$= 3 + 1 + \frac{1}{3} - \frac{3}{4}$$
> $$= 3 + \frac{12}{12} + \frac{4}{12} - \frac{9}{12}$$
> $$= 3 + \frac{12+4-9}{12}$$
> $$= 3 + \frac{7}{12}$$
> $$= 3\frac{7}{12}$$
>
> $\frac{3}{4}$ is bigger than $\frac{1}{3}$ so we take one of the whole units and change it into a fraction.

Find

13 $8\frac{4}{5} - 5\frac{1}{2}$ **17** $7\frac{1}{2} - 5\frac{3}{4}$ **21** $8\frac{5}{7} - 5\frac{3}{4}$

14 $5\frac{7}{9} - 3\frac{5}{7}$ **18** $4\frac{3}{5} - 1\frac{1}{4}$ **22** $3\frac{1}{2} - 1\frac{7}{8}$

15 $4\frac{5}{8} - 1\frac{1}{3}$ **19** $7\frac{6}{7} - 4\frac{3}{5}$ **23** $2\frac{1}{2} - 1\frac{3}{4}$

16 $6\frac{3}{4} - 3\frac{6}{7}$ **20** $8\frac{8}{11} - 2\frac{2}{3}$ **24** $5\frac{4}{7} - 3\frac{4}{5}$

25 $3\frac{2}{3} - 1\frac{4}{5}$ **29** $5\frac{6}{7} - 3\frac{3}{4}$ **33** $9\frac{2}{9} - 3\frac{6}{7}$

26 $10\frac{1}{2} - 5\frac{2}{3}$ **30** $6\frac{1}{8} - 3\frac{7}{12}$ **34** $4\frac{1}{3} - 3\frac{5}{8}$

27 $3\frac{1}{4} - 1\frac{7}{8}$ **31** $8\frac{2}{3} - 7\frac{8}{9}$ **35** $9\frac{7}{10} - 5\frac{4}{5}$

28 $5\frac{3}{5} - 2\frac{9}{10}$ **32** $4\frac{1}{6} - 2\frac{2}{3}$ **36** $2\frac{5}{12} - 1\frac{3}{4}$

37 Sheila cuts a piece of metal $5\frac{1}{2}$ inches long from a bar $27\frac{7}{10}$ inches long. What length remains?

38 A recipe for frozen Christmas puddings lists the main ingredients as: $1\frac{1}{2}$ cups of vanilla wafer crumbs, $\frac{1}{2}$ cup chopped nuts, $\frac{1}{2}$ cup chopped dates, $\frac{1}{2}$ cup chopped fruit peel, $\frac{1}{4}$ cup hot orange juice, $\frac{1}{3}$ cup sugar and 1 cup whipped cream. If all the ingredients would fill $4\frac{3}{4}$ cups how many cups of unlisted ingredients are there?

39 How much less than 1 is the difference between $5\frac{2}{3}$ and $4\frac{7}{8}$?

40 How much more than 2 is the difference between $3\frac{4}{5}$ and $6\frac{3}{4}$?

41 Which is the greater and by how much: the difference between $4\frac{7}{8}$ and $9\frac{1}{3}$ or the sum of $1\frac{3}{4}$ and $2\frac{3}{10}$?

MIXED EXERCISE

EXERCISE 4L

1 a Write $\frac{5}{6}$ as an equivalent fraction with a numerator of 25.

  b Write $\frac{4}{9}$ as an equivalent fraction with a denominator of 36.

2 Simplify the following fractions.

  a $\frac{16}{32}$ **b** $\frac{35}{55}$ **c** $\frac{49}{63}$

3 Find   **a** $\frac{4}{11} + \frac{3}{11}$ **b** $\frac{5}{12} + \frac{1}{6}$ **c** $\frac{5}{24} + \frac{1}{4}$ **d** $\frac{3}{10} + \frac{41}{100} + \frac{1}{4}$

4 Find   **a** $\frac{5}{9} - \frac{2}{9}$ **b** $\frac{2}{3} - \frac{5}{12}$ **c** $\frac{7}{11} - \frac{3}{8}$ **d** $\frac{2}{3} - \frac{3}{4} + \frac{5}{12}$

5 **a** Change **i** $\frac{68}{5}$ into a mixed number

   ii $2\frac{3}{7}$ into an improper fraction

   b Calculate $57 \div 8$ giving your answer as a mixed number.

6 Find   **a** $4\frac{2}{9} + 3\frac{1}{3}$ **b** $4\frac{2}{5} - 1\frac{1}{4}$ **c** $5\frac{2}{5} - 3\frac{7}{10}$ **d** $6\frac{3}{4} + 2\frac{5}{9}$

INVESTIGATION

a Use the digits 2, 5, 7 and 9 to write down all the fractions it is possible to make, using a single digit on the top and a single digit on the bottom. Some of these, for example $\frac{7}{5}$, will be improper fractions. (You should have 16 fractions altogether.)

b How many fractions use the same digit twice, e.g. $\frac{7}{7}$?

c Which fraction is   **i** smallest   **ii** largest?

d Which fractions have a value that is
   i less than   **ii** 1   **iii** more than 1 ?

e Write the sixteen fractions in order of size starting with the smallest.

f Copy and fill in the table so that the fractions in the top row all have a numerator of 2 and the denominators increase in size as you move from left to right.

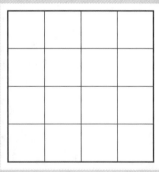

g Similarly for the second line but with every numerator 5.

h Likewise in the third line every numerator must be 7 and in the last line every numerator must be 9.

i What do you notice about the fractions in the diagonal starting with the fraction $\frac{2}{2}$?

j What do you notice about the values of all the fractions that are
   i above this diagonal   **ii** below this diagonal?

TRIANGLES AND QUADRILATERALS

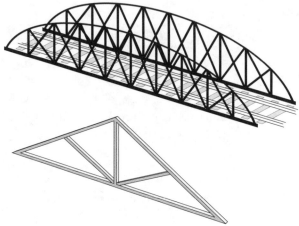

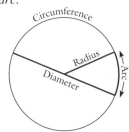

The diagrams show part of a railway bridge and a roof truss for a house.

- After these have been designed they need to be drawn accurately before they can be made.
- A modern bridge builder would produce accurate drawings using a computer but the roof truss is still simple enough to draw using pencil and paper methods.

To make accurate drawings of simple shapes you need

| a *sharp* pencil | a pair of compasses |
| a ruler | a protractor. |

USING A PAIR OF COMPASSES

We use a pair of compasses to draw a circle or an arc of a circle.

The edge of a circle is called the *circumference*.

Part of the circumference of a circle is called an *arc*.

All points on the circumference are the same distance from the centre.

A straight line drawn from the centre of a circle to the circumference is a *radius*.

A straight line drawn through the centre of a circle from edge to edge is a *diameter*.

Using a pair of compasses needs practice.

Draw several circles.
Make some of them small and some large.
You should not be able to see the place
where you start and finish.

Draw a circle of radius 7 cm.
Draw a diameter of the circle and measure it.
Is it the correct length?

Now try drawing the daisy pattern below.

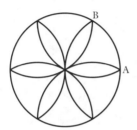

Draw a circle of radius 5 cm. Keeping the
radius the same, put the point of the
compasses at A and draw an arc to meet the
circle in two places, one of which is B. Move
the point to B and repeat. Carry on moving
the point of your compasses round the circle
until the pattern is complete.

Repeat the daisy pattern but this time draw complete circles instead of
arcs.

There are some more patterns using compasses on pages 111 and 112.

**DRAWING
STRAIGHT LINES
OF A GIVEN
LENGTH**

To draw a straight line that is 5 cm long, start by using your ruler to draw
a line that is *longer* than 5 cm.
Then mark a point on this line near one end as shown. Label it A.

Next set your compasses to
measure 5 cm on your ruler.

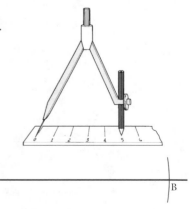

Then put the point of the
compasses on the line at A and
draw an arc to cut the line as
shown.

The length of line between A and B should be 5 cm. Measure it with
your ruler.

EXERCISE 5A   Draw, as accurately as you can, straight lines of the following lengths.

1 6 cm   **3** 12 cm   **5** 8.5 cm   **7** 4.5 cm

2 2 cm   **4** 9 cm   **6** 3.5 cm   **8** 6.8 cm

TRIANGLES   A triangle has three sides and three angles.

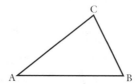

The corners of the triangle are called vertices. (One corner is called a vertex.) So that we can refer to one particular side, or to one particular angle, we label the vertices using capital letters.

In the diagram above we used the letters A, B and C so we can now talk about 'the triangle ABC' or '△ABC'.

The side between A and B is called 'the side AB' or AB.

The side between A and C is called 'the side AC' or AC.

The side between B and C is called 'the side BC' or BC.

The angle at the corner A is called 'angle A' or $\widehat{A}$ for short.

We can also describe the angle at A using the three letters on the arms that enclose it, with A in the middle, i.e. $C\widehat{A}B$ or $B\widehat{A}C$.

EXERCISE 5B   **1** Write down the name of the side which is 4 cm long.

Write down the name of the side which is 2 cm long.

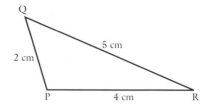

2 Write down the name of

a the side which is 2.5 cm long

b the side which is 2 cm long

c the angle which is 70°.

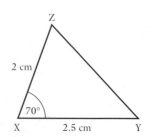

In the following questions, draw a freehand copy of the triangle and mark the given measurements on your drawing.

A FREEHAND COPY MEANS THAT THE COPY DOES NOT HAVE TO BE EXACTLY THE SAME AS THE ORIGINAL. THE COPY SHOULD BE NEAT, SO USE A STRAIGHT EDGE TO DRAW THE SIDES.

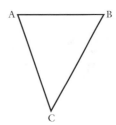

3 In $\triangle ABC$, $AB = 4\,cm$, $\widehat{B} = 60°$, $\widehat{C} = 50°$.

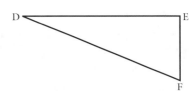

4 In $\triangle DEF$, $\widehat{E} = 90°$, $\widehat{F} = 70°$, $EF = 3\,cm$.

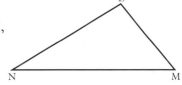

5 In $\triangle LMN$, $\widehat{L} = 100°$, $\widehat{N} = 30°$, $NL = 2.5\,cm$.

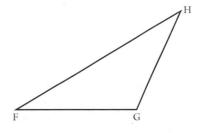

6 In $\triangle FGH$, $FG = 3.5\,cm$, $GH = 3\,cm$, $\widehat{H} = 35°$.

Make a freehand drawing of the following triangles. Label each one and mark the measurements given.

7 $\triangle ABC$ in which $AB = 10\,cm$, $BC = 8\,cm$ and $\widehat{B} = 60°$

8 $\triangle PQR$ in which $\widehat{P} = 90°$, $\widehat{Q} = 30°$ and $PQ = 6\,cm$

9 $\triangle DEF$ in which $DE = 8\,cm$, $\widehat{D} = 50°$ and $DF = 6\,cm$

10 $\triangle XYZ$ in which $XY = 10\,cm$, $\widehat{X} = 30°$ and $\widehat{Y} = 80°$

**ANGLES OF A
TRIANGLE**

Draw a large triangle of any shape. Use a straight edge to draw the sides. Measure each angle in this triangle, turning your page to a convenient position when necessary. Add up the sizes of the three angles.

Draw another triangle of a different shape. Again measure each angle and then add up their sizes.

Now try this: on a piece of paper draw a triangle of any shape and cut it out. Next tear off each corner and place the three corners together.

They should look like this:

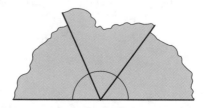

> The three angles of a triangle add up to 180°.

EXERCISE 5C

Find the size of angle A.

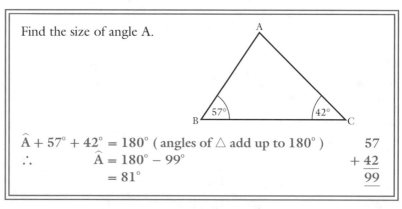

$\hat{A} + 57° + 42° = 180°$ (angles of $\triangle$ add up to $180°$)

$\therefore \qquad \hat{A} = 180° - 99°$

$\qquad = 81°$

$\begin{array}{r} 57 \\ + 42 \\ \hline 99 \\ \hline \end{array}$

Find the size of angle A (an angle marked with a square is a right angle).

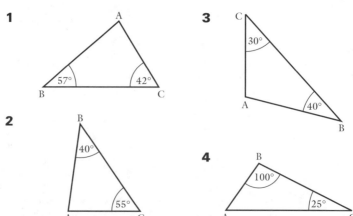

1

2

3

4

5

6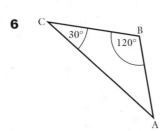

7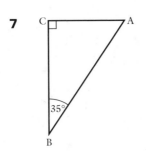

8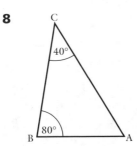

9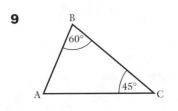

10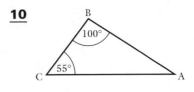

11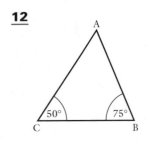

12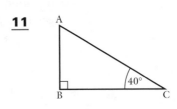

13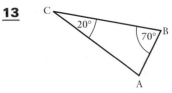

14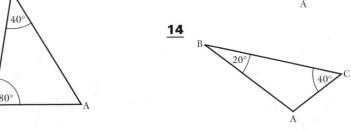

15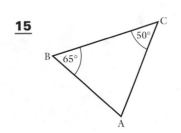

Remember these facts which are needed for the remaining questions in this exercise:

- Vertically opposite angles are equal.
- Angles on a straight line add up to 180°.
- Angles of a triangle add up to 180°.

In each question make a freehand copy of the diagram and mark the sizes of the angles that you are asked to find.

16 Find angles $d°$ and $f°$.

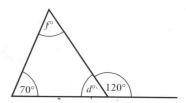

17 Find angles $s°$ and $t°$.

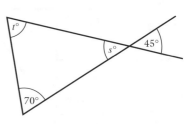

18 Find each of the equal angles $x°$.

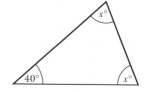

19 Find angles $p°$ and $q°$.

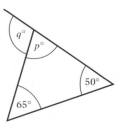

20 Find each of the equal angles $g°$.

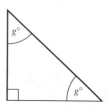

21 Find each of the equal angles $x°$.

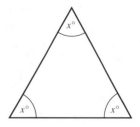

22 Find angles $s°$ and $t°$.

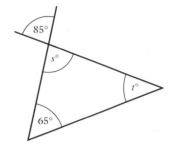

23 Find each of the equal angles $q°$ and angle $p°$.

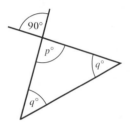

24 Angle $h°$ is twice angle $j°$. Find angles $h°$ and $j°$.

25

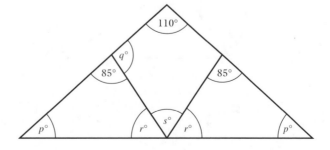

This section of a roof is symmetrical about the vertical line through its highest point. Find the angles marked $p°$, $q°$, $r°$ and $s°$.

CONSTRUCTING TRIANGLES GIVEN ONE SIDE AND TWO ANGLES

If we are given enough information about a triangle we can make an accurate drawing of that triangle. The mathematical word for 'make an accurate drawing of' is 'construct'.

For example: construct $\triangle ABC$ in which $AB = 7\,cm$, $\widehat{A} = 30°$ and $\widehat{B} = 40°$.

First make a freehand sketch of $\triangle ABC$ and put all the given measurements in your sketch.

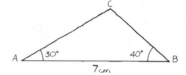

Next draw the line AB making it 7 cm long. Label the ends.

Then use your protractor to make an angle of 30° at A.

Next make an angle of 40° at B. If necessary extend the arms of the angles until they cross; this is the point C.

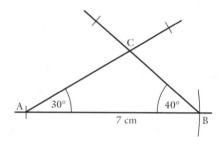

We can calculate $A\widehat{C}B$ because all three angles add up to $180°$ so $A\widehat{C}B = 110°$. Now as a check we can measure $A\widehat{C}B$ in our construction.

EXERCISE 5D

Construct the following triangles. Calculate the third angle in each triangle and then measure this angle to check the accuracy of your construction.

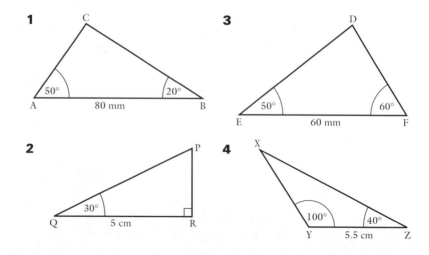

1

50° 80 mm 20°
A   B
C

3

50° 60 mm 60°
E   F
D

2

30° 5 cm
Q   R
P

4

100° 5.5 cm 40°
Y   Z
X

5 △UVW in which $\hat{V} = 35°$, VW $= 5.5$ cm, $\hat{W} = 75°$

6 △FGH in which $\hat{F} = 55°$, $\hat{G} = 70°$, FG $= 4.5$ cm

7 △KLM in which KM $= 10$ cm, $\hat{K} = 45°$, $\hat{M} = 45°$

CONSTRUCTING TRIANGLES GIVEN TWO SIDES AND THE ANGLE BETWEEN THE TWO SIDES

To construct △PQR in which PQ $= 4.5$ cm, PR $= 5.5$ cm and $\hat{P} = 35°$, first draw a freehand sketch of △PQR and put in all the measurements that you are given.

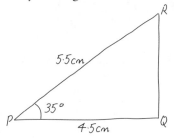

Draw one of the sides whose length you know; we will draw PQ.

Now using your protractor make an angle of 35° at P. Make the arm of the angle quite long.

Next use your compasses to measure the length of PR on your ruler.

Then with the point of your compasses at P, draw an arc to cut the arm of the angle. This is the point R.

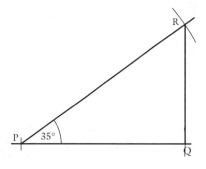

Now join R and Q.

EXERCISE 5E

Construct each of the following triangles and measure the third side.

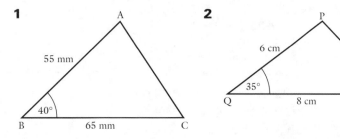

3

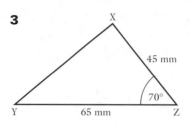

4

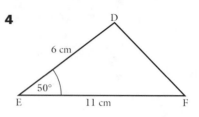

5 △HJK in which HK = 4.2 cm, $\widehat{H}$ = 45°, HJ = 5.3 cm

6 △ABC in which AC = 6.3 cm, $\widehat{C}$ = 48°, CB = 5.1 cm

7 △XYZ in which $\widehat{Y}$ = 65°, XY = 3.8 cm, YZ = 4.2 cm

CONSTRUCTING TRIANGLES GIVEN THE LENGTHS OF THE THREE SIDES

To construct △XYZ in which XY = 5.5 cm, XZ = 3.5 cm and YZ = 6.5 cm, first draw a freehand sketch of the triangle and put in all the given measurements.

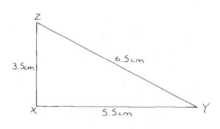

Next draw one side; we will draw XY.

Then set your compasses to the length of XZ on your ruler. With the point of your compasses at X draw a wide arc.

Next set your compasses to the length of YZ on your ruler. Then with the point of your compasses at Y draw another large arc to cut the first arc. Where the two arcs cross is the point Z. Join ZX and ZY.

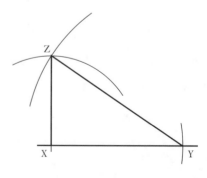

EXERCISE 5F

Construct the following triangles.

1

70 mm   B   80 mm

A   120 mm   C

3

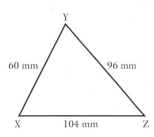

60 mm   Y   96 mm

X   104 mm   Z

2

4.5 cm   P   6 cm

Q   8 cm   R

4

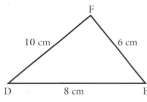

10 cm   F   6 cm

D   8 cm   E

5 △ABC in which AB = 7.3 cm, BC = 6.1 cm, AC = 4.7 cm

6 △DEF in which DE = 10.4 cm, EF = 7.4 cm, DF = 8.2 cm

7 △PQR in which PQ = 8.8 cm, QR = 6.6 cm, PR = 11 cm

EXERCISE 5G

Construct the following triangles. Remember to draw a freehand diagram of the triangle first and then decide which method you need to use.

1 △ABC in which AB = 7 cm, $\widehat{A} = 30°$, $\widehat{B} = 50°$

2 △PQR in which PQ = 50 mm, QR = 40 mm, RP = 70 mm

3 △BCD in which $\widehat{B} = 60°$, BC = 5 cm, BD = 4 cm

4 △WXY in which WX = 5 cm, XY = 6 cm, $\widehat{X} = 90°$

5 △KLM in which KL = 64 mm, LM = 82 mm, KM = 126 mm

6 △ABC in which $\widehat{A} = 45°$, AC = 8 cm, $\widehat{C} = 110°$

7 △CDE in which CD = DE = 60 mm, $\widehat{D} = 60°$

8 Try to construct a triangle ABC in which $\widehat{A} = 30°$, AB = 5 cm, BC = 3 cm.

9 Construct two triangles which fit the following measurements: △PQR in which $\widehat{P} = 60°$, PQ = 6 cm, QR = 5.5 cm.

10 Construct △ABC in which $\widehat{A} = 120°$, AB = 4 cm, BC = 6 cm. Can you construct more than one triangle that fits these measurements?

QUADRILATERALS A quadrilateral has four sides. These shapes are examples of quadrilaterals:

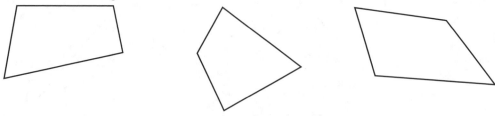

The following diagrams are also quadrilaterals, but each one is a 'special' quadrilateral with its own name:

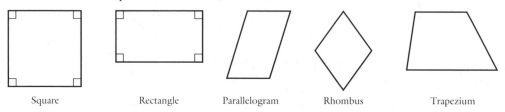

| Square | Rectangle | Parallelogram | Rhombus | Trapezium |

PARALLEL LINES If a pair of opposite sides of a square are extended, they will never meet.

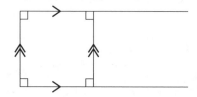

A pair of lines like these are called *parallel* lines. We use arrows to mark a pair of lines that are parallel.

A square has two pairs of parallel sides.

THE SUM OF THE ANGLES OF A QUADRILATERAL Draw yourself a large quadrilateral, but do not make it one of the special cases. Measure each angle and then add up the sizes of the four angles.

Do this again with another three quadrilaterals.

Now try this: on a piece of paper draw a quadrilateral. Tear off each corner and place the vertices together. It should look like this:

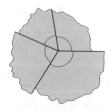

> The sum of the four angles of a quadrilateral is 360°.

This is true of any quadrilateral whatever its shape or size.

EXERCISE 5H Make a freehand copy of the following diagrams and mark on your diagram the sizes of the required angles. You can also write in the sizes of any other angles that you may need to find.

In questions **1** to **10** find the size of the angle marked $d°$.

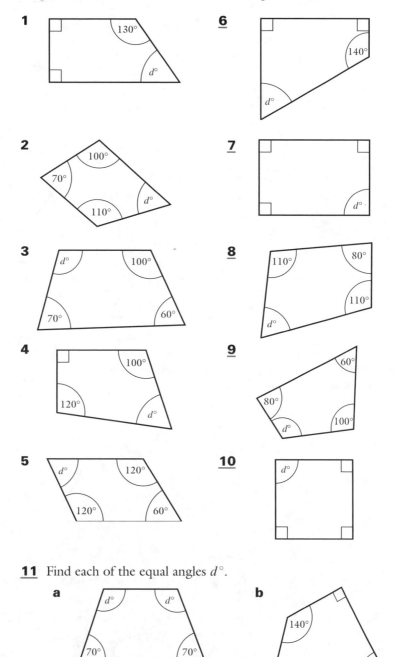

1

130°

$d°$

6

140°

$d°$

2

100°

70°

110°

$d°$

7

$d°$

3

$d°$ 100°

70°   60°

8

110°   80°

110°

$d°$

4

100°

120°

$d°$

9

60°

80°

100°

$d°$

5

$d°$ 120°

120°   60°

10

$d°$

11 Find each of the equal angles $d°$.

a

$d°$ $d°$

70°   70°

b

140°

$d°$

$d°$

12 Angle $e°$ is twice angle $d°$.
Find angles $d°$ and $e°$.

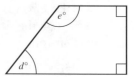

13 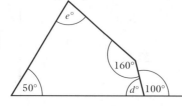 Find angles $d°$ and $e°$.

14 Find each of the equal angles $e°$.

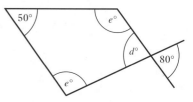

15 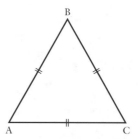 Angles $d°$ and $e°$ are supplementary. Find each of the equal angles $e°$.

EQUILATERAL AND ISOSCELES TRIANGLES

A triangle in which all three sides are the same length is called an *equilateral triangle*.

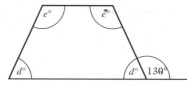

(When lines are marked ——||——, it means they are the same length.)

Construct an equilateral triangle in which the sides are each of length 6 cm. Label the vertices A, B and C.

On a separate piece of paper construct a triangle of the same size and cut it out. Label the angles A, B and C inside the triangle.

Place it on your first triangle. Now turn it round and it should still fit exactly. What do you think this means about the three angles? Measure each angle in the triangle.

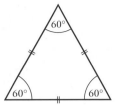

In an equilateral triangle all three sides are the same length and each of the three angles is 60 °.

A triangle in which two sides are equal is called an *isosceles triangle*.

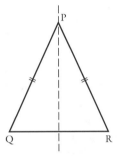

On a piece of paper construct an isosceles triangle PQR in which PQ = 8 cm, PR = 8 cm and $\widehat{P} = 80°$. Cut it out and fold the triangle through P so that the corners at Q and R meet. You should find that $\widehat{Q} = \widehat{R}$. (The fold line is a line of symmetry.)

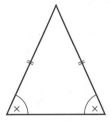

In an isosceles triangle two sides are equal and the two angles at the base of the equal sides are equal.

EXERCISE 5I

In questions **1** to **6** make a freehand sketch of the triangle and mark angles that are equal.

1

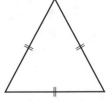

2

3

5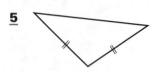

4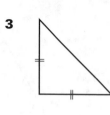

6

Find angle $d°$. Give reasons for your working.

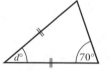

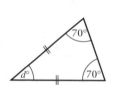 The angles at the base of the equal sides are both 70°.

$\therefore$ $d° + 140° = 180°$
(angles of $\triangle$ add up to 180°)

$\therefore$ angle $d°$ is 40°

In questions **7** to **18** find angle $d°$. Give reasons for your working.

7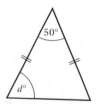

9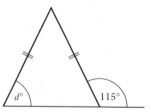

8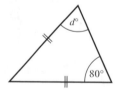

10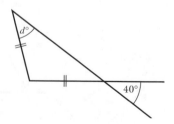

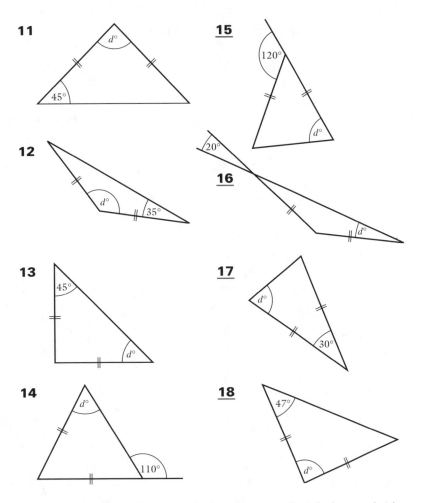

In questions **19** to **22** make a freehand copy and mark the equal sides.

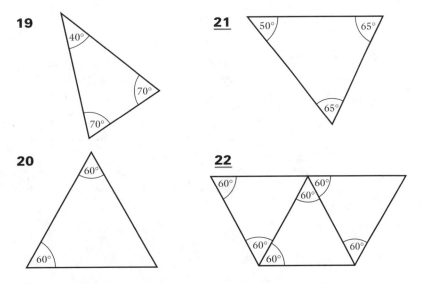

In questions **23** to **28** find angles $d°$ and $e°$.

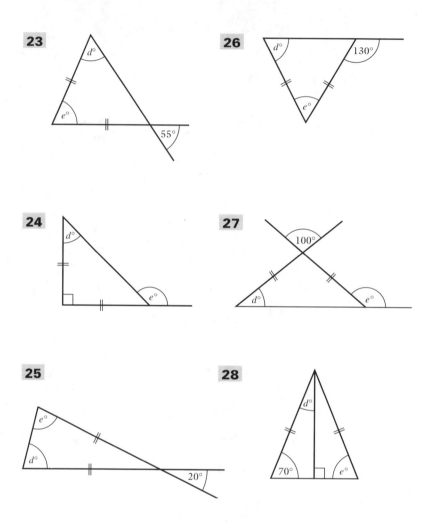

23

24

25

26

27

28

29 The diagram shows a section from a road bridge. The four inclined girders are the same length. Angles $d°$ and $e°$ are supplementary. Find the angles marked $d°$, $e°$, $f°$ and $g°$.

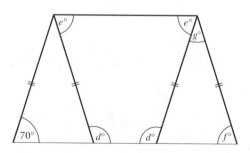

MIXED EXERCISE

EXERCISE 5J

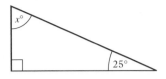

1 Find the size of the angle marked $x°$.

2

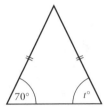

Find the size of the angle marked $t°$.

3 Find the size of the angle marked $y°$.

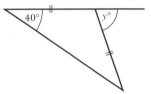

4 Construct $\triangle ABC$ in which $AB = 6$ cm, $BC = 4$ cm and $\hat{B} = 40°$. Measure AC.

5 Construct $\triangle ABC$ in which $BC = 10$ cm, $AB = 6$ cm, $AC = 8$ cm. Measure $\hat{A}$.

PRACTICAL WORK

The patterns below are made using a pair of compasses. Try copying them. Some instructions are given which should help.

1

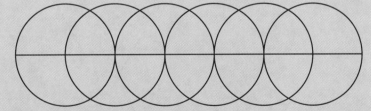

Draw a straight line. Open your compasses to a radius of 3 cm and draw a circle with its centre on the line. Move the point of the compasses 3 cm along the line and draw another circle. Repeat as often as you can.

2 Draw a square of side 4 cm. Open your compasses to a radius of 4 cm and with the point on one corner of the square draw an arc across the square. Repeat on the other three corners.

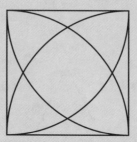

Try the same pattern, but leave out the sides of the square; just mark the corners. A block of four of them looks good.

3 On a piece of paper construct an equilateral triangle of side 4 cm. Construct an equilateral triangle, again of side 4 cm, on each of the three sides of the first triangle. Add tabs as shown.

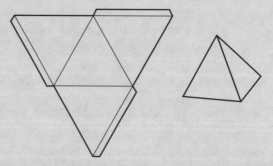

Cut out the complete diagram. Fold the outer triangles up so that the corners meet. Stick the edges together using the tabs. You have made a tetrahedron. (These make good Christmas tree decorations if made out of foil-covered paper.)

PUZZLES

1 This cross can be divided into 4 identical pieces in at least 3 different ways.
Draw diagrams to show how this is possible.

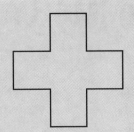

2

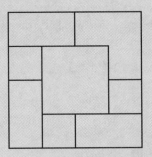

Eight serviettes are placed flat but overlapping on a table and give the outlines shown in the diagram. In which order must they be removed if the top one is always taken off next?

INVESTIGATION

Five different-shaped triangles can be drawn on a 2 × 2 grid.

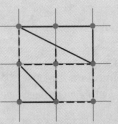

Two of them are shown. Sketch the other three.
Remember that is the same as

Investigate the number of different triangles that can be drawn on a 3 × 3 grid.
Extend your investigation to a 4 × 4 grid and then to a 5 × 5 grid.
Can you find a connection between the number of different triangles that can be drawn and the length of the side of the grid?

SUMMARY 2

MIXED ADDITION AND SUBTRACTION

The sign in front of a number refers to that number only.

The order in which you add or subtract numbers does not matter, so $1 - 5 + 8$ can be calculated in the order $1 + 8 - 5$, i.e. $9 - 5 = 4$

MIXED OPERATIONS OF $\times, \div, +, -$ AND BRACKETS

When a calculation involves a mixture of operations, start by calculating anything inside brackets, then follow the rule 'do the multiplication and division first',

e.g.
$$2 + 3 \times 2 = 2 + 6 \qquad \text{and} \qquad (2 + 3) \times 2 = 5 \times 2$$
$$= 8 \qquad\qquad\qquad\qquad = 10$$

INDEX NUMBERS

The small 2 in 3^2 is called an index and it tells you how many 3s are multiplied together,

e.g. 3^2 means 3×3 and 3^5 means $3 \times 3 \times 3 \times 3 \times 3$

COMMON FACTORS

A factor of a number will divide into the number exactly.

When two or more numbers have the same factor, it is called a common factor,

e.g.   12 and 16 have a common factor of 2 (and of 4).

COMMON MULTIPLES

A multiple of a number has that number as a factor,

e.g.   12 is a multiple of 3.

A common multiple of two or more numbers can be divided exactly by each of those numbers,

e.g.   12 is a common multiple of 2, 3, 4, 6 and 12.

RECTANGULAR NUMBERS

These can be drawn as a rectangular grid of dots, e.g. 6:

SQUARE NUMBERS

These can be drawn as a square grid of dots, e.g. 4:

TRIANGULAR NUMBERS

These can be drawn as a triangular grid of dots, e.g. 6:

ADDITION AND SUBTRACTION OF FRACTIONS

Fractions can be added or subtracted when they have the same denominator,

e.g.   to add $\frac{1}{2}$ to $\frac{1}{3}$ we must first change them into equivalent fractions with the same denominators,

i.e. $\frac{1}{2} + \frac{1}{3} = \frac{1}{2} \times \frac{3}{3} + \frac{1}{3} \times \frac{2}{2} = \frac{3}{6} + \frac{2}{6} = \frac{5}{6}$

MIXED NUMBERS AND IMPROPER FRACTIONS

$1\frac{3}{4}$ is called a mixed number.

$$1\frac{3}{4} = 1 + \frac{3}{4} = \frac{4}{4} + \frac{3}{4} = \frac{7}{4}$$

$\frac{7}{4}$ is called an improper fraction.

ANGLES

One complete revolution $= 4$ right angles $= 360°$.

1 right angle $= 90°$.

An acute angle is less than one right angle.

An obtuse angle is larger than 1 right angle but less than 2 right angles.

A reflex angle is larger than two right angles.

Vertically opposite angles are equal.

Angles on a straight line add up to $180°$.

Two angles that add up to $180°$ are called supplementary angles.

Angles at a point add up to $360°$.

TRIANGLES

The three angles in any triangle add up to $180°$.

An equilateral triangle has three equal sides and each angle is $60°$.

An isosceles triangle has two equal sides and the angles at the base of these sides are equal.

QUADRILATERALS A quadrilateral has four sides.
The four angles in a quadrilateral add up to 360°.

**REVISION
EXERCISE 2.1
(Chapters 1 and 2)**

Do not use a calculator for this exercise.

1 Find

   a $5 \times 3 \times 2 \times 2$ **b** 32×400 **c** 28×21 **d** $7200 \div 30$

2 Find

   a $8 \times (3 + 4)$ **c** $6 + 3 \times 7 - 12 \div 4$
   b $36 \div 9 + 3$ **d** $4 \times 5 \times 6$

3 Find the missing digits in the following calculations.

   a $4 + \square \times 3 = 19$ **b** $3 \times \square \times 5 = 30$ **c** $4 \times 5 \times \square = 140$

4 Find, giving the remainder if there is one

   a $76 \div 6$ **b** $327 \div 43$ **c** $704 \div 16$ **d** $624 \div 25$

5 Find

   a 34×67 **b** 592×54 **c** $3010 \div 70$ **d** $5 \times 20 \div 4 - 6 \times 4$

6 How many degrees does a hand of a clock turn through when it moves

   a from 7 to 12   **b** from 9 to 3   **c** from 2 to 5?

7 Which of these statements are true and which are false?

   a The difference between an obtuse angle and an acute angle is always less than 90°.

   b 190° is an example of an obtuse angle.

   c Every reflex angle is bigger than every obtuse angle.

   d The difference between a reflex angle and an obtuse angle is sometimes less than 90°.

8 Estimate the size of each of the following angles.

   a   **b**   **c**

9 Find the size of each marked angle.

a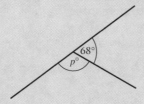

b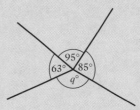

10 Find the size of each marked angle.

a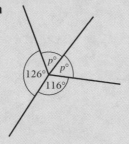

b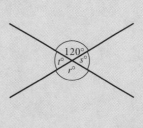

REVISION EXERCISE 2.2
(Chapters 3, 4 and 5)

Do not use a calculator for this exercise.

1 **a** Write down all the multiples of 7 between 30 and 70.

b Write down all the prime numbers between 20 and 40.

c Write 20 as the sum of two prime numbers.

2 **a** Write $3 \times 3 \times 3 \times 3 \times 3$ in index form.

b Find the value of **i** 7^2 **ii** 3^4 **iii** five cubed

3 **a** Which of the following numbers are divisible by 3?
i 52 **ii** 137 **iii** 591

b Is 1242 divisible by 18?

4 **a** Express 112 in prime factors in index form.

b Find the largest whole number that will divide exactly into
i 28, 42 and 84 **ii** 45, 60 and 75

c Which of the numbers between 10 and 30 inclusive are
i rectangular numbers
ii square numbers
iii triangular numbers?

5 Change each fraction into an equivalent fraction with a denominator of 24.

a $\frac{1}{3}$ **b** $\frac{3}{4}$ **c** $\frac{1}{6}$ **d** $\frac{7}{12}$ **e** $\frac{7}{8}$

6 a Change into a mixed number   **i** $\frac{17}{3}$ **ii** $\frac{29}{4}$ **iii** $\frac{33}{9}$

   b Change into an improper fraction   **i** $5\frac{1}{3}$ **ii** $7\frac{3}{4}$ **iii** $6\frac{4}{7}$

7 Find, simplifying the answers where you can

   a $\frac{7}{12}+\frac{3}{12}$ **b** $\frac{11}{31}+\frac{13}{31}+\frac{7}{31}$ **c** $\frac{1}{3}+\frac{1}{9}+\frac{1}{12}$ **d** $\frac{11}{14}-\frac{6}{7}+\frac{1}{2}$

8 Find   **a** $4\frac{1}{4}+2\frac{2}{5}$ **b** $5\frac{2}{3}+1\frac{4}{7}$ **c** $7\frac{5}{8}-3\frac{1}{2}$ **d** $10\frac{1}{3}-7\frac{3}{4}$

9 Find the size of the angle A.

   a 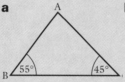   **b** 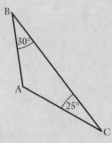   **c**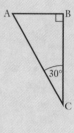

10 Find angles $d°$ and $e°$.

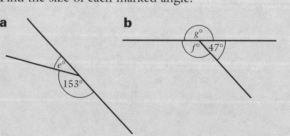

REVISION
EXERCISE 2.3
(Chapters 1 to 5)

Do not use a calculator for this exercise.

1 Find

   a $1080 \div 40$ **b** 37×82 **c** $7380 \div 60$ **d** 152×805

2 Find

   a $12 \div 4 - 3 + 1 + 5 \times 3$

   b $52 \times (37 - 17)$

   c $48 \div 4 - 15 \div 3 \times 2$

3 Find the size of each marked angle.

   a   **b**   **c**

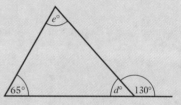

4 Find the size of each marked angle.

a

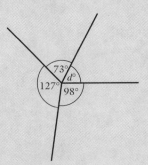

b

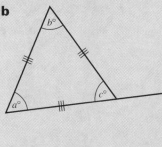

5 a Find the first two prime numbers after 100.

b Write the product $5 \times 5 \times 5 \times 7 \times 7$ in index form.

c Is 2075 divisible by 15?

6 a Find the smallest whole number that both 10 and 35 will divide into exactly.

b Write 47 as the sum of three odd prime numbers.

c Express 160 in prime factors in index form.

d What is the first triangular number after 35?

7 Find   **a** $\frac{1}{5} + \frac{1}{10}$ **b** $\frac{2}{3} + \frac{1}{7}$ **c** $1\frac{1}{3} + \frac{3}{4}$ **d** $4\frac{7}{12} - 2\frac{1}{6}$

8 a Write $\frac{4}{5}$ as an equivalent fraction

   i with denominator 20   **ii** with numerator 20.

b In a test $\frac{2}{3}$ of the pupils scored more than 50 and $\frac{3}{8}$ scored 70 or more. What fraction of the class scored more than 50 but less than 70?

9 Find the marked angles.

a

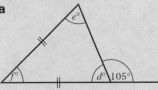

b

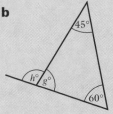

c

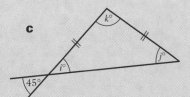

10 Find the size of each marked angle.

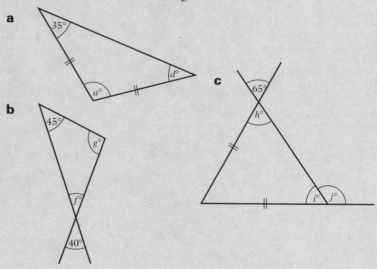

**REVISION
EXERCISE 2.4
(Chapters 1 to 5)**

Do not use a calculator for this exercise.

1 Find

    a $2 \times 5 \times 4 \times 6 \times 7$ **c** 23×8000

    b 85×30 **d** $101\,000 \div 500$

2 **a** Divide 2063 by 102, giving the remainder if there is one.

    b A club started the year with 56 members. During the year 19
       members left and 25 people joined. How many people belonged
       to the club at the end of the year?

3 Find the size of each marked angle.

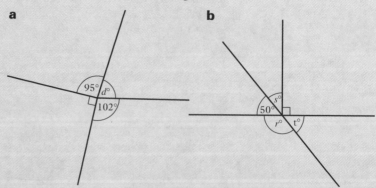

4 **a** If you start facing east and turn clockwise through 180°, in which
       direction are you facing?

    b If you start facing south and turn anticlockwise through 90°, in
       which direction are you facing?

5 a Find the largest whole number that will divide exactly into 20, 40 and 50.

b Find the smallest whole number that 36 and 45 will divide into exactly.

c A committee room measures 900 cm by 1250 cm. Find the size of the largest square tile that can be used to tile the floor without cutting.

6 a Express 280 in prime factors in index form.

b Write down
   i the next rectangular number after 16
   ii the next square number after 26
   iii the next triangular number after 20
   iv the next prime number after 25.

c Find the least sum of money that 15 p and 27 p will divide into exactly.

7 a Simplify the fractions   **i** $\frac{36}{48}$ **ii** $\frac{15}{25}$ **iii** $\frac{54}{90}$ **iv** $\frac{91}{104}$

b Find, giving your answer as a mixed number
   i $27 \div 6$ **ii** $43 \div 7$

8 Find

a $\frac{7}{12} + \frac{1}{8}$ **c** $1\frac{1}{4} - \frac{1}{2}$ **e** $4\frac{3}{8} - 1\frac{7}{12}$

b $\frac{2}{3} - \frac{1}{5}$ **d** $9\frac{1}{3} + 4\frac{5}{6}$ **f** $3\frac{2}{3} - 1\frac{7}{8}$

9 Construct a triangle ABC in which AB = 45 mm, BC = 55 mm and $\widehat{B} = 50°$. Measure AC.

10 Find the size of the angle marked $t°$.

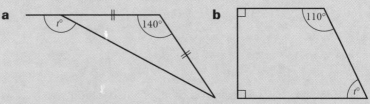

DECIMALS

6

Sabina went shopping with a £50 note.

She paid bills for £8.19, £3.99, £14.95 and £16.99.
She wanted to check her change.

To solve this and similar problems she needs to be able to add and subtract decimals. This work was considered in Chapter 9 of Book 7B. If you need to revise it use Revision Exercise 1.2 question 10 (page 10).

- Harri wants 36 pieces of 30 mm square timber, each 1.24 m long. The builders' merchant has a large quantity of this timber at a reduced price provided that Harri is willing to take 6.1 m lengths. Harri wonders whether this is the cheapest way of buying what he wants. Would it be better to buy the exact lengths he needs at £1.20 per metre, which is 20 p more per metre than the reduced price?

- A pharmacist finds the easiest way to count tablets is by weighing them. She knows that 30 of a particular tablet weigh 22.5 g. She needs 100 tablets for a prescription.

To solve these simple everyday problems requires the ability to multiply and divide decimals.

EXERCISE 6A

1 Can you think of any occasion last week when being able to multiply or divide decimals without a calculator, would have been useful?

2 Which of the following people need to be able to multiply and divide decimals?

    a a carpenter   **c** a builder   **e** a banker

    b a shopkeeper   **d** an engineer   **f** a nurse?

3 Discuss in which of the following situations it is an advantage to be able to multiply and/or divide decimals.

    a Changing pounds into foreign currency to go abroad.

    b Buying a quantity of 50 kg bags of cement which is priced by the tonne.

    c Buying tickets for a group of pupils to go to a concert.

You should now be convinced that everyone needs to be able to multiply and divide decimals.

MULTIPLICATION BY 10, 100, 1000...

We know that $32 \times 10 = 320$.
Multiplying by 10 has made the number of units become the number of tens, and the number of tens become the number of hundreds, so that all figures have moved one place to the left.
Now consider 0.2×10.
When multiplied by 10, tenths become units (one tenth $\times 10 = 1$),

so	units	tenths		units
	0 .	2	$\times$ 10 =	2

Again the figure has moved one place to the left.
Multiplying by 100 means multiplying by 10 and then by 10 again, so the figures move 2 places to the left.

	tens	units	tenths	hundredths	thousandths	
		0 .	4	2	6	$\times$ 100
=	4	2 .	6			

Notice that the figures move to the left while the point stays put but without headings it looks as though the figures stay put and the point moves to the right.
When necessary we fill an empty space with a nought.

units	tenths			hundreds	tens	units
4 .	2	$\times$ 100	=	4	2	0

EXERCISE 6B

1 Key in 5.42 on your calculator.

    a Multiply it by 10.

    b Multiply your answer by 10.

    c Multiply this answer by 10.

What happens to the figures 542 each time you multiply by 10?

Without using a calculator find the value of

a 3.68×10 **b** 3.68×1000

a $3.68 \times 10 = 36.8$

The decimal point moves one place to the right.

b $3.68 \times 1000 = 3680$

THE DECIMAL POINT MOVES 3 PLACES TO THE RIGHT
$3.68 \times 1000 = 3680$. WE FILL THE 'EMPTY' SPACE WITH ZERO.

Find, without using a calculator

2 7.2×100 **7** 0.66×10 **12** 0.204×1000

3 4.24×10 **8** 17.3×1000 **13** 2.73×1000

4 0.042×100 **9** 45.03×100 **14** 0.074×100

5 0.007×1000 **10** 4.92×100 **15** 0.009×10

6 8.4×10 **11** 0.57×100 **16** 4.007×1000

17 A £1 coin is 2.81 mm thick. How high is a pile of 10 similar coins?

18 Eryl has a ten-by-ten sheet of postage stamps. Each stamp is 2.05 cm wide and 2.45 cm long. Find the dimensions of the sheet.

19 Hanwar is cutting pieces off a large ball of string. Each piece is 14.5 cm long. He cuts off 100 pieces.
Find the total length of the string he cuts off.

20 A nail weighs 1.05 g. What is the weight of 1000 identical nails?

21 A book is 16.5 cm wide and 23.6 cm long.

   a One hundred of these books are placed side-by-side in a line so that their long edges touch. How long is the line?

   b If 100 of these books are placed in a line, short end to short end, how far will they stretch? How much longer is this line of books than the line referred to in part **a**?

DIVISION BY 10, 100, 1000...

When we divide by 10, the hundreds become tens; the tens become units

hundreds	tens	units				tens	units
6	4	0	$\div 10$	=		6	4

The figures move one place to the right and the number becomes smaller but it looks as though the decimal point moves to the left, e.g.

$$2.83 \div 10 = 0.283$$

To divide by 100 the point is moved two places to the left,

e.g. $7.2 \div 100 = 0.072$

To divide by 1000 the point is moved three places to the left,

e.g. $54.6 \div 1000 = 0.0546$

EXERCISE 6C

1 Key in 238.7 on your calculator.

a Divide it by 10. **c** Divide this answer by 10.

b Divide your answer by 10. **d** Divide your last answer by 10.

What happens to the decimal point each time you divide by 10?

Find, without using a calculator, the value of

a $3.2 \div 10$ **b** $43 \div 1000$

a $3.2 \div 10 = 0.32$

TO DIVIDE BY 10 MOVE THE DECIMAL POINT 1 PLACE TO THE LEFT.

b $43 \div 1000 = 0.043$

TO DIVIDE BY 1000 MOVE THE DECIMAL POINT 3 PLACES TO THE LEFT; 0.043. I NEED TO FILL THE 'EMPTY' SPACE WITH A NOUGHT.

Without using a calculator, find the value of

2 $3.4 \div 10$ **5** $7.56 \div 1000$ **8** $16.09 \div 10$

3 $76.49 \div 100$ **6** $5.8 \div 100$ **9** $63.4 \div 1000$

4 $0.44 \div 10$ **7** $0.865 \div 1000$ **10** $0.82 \div 100$

11 $675.4 \div 10$ **14** $5.06 \div 100$

12 $23.66 \div 100$ **15** $0.077 \div 10$

13 $0.45 \div 1000$ **16** $34.82 \div 100$

17 A pile of ten 20p coins is 1.6 cm high. How thick is one 20p coin?

18 Peter builds a tower using ten coloured cubes. The tower is 36 cm high. What is the length of an edge of one cube?

19 In a factory storage park, 100 cars of a particular model are parked nose-to-tail. They stretch for 3950 m. What is the length of one car?

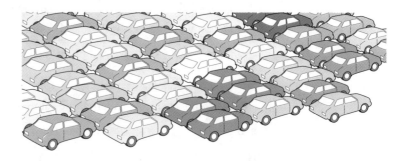

20 When laid end to end, 100 screws stretch a distance of 520 cm. What is the length of 1 screw?

21 A retailer buys 1000 copies of a best seller from a publisher for £2700. How much is the retailer paying per copy?

22 A machine produces nails by cutting them from a coil of wire 2 mm thick. The length of wire needed to cut 1000 identical nails measures 23.5 m. How long, in millimetres, is each nail?

23 One million 10 cent coins weigh 3.75 tonnes. What is the weight, in grams, of one coin?

The next exercise contains a mixture of questions requiring multiplication or division by 10, 100, 1000, ...

EXERCISE 6D　　Find, without using a calculator

1 $1.6 \div 10$	**5** 14.3×100	**9** $140 \div 1000$
2 1.6×100	**6** $27.3 \div 100$	**10** 7.8×1000
3 $0.067 \div 10$	**7** $1.63 \div 100$	**11** $56 \div 10$
4 0.32×10	**8** 45.3×100	**12** 0.006×100
13 $8.2 \div 100$	**16** $0.77 \div 100$	**19** $0.045 \div 1000$
14 $0.078 \div 100$	**17** $0.58 \div 1000$	**20** 0.041×1000
15 $2.34 \div 100$	**18** $78.6 \div 10$	**21** 0.098×100

22 Sixty-seven metres of string is shared equally among 10 people. What length of string does each person get?

23 Find the cost of 100 articles at £1.64 each.

24 Which of the following is larger, and by how much:
$$0.47 \times 100 \quad \text{or} \quad 560 \div 10 ?$$

25 Which of the following is smaller, and by how much:
$$1.36 \div 10 \quad \text{or} \quad 0.046 \times 100 ?$$

26 Find the cost of 1000 books at £2.62 each.

27 Multiply 2.7 by 100 and then divide the result by 1000.

28 Divide 740 by 100, and then divide the result by 10.

29 Add 14.9 to 3.45 and divide the result by 10.

30 Take 3.76 from 10 and multiply the result by 100.

31 A lorry is carrying 1000 boxes.
If each box weighs 1.34 kg what load is the lorry carrying?

32 100 cars, each 4.245 m long, are parked nose-to-tail in a straight line. How far is it from the front of the first car to the tail of the last one?

33 A book weighs 0.66 kg. How much will 10 000 books weigh?

34 Which is the larger, and by how much:
the difference between 4.6 and 15.9, multiplied by 10,
or the sum of 150.3 and 52, divided by 100?

35 A box contains 100 nails, each nail weighing 0.88 g.
Find the weight, in grams, of the nails in

   a 1 box   **b** 100 boxes.

MULTIPLICATION BY WHOLE NUMBERS

A decimal can be multiplied by a whole number in the same way as one whole number can be multiplied by another. It is easier to keep the decimal point in the correct place when the calculation is set out in columns, e.g.

$$1.87 \times 6 = 11.22 \qquad \begin{array}{r} 1.87 \\ \times \quad 6 \\ \hline 11.22 \end{array}$$

EXERCISE 6E

Find, without using a calculator

1	1.3×4	**6**	2.81×3	**11**	3.9×5
2	2.7×5	**7**	1.95×2	**12**	2.68×5
3	0.8×8	**8**	52.4×4	**13**	0.126×4
4	4.2×3	**9**	812.4×4	**14**	53.72×6
5	3.4×6	**10**	342.4×5	**15**	63.02×8

16 Find the cost of eight tapes at £5.99 each.

17 Find the weight of seven similar pens if one pen weighs 9.5 g.

18 Five cubes, each of edge 4.3 cm are piled one on top of the other to form a tower. How high is the tower?

19 Nine ball-point pens, each 13.2 cm long, are placed end-to-end on a table. How far do they stretch?

20 A tumbler has a capacity of 0.27 litres. How much water is needed to fill half-a-dozen similar tumblers?

21 Four lorries, each 7.34 m long, are parked nose-to-tail in a straight line. How far is it from the front of the first lorry to the back of the last one?

22 In a block of flats the distance from the floor of one flat to the floor of the one above is 2.94 m. How far is it from the floor of a first floor flat to the floor of the flat that is immediately above it, but on the ninth floor?

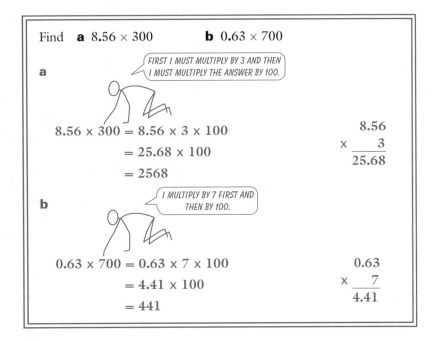

Find   **a** 8.56 × 300   **b** 0.63 × 700

a

FIRST I MUST MULTIPLY BY 3 AND THEN I MUST MULTIPLY THE ANSWER BY 100.

8.56 x 300 = 8.56 x 3 x 100

            = 25.68 x 100

            = 2568

                              8.56
                       x   3
                        25.68

b

I MULTIPLY BY 7 FIRST AND THEN BY 100.

0.63 x 700 = 0.63 x 7 x 100

            = 4.41 x 100

            = 441

                              0.63
                       x   7
                        4.41

Find, without using a calculator

23 3.4 × 30	**26** 5.67 × 400	**29** 0.86 × 700
24 0.56 × 500	**27** 0.083 × 600	**30** 32.6 × 90
25 6.40 × 80	**28** 2.75 × 50	**31** 0.72 × 60

32 Find the cost of seven magazines at £2.95 each.

33 A book is 1.74 cm thick. How high is a pile of five similar books?

34 The thickness of a piece of paper is 0.035 mm. What is the thickness of a ream (500 sheets)?

35 A coloured pencil weighs 6.8 g. A pack holds seven pencils and the weight of the pack is equal to the weight of two pencils. What is the total weight of the pack and its pencils?

DIVISION BY WHOLE NUMBERS

We can see that

	units	tenths					units	tenths
	0 .	6	÷	2	=		0 .	3

because 6 tenths ÷ 2 = 3 tenths. So we may divide by a whole number in the usual way as long as we keep the figures in the correct columns and the points are in line.

EXERCISE 6F

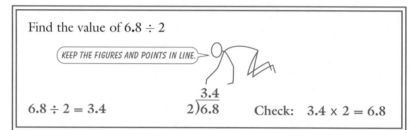

Find the value of 6.8 ÷ 2

KEEP THE FIGURES AND POINTS IN LINE.

6.8 ÷ 2 = 3.4

$$\begin{array}{r} 3.4 \\ 2\overline{)6.8} \end{array}$$

Check: 3.4 x 2 = 6.8

Without using a calculator, find the value of

1 0.4 ÷ 2

2 3.2 ÷ 2

3 0.63 ÷ 3

4 7.8 ÷ 3

5 9.6 ÷ 6

6 0.9 ÷ 9

7 0.95 ÷ 5

8 0.672 ÷ 3

9 26.6 ÷ 7

10 67.2 ÷ 8

11 42.6 ÷ 2

12 7.53 ÷ 3

13 6.56 ÷ 4

14 0.75 ÷ 5

15 28.8 ÷ 8

16 0.798 ÷ 7

17 16.2 ÷ 6

18 9.81 ÷ 9

19 A pile of four 1 p coins is 5.36 mm high.
What is the thickness of one coin?

20 Six screws weigh 14.4 g.
What is the weight of one screw?

21 Eight boxed exercise benches are stacked one on top of the other and reach a height of 1.52 m.
How deep is one box?

22 Fencing posts are placed equal distances apart around the edge of a rectangular field. Measuring from one corner the distance from the first post to the eighth post is 112.7 m.
How far is it between consecutive posts?

Sometimes it is necessary to fill in spaces with noughts.

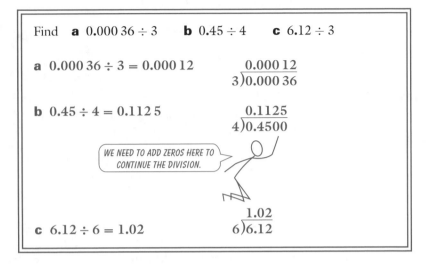

Find **a** $0.000\,36 \div 3$ **b** $0.45 \div 4$ **c** $6.12 \div 3$

a $0.000\,36 \div 3 = 0.000\,12$
$$\begin{array}{r} 0.000\,12 \\ 3\overline{)0.000\,36} \end{array}$$

b $0.45 \div 4 = 0.112\,5$
$$\begin{array}{r} 0.1125 \\ 4\overline{)0.4500} \end{array}$$

WE NEED TO ADD ZEROS HERE TO CONTINUE THE DIVISION.

c $6.12 \div 6 = 1.02$
$$\begin{array}{r} 1.02 \\ 6\overline{)6.12} \end{array}$$

Find, without using a calculator

23 $0.057 \div 3$ **29** $0.036 \div 6$ **35** $0.0285 \div 5$

24 $0.0065 \div 5$ **30** $1.62 \div 2$ **36** $0.038 \div 2$

25 $0.008\,72 \div 4$ **31** $0.5215 \div 5$ **37** $0.24 \div 5$

26 $0.0076 \div 4$ **32** $6.3 \div 7$ **38** $0.714 \div 7$

27 $0.81 \div 9$ **33** $1.232 \div 4$ **39** $0.3 \div 8$

28 $0.012 \div 6$ **34** $0.6552 \div 6$ **40** $9.54 \div 9$

41 A metal rod $0.46\,\text{m}$ long is sawn into four equal pieces. Find the length of each piece.

42 A pamphlet containing eight leaves is $0.256\,\text{mm}$ thick. How thick is each leaf?

43 A hiker walked $19.2\,\text{km}$ in 3 hours. If she walked at a steady rate how far did she walk in each hour?

44 A tailor used $30.6\,\text{m}$ to make nine similar suits. What length of material did he use to make one suit?

45 Pat received 55.44 French francs in exchange for £6. How many francs did he get for £1?

DIVISION BY 20, 300, 7000, ...

Suppose we wish to divide 4.8 by 20. We can do this by dividing first by 10 and then by dividing by 2,

i.e. $4.8 \div 10 = 0.48$ and $0.48 \div 2 = 0.24$

So $4.8 \div 20 = 0.24$

EXERCISE 6G

Find, without using a calculator, $291.9 \div 30$.

$291.9 \div 10 = 29.19$

$29.19 \div 3 = 9.73$

DIVIDE BY 10 FIRST, THEN DIVIDE BY 3.

$$\begin{array}{r} 9.73 \\ 3{\overline{)29.19}} \end{array}$$

So $291.9 \div 30 = 9.73$

Find, without using a calculator

1 $26.4 \div 20$

2 $157.8 \div 30$

3 $40.2 \div 600$

4 $105.6 \div 40$

5 $15.93 \div 90$

6 $1.944 \div 800$

7 $19.5 \div 50$

8 $2.94 \div 70$

9 $59.1 \div 300$

10 A ship sailed 396.4 nautical miles at a steady speed in 20 hours. How many nautical miles did it sail in one hour?

11 In a carefully monitored test a car travelled 199.2 miles on 30 litres of fuel. If it used fuel at a constant rate how many miles did it travel on one litre?

12 A company pays £14.70 for a delivery of 70 small components. Find the cost, in pounds, of one component.

STANDARD DECIMALS AND FRACTIONS

It is worthwhile knowing a few equivalent fractions, decimals and percentages. For example

$$\tfrac{1}{2} = 0.5 = 50\% \qquad \tfrac{1}{4} = 0.25 = 25\% \qquad \tfrac{1}{8} = 0.125 = 12.5\%$$

Notice that $0.4 = \tfrac{4}{10} = \tfrac{2}{5}$

EXERCISE 6H

Write the following decimals as fractions in their lowest terms, without any working if possible.

1 0.2

2 0.3

3 0.5

4 0.75

5 0.6	**7** 0.9	**9** 0.04	**11** 0.005
6 0.7	**8** 0.05	**10** 0.8	**12** 0.06

**MULTIPLICATION
BY A DECIMAL**

So far we have multiplied by a multiple of 10 and by a whole number. We have also divided by a multiple of 10, that is, by 10, 100, 1000, ...

Using this knowledge enables us to multiply any two decimals together.

Suppose we wish to find 0.3×0.2

$$\text{Since } 0.2 = 2 \div 10 \qquad 0.3 \times 0.2 = 0.3 \times 2 \div 10$$
$$= 0.6 \div 10$$
$$= 0.06$$

EXERCISE 6I

> Find 0.05×0.7
>
> $$0.05 \times 0.7 = 0.05 \times 7 \div 10 \qquad \boxed{0.7 = 7 \div 10}$$
> $$= 0.35 \div 10$$
> $$= 0.035$$

Find, without using a calculator

1 0.04×0.2	**3** 0.003×6	**5** 0.001×0.3
2 0.1×0.1	**4** 3×0.02	**6** 0.4×0.001

7 Compare the number of decimal places in your answers with the number of decimal places in the numbers being multiplied. What do you notice?

From the exercise above, we see that if we add together the number of figures after the decimal point in the numbers being multiplied together, we get the number of figures after the point in the answer. This fact can be used to multiply any two decimals together. The number of figures after the point is called the *number of decimal places.*

For example, to work out 0.05×0.7
we first find $5 \times 7 = 35$
then 0.05 has 2 decimal places and 0.7 has 1 decimal place,
so the answer has $(2 + 1)$ decimal places, i.e. 3 decimal places.

$$\therefore \qquad 0.05 \times 0.7 = 0.035$$

EXERCISE 6J

Calculate the products   **a** 0.08×0.4 **b** 6×0.002

a   0.08   ×   0.4   =   0.032 $(8 \times 4 = 32)$
    (2 places)   (1 place)   (3 places)

b   6   ×   0.002   =   0.012 $(6 \times 2 = 12)$
    (0 places)   (3 places)   (3 places)

Calculate the following products. Do not use a calculator.

1 0.6×0.3 **4** 0.12×0.09 **7** 0.08×0.08

2 0.04×0.06 **5** 0.07×0.003 **8** 3×0.006

3 0.009×2 **6** 0.5×0.07 **9** 0.7×0.06

10 0.07×1.2 **12** 0.09×0.9 **14** 0.7×0.11

11 4×0.009 **13** 0.0008×11 **15** 0.04×7

16 Joe saws a length of wood into 7 equal pieces each 23.7 cm long. If each saw cut consumes 0.1 cm, how long was the length of wood before he started sawing?

Noughts appearing after the decimal point, in the middle or at either end, must be included when counting the places.

Find   **a** 0.252×0.4 **b** 2.5×6 **c** 300×0.2

a   0.252   ×   0.4   =   0.1008   252
    (3 places)   (1 place)   (4 places)   ×   4
                                                         1008

b   2.5   ×   6   =   15.0   25
    (1 place)   (0 places)   (1 place)   ×   6
                                                        150

c   300   ×   0.02   =   6.00 $300 \times 2 = 600$
    (0 places)   (2 places)   (2 places)

Calculate the following products. Do not use a calculator.

17 0.751×0.2 **20** 400×0.6 **23** 320×0.07

18 3.2×0.5 **21** 31.5×2 **24** 0.4×0.0055

19 0.35×4 **22** 5.6×0.02 **25** 0.5×0.006

26 1.6×0.4 **29** 4×1.6 **32** 0.16×4

27 1.6×0.5 **30** 5×0.016 **33** 0.0016×5

28 0.16×0.005 **31** $16\,000 \times 0.05$ **34** 310×0.04

35 A metal washer is 1.25 mm thick. Six washers are placed on each of the two supports of a gate in order to raise it. By how much is the gate raised?

36 Find the cost of 8 articles at £43.50 each.

Calculate 0.26×1.3

$$0.26 \quad \times \quad 1.3 \quad = \quad 0.338$$
(2 places)   (1 place)   (3 places)

```
    26
  x 13
    78
   260
   338
```

Calculate the following products. Do not use a calculator.

37 4.2×1.6 **40** 310×1.4 **43** 0.0232×0.034

38 52×0.24 **41** 1.623×0.27 **44** 0.0016×1600

39 $0.68 \div 0.14$ **42** 13.2×2.5 **45** 0.34×0.31

46 A sheet of paper is 0.065 mm thick.
How thick is a pile of 240 sheets?

47 Find the weight of 34 books if each book weighs 1.35 kg.

48 A fire engine travels 0.675 miles in each minute.
How far will it travel in **a** 4 minutes **b** 12 minutes?

49 a In Ruritania the 88 ten cent coins in a bag weigh 330 g. What is the weight of one ten cent coin?

b The weight of the ten cent coins in another bag is 165 g. What is the value, in dollars, of these coins? (100 c = $ 1)

50 A taxi, that can travel at 0.6 miles per minute, had a call at 10.22 to pick up a fare at a passenger's home which was 4.5 miles away. The passenger wished to be taken to the station to catch a train due at 10.50. The taxi driver answered the call immediately, spent 1.5 minutes loading the passenger and her luggage, and drove the 6.5 miles to the station.

a How long did the taxi take to get to the passenger?

b How long did the taxi take to drive the passenger to the station?

c At what time did the passenger arrive at the station?

d If 3.25 minutes were allowed to get from the taxi to the station platform, did the passenger catch the train?
If so how much time did she have to spare?

CHANGING FRACTIONS TO DECIMALS

In Chapter 4 we saw that $\frac{5}{8}$ can be interpreted as meaning $5 \div 8$

By placing zeros after the decimal point, this division can be evaluated as a decimal

i.e.

$$\frac{0.625}{8)5.000} \qquad \text{hence } \tfrac{5}{8} = 0.625$$

Any fraction can be treated in the same way, i.e.

> to change a fraction to a decimal,
> divide the numerator by the denominator.

EXERCISE 6K

Express as a decimal　　**a** $\frac{3}{5}$　**b** $\frac{6}{25}$

a $\frac{3}{5} = 0.6$
$$5\overline{)3.0}\quad 0.6$$

b $\frac{6}{25} = 0.24$
$$25\overline{)6.00}\quad 0.24$$

Do not use a calculator in this exercise.

Express each fraction as a decimal.

1 $\frac{7}{10}$　　**5** $\frac{4}{5}$　　**9** $\frac{1}{8}$　　**13** $\frac{3}{8}$

2 $\frac{3}{4}$　　**6** $\frac{7}{20}$　　**10** $\frac{7}{8}$　　**14** $\frac{14}{25}$

3 $\frac{1}{2}$　　**7** $\frac{3}{20}$　　**11** $\frac{3}{40}$　　**15** $\frac{5}{16}$

4 $\frac{1}{5}$　　**8** $\frac{8}{25}$　　**12** $\frac{19}{50}$　　**16** $\frac{19}{25}$

DIVISION BY DECIMALS WITHOUT USING A CALCULATOR

We know how to divide a decimal by a whole number,

e.g.　　$2.7 \div 2 = 1.35$　　$2\overline{)2.70}\quad 1.35$

We use this knowledge to divide by a decimal because division by a decimal can always be changed to division by a whole number.

For example, $3.45 \div 0.5 = \frac{3.45}{0.5}$, and $\frac{3.45}{0.5}$ can be changed to an equivalent fraction with 5 as the denominator by multiplying top and bottom by 10, so

$$\frac{3.45}{0.5} = \frac{34.5}{5} = 34.5 \div 5 = 6.9$$

Similarly　　$0.48 \div 0.004 = \frac{0.48}{0.004}$

$$= \frac{480}{4} = 120$$

The method used in these examples can be extended to give a general rule for division by a decimal.

To change division by a decimal to division by a whole number, multiply both the top number and the bottom number by 10, 100, ... to change the bottom number into a whole number.

EXERCISE 6L

Without using a calculator, find the value of

a $4.4 \div 0.5$ **b** $1.4 \div 0.04$

a $4.4 \div 0.5 = \dfrac{4.4}{0.5} = \dfrac{44}{5} = 8.8$

MULTIPLY THE TOP AND BOTTOM BY 10 SO THAT 0.5 BECOMES A WHOLE NUMBER.

b $1.4 \div 0.04 = \dfrac{1.4}{0.04} = \dfrac{140}{4} = 35$

Multiply the top and bottom by 100 so that 0.04 becomes a whole number.

Without using a calculator, find the value of

1 $0.4 \div 0.1$

2 $2 \div 0.2$

3 $1.4 \div 0.07$

4 $0.36 \div 1.2$

5 $2.5 \div 0.5$

6 $0.1 \div 0.01$

7 $0.8 \div 0.04$

8 $6.09 \div 0.3$

9 $0.49 \div 0.7$

10 $35.5 \div 0.05$

11 $6.4 \div 0.08$

12 $0.081 \div 0.9$

13 $5.12 \div 0.4$

14 $1.04 \div 0.8$

15 $0.348 \div 0.006$

16 $0.217 \div 0.07$

17 $0.0312 \div 0.06$

18 $0.0504 \div 0.007$

19 $0.0369 \div 0.9$

20 $0.00063 \div 0.009$

21 $0.000024 \div 0.004$

22 One tablet contains 0.12 mg of vitamin C. How many tablets can be made from 180 mg of vitamin C?

23 One ingredient of bath oil is oil of juniper. Each bottle contains 2.5 ml of this oil and the total amount of oil of juniper in the bottles in one carton is 32.5 ml. How many bottles are there in the carton?

24 A capsule contains 0.14 mg of vitamin E and the total amount of vitamin E in a box of capsules is 6.72 mg. How many capsules are there in the box?

25 The cost of 0.8 kg of apples is £1.20. What is the cost of 1 kg?

26 The weight of 0.03 m^3 of copper is 26.7 kg. What is the weight of 1 m^3?

MIXED EXERCISE

EXERCISE 6M

Do not use a calculator in this exercise.

Find the value of

1 **a** 3.74×100 **c** 0.13×1000 **e** $5.02 \div 10$
   b 0.072×10 **d** $0.67 \div 100$ **f** $15.8 \div 1000$

2 **a** 2.6×3 **c** 83.7×7 **e** 0.93×500
   b 5.6×5 **d** 7.2×30 **f** 0.054×80

3 **a** $6.8 \div 2$ **c** $0.56 \div 8$ **e** $4.8 \div 0.6$
   b $31.8 \div 6$ **d** $12 \div 0.3$ **f** $0.63 \div 0.7$

4 **a** $63.4 \div 20$ **b** $3.25 \div 500$ **c** $1.6 \div 800$

5 **a** 0.5×0.8 **c** 4.6×0.3 **e** $1.2 \div 0.08$
   b 2.1×0.06 **d** $5.6 \div 0.5$ **f** $5.2 \div 0.004$

6 Write each decimal as a fraction in its lowest terms.

   a 0.8 **b** 0.05 **c** 0.12 **d** 0.625

7 Express each fraction as a decimal.

   a $\frac{2}{5}$ **b** $\frac{13}{20}$ **c** $\frac{13}{25}$ **d** $\frac{47}{80}$

8 $2000 \, cm^3$ of a hard semi-precious stone has a mass of $5.23 \, kg$. What is the mass of $1 \, cm^3$ of this stone?

9 Find the cost of $4.3 \, kg$ of potatoes at £0.60 per kilogram.

PUZZLE

I am a decimal number.
I have two figures before the decimal point and two figures after it.
I read the same backwards as forwards.
My first digit is larger than my second digit.
All my digits are prime numbers.
The sum of my digits is 16.
What number am I?

USING A
CALCULATOR

Hannah asked Paul how long it would take her to cycle to his house. Paul said 'It's about 8 km, and if you cycle at about 13 km/hour, it will take you about, ..., I need my calculator, ..., I make that 36.923 076 minutes.'
"Humph !?" said Hannah, as well she might !

To find the time, Paul used a distance and a speed that are clearly only approximate. So it is ridiculous to give an answer that appears to be very precise because of the large number of figures in it, when in fact it cannot be.

Hannah's question cannot have an exact answer anyway because the speed at which she can cycle depends on factors such as weather, other traffic, and so on. These are unknown. A more sensible reply would be '30 to 40 minutes.'

This situation illustrates that

* the answers we give to questions should not apparently be more accurate than the information given, nor more accurate than the context in which the question is asked.

* when we use calculators, we need to interpret the number in the display at the appropriate level of accuracy.

EXERCISE 7A   Discuss how accurate the replies to these questions should be.

1 How long is that carpet?

2 Bus fares are going up by 6%. My fare to school is 45 pence now. How much will it be after the increase?

3 Gold weighs 19.3 grams per cm^3. What is the volume of gold in an ingot weighing 56.4 grams?

4 There is 0.725 mg of vitamin C in one tablet. How many tablets can be made from 100 mg of vitamin C?

5 Use your calculator to find an answer to question **4**. Write down the number shown in the display. Is this number an appropriate answer for question **4**?

6 Find an answer to this problem without using a calculator, and discuss what you find.
A plank, 120 centimetres long, is to be cut into 7 pieces of equal length. How long should each piece be?

CORRECTING TO A GIVEN NUMBER OF DECIMAL PLACES

Discussion of the examples above shows that the arithmetic used to find an answer to a problem can give many more figures than we need. We then have to decide where to stop and give the answer to the nearest whole number, or tenth, or hundredth, and so on.

In question **6**, we might decide that approximating to the nearest centimetre is a reasonable degree of accuracy for the length.
This means that we have to correct the calculation to the nearest tenth, i.e. to 1 decimal place.

Consider the numbers 1.6, 1.62, 1.65, 1.67, 1.7.
If we write 1.6 as 1.60 and 1.7 as 1.70, and show the numbers on a scale, we can compare them.

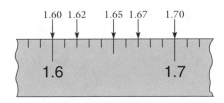

Now we can see that 1.62 is nearer to 1.60 than to 1.70 so we write

$$1.6|2 = 1.6 \text{ correct to 1 decimal place}$$

We can also see that 1.67 is nearer to 1.70 than to 1.60 so we write

$$1.6|7 = 1.7 \text{ correct to 1 decimal place}$$

It is not so obvious what to do with 1.65 as it is exactly halfway between 1.60 and 1.70. To save arguments, if the figure after the cut-off line is 5, we add 1 to the figure before, that is, we round up. Therefore we write

$$1.6|5 = 1.7 \text{ correct to 1 decimal place}$$

We use the same rule when we correct to any given number of decimal places (d.p.); we mark a cut-off line after the place we want to correct to, then if the figure after this line is 5 or more we round up, otherwise we round down.

Give 10.9315 correct to

a the nearest whole number   **b** 1 decimal place.

a 10.9315 = 11   (correct to the nearest whole number)

b 10.91315 = 10.9 (correct to 1 decimal place)

Give the following numbers correct to the nearest whole number.

1 13.9   **4** 6.783   **7** 58.4

2 6.34   **5** 109.7   **8** 3.9999

3 26.5   **6** 0.98   **9** 74.09

Give the following numbers correct to 1 decimal place.

10 6.145   **13** 2.78   **16** 4.45

11 15.29   **14** 26.49   **17** 152.921

12 0.176   **15** 0.0553   **18** 0.192

Give **a** 4.699 correct to 2 decimal places

  b 0.007 correct to 3 decimal places.

a 4.699 = 4.70 (correct to 2 decimal places)

```
 4.69
+  1
 4.70
```
WE KEEP THIS ZERO TO SHOW THAT THE
NUMBER HAS BEEN CORRECTED TO 2 d.p.

b 0.0007 = 0.001 (correct to 3 decimal places)

Give the following numbers correct to 2 decimal places.

19 0.328   **24** 0.6947   **29** 0.178

20 0.322   **25** 0.8351   **30** 1.582

21 1.2671   **26** 3.927   **31** 4.995

22 2.345   **27** 0.0084   **32** 0.0115

23 0.0416   **28** 3.9999   **33** 8.0293

Give the following numbers correct to the number of decimal places indicated in the brackets.

34 1.784 (1)   **40** 1.639 (1)

35 42.64 (1)   **41** 1.689 (nearest whole number)

36 1.0092 (2)   **42** 3.4984 (2)

37 0.00942 (4)   **43** 3.4984 (1)

38 0.7345 (3)   **44** 0.00384 (4)

39 1.639 (2)   **45** 18.499 (nearest whole number)

Give the following quantities correct to the number of decimal places indicated in the brackets.

46 8.56 cm (1)   **52** 18.95 m (1)

47 4.4227 litres (3)   **53** 0.0025 kg (3)

48 8.098 mm (2)   **54** 26.039 seconds (1)

49 0.892 grams (1)   **55** 3.666 litres (2)

50 14.7882 kg (3)   **56** 12.064 mm (1)

51 0.038 cm (2)   **57** 26.3948 kg (2)

CORRECTION TO A NUMBER OF DECIMAL PLACES

If we are asked to give an answer correct to a certain number of decimal places, we work out one more decimal place than is asked for. Then we can find the size of the last figure required.

EXERCISE 7C

Do not use a calculator.

Find $4.28 \div 6$ giving your answer correct to 2 decimal places.

$$4.28 \div 6 = 0.71|3\ldots$$

$$\begin{array}{r} 0.713\ldots \\ 6\overline{)4.28^20} \end{array}$$

$$= 0.71 \quad (\text{correct to 2 decimal places})$$

Calculate, giving your answers correct to 2 decimal places.

1 $0.496 \div 3$ **4** $12.2 \div 6$ **7** $0.68 \div 6$

2 $6.49 \div 7$ **5** $25.68 \div 9$ **8** $0.99 \div 8$

3 $3.12 \div 9$ **6** $2.35 \div 4$ **9** $1.73 \div 8$

Without using your calculator, solve these problems giving your answer as accurately as you think is reasonable.

10 The perimeter of a square field is 67 metres. How long is each side?

11 A sack of flour weighs 30 kg.
The flour is shared equally among 7 people.
What weight of flour does each person get?

FLOUR

12 The length of this ribbon is 0.12 metres.
It is cut into 9 equal lengths.
How long is each piece?

USING A CALCULATOR

When we use a calculator, the display often fills up with many more figures than we need.

For example, when using a calculator to find $11 \div 17$, the display shows

We do not need to write all these figures down.

If the answer is to be given correct to two decimal places, we only need write down the first three decimal places,

The line after the second decimal place is a reminder to look at the next figure.

i.e. $11 \div 17 = 0.64|7\ldots$

$= 0.65$ (correct to 2 d.p.)

EXERCISE 7D

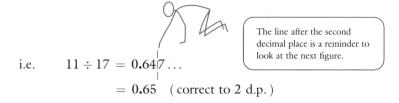

Find the value of $2.19 \div 0.472$, giving the answer correct to 2 decimal places.

$2.19 \div 0.472 = 4.63|9\ldots$

$= 4.64$ (correct to 2 d.p.)

Find, giving your answers correct to 1 decimal place.

1 $14.6 \div 7$ **3** $25 \div 13$ **5** 36.02×0.94

2 $6.15 \div 0.37$ **4** 2.09×8.37 **6** 0.987×0.36

Find, giving your answers correct to 2 decimal places.

7 $25.7 \div 0.29$ **9** 24.17×0.078 **11** $27.5 \div 126.9$

8 $8.3 \div 1.7$ **10** $15 \div 27$ **12** 0.5789×1.956

13 a Divide 14.6 by 2.5. Is the answer bigger or smaller than 14.6?

     b Divide 14.6 by some other numbers that are bigger than 1. Are the answers bigger or smaller than 14.6?

     c Divide 14.6 by 0.3. What do you notice about the size of the answer this time?

     d Divide 14.6 by some other numbers that are smaller than 1. Does the same thing happen as you found in part **c**?

14 Investigate what happens to the number 0.3 when it is divided by

a a number greater than 1

b a number less than 1.

15 Investigate what happens when a number is multiplied by

a a number larger than 1

b a number smaller than 1.

Use what you found in parts **a** and **b** to write down the words that are missing from these sentences.

c When a number is multiplied by a number greater than one, the answer is _____ than the original number.

d When a number is multiplied by a number less than one, the answer is _____ than the original number.

ESTIMATING RESULTS

Questions **13** to **15** in the last exercise illustrate that

> multiplying by a number greater than 1, increases a quantity, and multiplying by a number less than 1, decreases a quantity.

However when we divide, the opposite happens:

> division by a number greater than 1 decreases the quantity, and division by a number less than 1 increases the quantity.

These facts can be used as a quick check on the reasonableness of an answer.

A further check can be made by rounding the numbers to easy ones so that the calculation can be done in your head or quickly on paper. For example, we can find a rough value for $14.25 \div 0.58$ by rounding 14.25 to 14, and rounding 0.58 to 0.6,

i.e. $14.25 \div 0.58$ is roughly equal to $14 \div 0.6 = 140 \div 6 \approx 23$

The calculator gives $14.25 \div 0.58$ as equal to $24.56\ldots$

This agrees quite well with the rough value, so we can be fairly confident that it is correct.

EXERCISE 7E

Estimate the value of 169.27×0.0395, then use a calculator to find the value correct to 3 decimal places.

Estimate: $169.27 \times 0.0395 \approx 170 \times 0.04 = 6.8$

Calculator: $169.27 \times 0.0395 = 6.686|1 \ldots$

$= 6.686$ (correct to 3 d.p.)

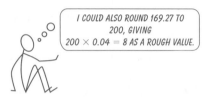

I COULD ALSO ROUND 169.27 TO 200, GIVING 200 × 0.04 = 8 AS A ROUGH VALUE.

First find a rough value, then use a calculator to find the value correct to the number of decimal places given in the brackets.

1 $32.9 \div 8$ (3)

2 $402 \div 7$ (1)

3 $9.76 \div 11$ (1)

4 $124 \div 17$ (1)

5 $0.45 \div 12$ (2)

6 $15.1 \div 16$ (1)

7 $519 \div 19$ (2)

8 $0.321 \div 17$ (2)

9 21.6×5.03 (2)

10 63.09×0.115 (2)

11 1.942×2.559 (3)

12 0.852×12.6 (1)

13 12.07×0.499 (1)

14 7.56×3.16 (1)

15 24.09×0.255 (2)

16 0.182×4.229 (3)

17 $2.3 \div 11$ (2)

18 $5.33 \div 1.08$ (1)

19 52.05×3.76 (2)

20 $2.584 \div 16$ (2)

21 112.5×0.629 (2)

22 $0.041 \div 0.13$ (2)

23 $64.07 \div 12.44$ (3)

24 0.792×2.017 (2)

25 Estimates suggest that the average man uses 12.3 calories per minute when swimming. Correct to one decimal place, how many calories are used when a man swims for

a 10 minutes   **b** 22 minutes   **c** 13.25 minutes?

26 There are an unknown number of identical screws in a bag. These screws weigh 120 g, correct to the nearest gram. One screw weighs 1.35 g, correct to 2 decimal places.

a How many screws are there in the bag?

b Explain why the calculation to find the answer to part **a** does not give a whole number as the result.

27 Before the covers are put on, a book has 350 pages.

a How many sheets of paper are there in this book?

b The book is 12.25 mm thick. How thick, correct to 2 decimal places, is each sheet?

c Another book, printed on the same paper and without covers, has 450 pages. How thick is this book?

28 Seven brothers and sisters are given £100 to be divided equally among them.

a Correct to the nearest penny, how much will each one receive? If each brother and sister received this amount, would £100 be enough? Give reasons for your answer.

b Repeat part **a** if they are given £10 000 instead of £100.

MIXED OPERATIONS USING A CALCULATOR

In Chapter 1 we saw that, when a calculation involves a mixture of signs, we work out the multiplications and divisions before doing any addition or subtraction. If brackets are used, the calculation inside the brackets is worked first.

For example, to calculate $2 + 3 \times 6$, we first find 3×6,

i.e. $$2 + 3 \times 6 = 2 + 18$$

$$= 20$$

A scientific calculator obeys the rule 'multiplication and division before addition and subtraction'.

When $2 + 3 \times 6$ is keyed in as $\boxed{2}$ $\boxed{+}$ $\boxed{3}$ $\boxed{\times}$ $\boxed{6}$ $\boxed{=}$, the calculator will work out 3×6 first.

If we need to do addition or subtraction first, we can use brackets to show this, i.e. $(2 + 3) \times 6$ means 'add 2 and 3 first'.

We can use the bracket keys on a calculator to find this in one operation,

i.e. press (2 + 3) × 6 =

Alternatively we can press the = key after entering 2 + 3, then we carry on with ×6,

i.e. press 2 + 3 = × 6 =

EXERCISE 7F

Use your calculator to find 2578 − 36 × 13

Estimate:

2578 − 36 × 13 ≈ 2500 − 40 × 10 = 2500 − 400 = 2100

 2 5 7 8 − 3 6 × 1 3 =

Calculator:

2578 − 36 × 13 = 2110

Use your calculator to find the answers, giving them correct to 2 decimal places when they are not exact. Do not forget to estimate the answer first.

1 $25 + 52 \times 26$

2 $279 \times 32 + 27$

3 $25 \times 52 + 26$

4 $398 \times 24 - 2560$

5 $579 + 46 - 37 \times 16$

6 $2965 \times 36 - 293 \times 178$

7 $36 - 216 \div 21$

8 $4088 \div 73 - 29$

9 $27 + 17 \div 58$

10 $1380 - 120 \times 18 \div 15$

11 $0.366 - 0.37 \times 0.52$

12 $0.0526 \times 0.372 + 0.027$

13 $6.924 + 1.56 \div 0.00793$

14 $0.638 \times 825 + 54.3$

15 $52 \times 0.0895 - 0.489$

16 $0.826 - 0.348 \times 0.582$

17 $24.78 \times 0.0724 + 8.25$

18 $0.00835 \times 0.617 - 0.00247$

19 $0.5824 + 1.054 \times 6.813$

20 $0.74 + 8.42 \div 0.56$

Use your calculator to find $(2.486 - 1.295) \times 3.057$ giving the answer corrected to 2 decimal places.

Estimate:

$(2.486 - 1.295) \times 3.057 \approx (2 - 1) \times 3 = 1 \times 3 = 3$

This can be done in one stage using the brackets buttons:

press $(\ 2\ \cdot\ 4\ 8\ 6\ -\ 1\ \cdot\ 2\ 9\ 5\ )$
$\times\ 3\ \cdot\ 0\ 5\ 7\ =$

It can also be done in two stages:

press $2\ \cdot\ 4\ 8\ 6\ -\ 1\ \cdot\ 2\ 9\ 5\ =$

and write down the result but do not clear the display.

Then press $\times\ 3\ \cdot\ 0\ 5\ 7\ =$

Calculator:

$(2.486 - 1.295) \times 3.057 = 3.640\ldots$

$\qquad\qquad\qquad\qquad = 3.64$ (correct to 2 d.p.)

First make an estimate of the answer and then use your calculator to find, correct to 3 decimal places

21 $54.6 \times (22.05 - 8.17)$ **25** $32.03 \times (17.09 - 16.9)$

22 $6.04 \div (1.958 - 0.872)$ **26** $0.51 \div (0.45 + 0.327)$

23 $(0.824 + 0.057) \times 27.45$ **27** $(1.033 + 0.29) \times 4.47$

24 $(27.98 - 21.25) \div 12.099$ **28** $(0.029 - 0.0084) \div 1.88$

USING A CALCULATOR TO WORK OUT POWERS

Remember that 2^3 means $2 \times 2 \times 2$.
Similarly 2.56^3 means $2.56 \times 2.56 \times 2.56$.

On a scientific calculator, the $\boxed{x^y}$ key can be used to work out powers of numbers,

e.g.   to find 2.56^3, press    $2\ \cdot\ 5\ 6\ \boxed{x^y}\ 3\ =$

We do not need to use the $\boxed{x^y}$ key in order to square numbers, as there is an $\boxed{x^2}$ button,

e.g.   to find 1.67^2, press $1\ \cdot\ 6\ 7\ \boxed{x^2}$

Note that these instructions apply to many *but not to all* calculators. You need to use the manual that comes with your calculator.

EXERCISE 7G

Find 1.2×0.34^3 correct to 2 decimal places.

$$\boxed{1}\ \boxed{.}\ \boxed{2}\ \boxed{\times}\ \boxed{0}\ \boxed{.}\ \boxed{3}\ \boxed{4}\ \boxed{x^y}\ \boxed{3}\ \boxed{=}$$

$1.2 \times 0.34^3 = 0.0471\ldots$

$\qquad\qquad = 0.05$ (correct to 2 d.p.)

Use your calculator to find, correct to 2 decimal places

1 1.56^2 **4** 2.78^6 **7** 56.8^3

2 4.59^3 **5** 1.9^3 **8** 3.05^5

3 1.7^4 **6** 12.7^2 **9** 0.73^5

10 0.35×1.2^2 **13** $3.27^4 \div 12.5$ **16** $19.45 \div 2.23^2$

11 $0.56^3 \div 0.16$ **14** $28.4 \div 1.6^4$ **17** 0.367×1.7^3

12 3.24×1.55^4 **15** 54.9×0.43^5 **18** $0.058 \div 0.445^2$

MIXED EXERCISE

EXERCISE 7H

1 This piece of Brie, when complete, weighed 3.75 kg. It is cut into 32 equal-sized portions. Find the weight of one portion, giving your answer as accurately as you think is reasonable.

2 The volume, in cubic centimetres, of this bar is found by calculating $(1.26 + 2.55) \times 24.28$. Find the volume of the bar correct to 1 decimal place.

3 Write each number correct to 2 decimal places.

   a 0.0497   **b** 1.096   **c** 12.333

4 Use your calculator to find, correct to 1 decimal place

    a 12.4^2 **b** $1.22 + 3.57 \div 0.252$ **c** 2.77^3

5 Without using your calculator, find, correct to 3 decimal places

    a $2 \div 11$ **b** $4 \div 30$ **c** $36 \div 7$

NUMBER PUZZLE

The digits 3, 4, 6 and 8 can be arranged as two pairs of two-figure numbers such that the products of the pairs gives the same result.

For example $43 \times 68 = 2924$

and $34 \times 86 = 2924$

Use your calculator to find other sets of 4 digits that, when arranged in pairs, behave like this.

Explain any tactics you used when solving this puzzle.

INVESTIGATION

a Investigate at least two ways of estimating the number of sweets in the jar. How accurate do you think you can be?

b Now estimate the number of coins on this table.

MULTIPLYING FRACTIONS

Fractions are part of every day language; the following sentences can be overheard anytime.

'I can get a third off the train fare with a young person's rail card.'

'My slice is only $\frac{1}{8}$ of the pie. If I give you half of it, you'll have more than I have.'

'Here is $6\frac{1}{2}$ in of wire. Cut it into $\frac{3}{8}$ in lengths – you should get at least 20 pieces out of it.'

- If you don't know what fractions mean, you cannot make much sense of these statements.
- The last two sentences contain statements which could be wrong.

In order to check whether these are correct, we need to be able to calculate with fractional quantities.

MULTIPLYING FRACTIONS

A particular fraction describes the size of part of a quantity.

For example, $\frac{3}{4}$ of £10 means 3 out of 4 equal-sized portions of £10.

In Chapter 3, we found how to add and subtract fractions. This will not help us to find, for example, the fraction of a pie that $\frac{1}{2}$ of one eighth of it is. We can, however, use a 'cake' diagram to illustrate what $\frac{1}{2}$ of $\frac{1}{8}$ means

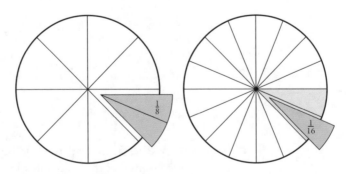

Now we can see that $\frac{1}{2}$ of $\frac{1}{8}$ of the pie is equal to $\frac{1}{16}$ of the pie.

The next step is to interpret the meaning of $\frac{1}{2}$ of $\frac{1}{8}$ in mathematical symbols;

when we have to find   '3 of a quantity',

we do so by calculating   '3 × the quantity'.

In the same way to find   '$\frac{1}{2}$ of a quantity',

we calculate   '$\frac{1}{2}$ × the quantity'.

Hence $\boxed{\dfrac{1}{2} \text{ of } \dfrac{1}{8} \text{ means calculate } \dfrac{1}{2} \times \dfrac{1}{8}}$

$\left(\text{and conversely, } \dfrac{1}{2} \times \dfrac{1}{8} \text{ means } \dfrac{1}{2} \text{ of } \dfrac{1}{8}.\right)$

From the cake diagram, we know that $\dfrac{1}{2} \times \dfrac{1}{8} = \dfrac{1}{16}$

EXERCISE 8A

Draw cake diagrams to find

1 $\dfrac{1}{2} \times \dfrac{1}{4}$ **3** $\dfrac{1}{2} \times \dfrac{3}{4}$ **5** $\dfrac{1}{3} \times \dfrac{2}{5}$

2 $\dfrac{1}{3} \times \dfrac{1}{2}$ **4** $\dfrac{2}{3} \times \dfrac{1}{3}$ **6** $\dfrac{1}{4} \times \dfrac{1}{3}$

7 Use a copy of the diagram to find

$\dfrac{3}{4} \times \dfrac{2}{3}$

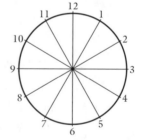

8 Use a copy of the diagram to find

$\dfrac{2}{5} \times \dfrac{3}{10}$

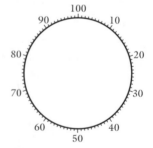

9 a For questions **1** to **6** find a relationship between the numerators in the given fractions and the numerator in the result.

    b Repeat part **a** for the denominators.

THE RULE FOR MULTIPLYING FRACTIONS

You may have discovered this rule in question **9** of the exercise on the previous page:

> Fractions are multiplied by multiplying together the numbers in the numerators *and* multiplying together the numbers in the denominators.

For example, $\frac{2}{3} \times \frac{4}{7} = \frac{2\times4}{3\times7} = \frac{8}{21}$

EXERCISE 8B

Calculate

1 $\frac{1}{2} \times \frac{3}{4}$

2 $\frac{2}{3} \times \frac{1}{5}$

3 $\frac{2}{7} \times \frac{3}{5}$

4 $\frac{1}{9} \times \frac{1}{2}$

5 $\frac{3}{4} \times \frac{1}{5}$

6 $\frac{2}{5} \times \frac{3}{5}$

7 $\frac{1}{2} \times \frac{1}{2}$

8 $\left(\frac{1}{3}\right)^2$

9 $\frac{1}{3} \times \frac{2}{5}$

10 $\frac{3}{5} \times \frac{3}{4}$

11 $\frac{2}{3} \times \frac{2}{3}$

12 $\left(\frac{2}{5}\right)^2$

Calculate $\frac{2}{3} \times \frac{3}{4}$

> The numbers can sometimes be simplified by cancelling common factors before finding the product.

$$\frac{2}{3} \times \frac{3}{4} = \frac{2^1}{{}_1 3} \times \frac{3^1}{{}_2 4} = \frac{1 \times 1}{1 \times 2}$$

$$= \frac{1}{2}$$

The diagram shows that

$\frac{2}{3}$ of $\frac{3}{4} = \frac{1}{2}$

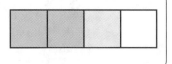

Calculate

13 $\frac{3}{4} \times \frac{4}{7}$

14 $\frac{2}{3} \times \frac{3}{7}$

15 $\frac{2}{3} \times \frac{3}{5}$

16 $\frac{2}{5} \times \frac{3}{4}$

17 $\frac{4}{7} \times \frac{5}{12}$

18 $\frac{2}{9} \times \frac{3}{7}$

Sometimes there is more than one common factor that can be cancelled.

Calculate $\dfrac{4}{25} \times \dfrac{15}{16}$

$\dfrac{\cancel{4}^{1}}{_{5}\cancel{25}} \times \dfrac{\cancel{15}^{3}}{_{4}\cancel{16}} = \dfrac{1 \times 3}{5 \times 4}$ (4 is a common factor, so is 5.)

$\qquad\qquad = \dfrac{3}{20}$

Calculate

19 $\dfrac{7}{8} \times \dfrac{4}{21}$ **21** $\dfrac{21}{22} \times \dfrac{11}{27}$ **23** $\dfrac{7}{9} \times \dfrac{3}{21}$

20 $\dfrac{3}{4} \times \dfrac{16}{21}$ **22** $\dfrac{8}{9} \times \dfrac{33}{44}$ **24** $\dfrac{3}{4} \times \dfrac{16}{21}$

25 $\dfrac{4}{5} \times \dfrac{15}{16}$ **27** $\dfrac{4}{15} \times \dfrac{25}{64}$ **29** $\dfrac{3}{7} \times \dfrac{28}{33}$

26 $\dfrac{10}{11} \times \dfrac{33}{35}$ **28** $\dfrac{2}{3} \times \dfrac{33}{40}$ **30** $\dfrac{48}{55} \times \dfrac{5}{12}$

31 A cook adds $\frac{1}{2}$ cup of water to a stew. The cup holds $\frac{1}{10}$ litre. What fraction of a litre is added to the stew?

32 There are some balls in a bag and $\frac{3}{8}$ of them are black. Two thirds of the black balls have white spots on them.
What fraction of the balls in the bag are black with white spots on them?

33 Three-quarters of the pupils in a class got a grade B in a chemistry exam. Two-fifths of those who got grade B in chemistry also got grade B in biology. What fraction of the class got Bs in both exams?

34 Three-quarters of the area of some reclaimed land is designated for housing and the rest is to be used for industrial development. One-fifth of the area set aside for housing is left as open space.

    a What fraction of the area of reclaimed land is to be used for industrial purposes?

    b What fraction of the area of reclaimed land is to be left as open space?

35 Place these fractions in order of size with the smaller first.

a $\frac{2}{3}$ of $\frac{1}{5}$, $\frac{1}{2} \times \frac{2}{5}$

c $\frac{3}{4}$ of $\frac{1}{2}$, $\frac{1}{8} \times \frac{3}{4}$

b $\frac{3}{4} \times \frac{1}{3}$, $\frac{1}{12}$ of eight-ninths.

d $\frac{1}{6} + \frac{2}{9}$, $\frac{2}{3} \times \frac{5}{6}$

36 State, with reasons, whether two-thirds of one-fifth is the same as one-third of two-fifths. Without working them out, state with reasons whether twelve-seventeenths of thirteen-nineteenths is the same as thirteen-seventeenths of twelve-nineteenths.

MULTIPLYING MIXED NUMBERS

Mixed numbers cannot be multiplied together unless they are first changed into improper fractions.

To find $3\frac{1}{2} \times 4\frac{1}{8}$,

we change $3\frac{1}{2}$ into $\frac{7}{2}$ and we change $4\frac{1}{8}$ into $\frac{33}{8}$, then

$$3\frac{1}{2} \times 4\frac{1}{8} = \frac{7}{2} \times \frac{33}{8}$$

$$= \frac{231}{16} = 14\frac{7}{16}$$

EXERCISE 8C

Calculate $2\frac{1}{3} \times 1\frac{1}{5}$

$$2\frac{1}{3} \times 1\frac{1}{5} = \frac{7}{{}_1 3} \times \frac{\cancel{6}^2}{5}$$

3 is a common factor of the top and bottom so it can be cancelled.

$$= \frac{14}{5} = 2\frac{4}{5}$$

Calculate

1 $1\frac{1}{2} \times \frac{2}{5}$

6 $1\frac{1}{4} \times \frac{2}{5}$

2 $2\frac{1}{2} \times \frac{4}{5}$

7 $2\frac{1}{3} \times \frac{3}{8}$

3 $3\frac{1}{4} \times \frac{3}{13}$

8 $\frac{10}{11} \times 2\frac{1}{5}$

4 $4\frac{2}{3} \times \frac{2}{5}$

9 $3\frac{1}{2} \times \frac{2}{3}$

5 $2\frac{1}{5} \times \frac{5}{22}$

10 $4\frac{1}{4} \times \frac{4}{21}$

11 $5\frac{1}{4} \times 2\frac{2}{3}$

16 $4\frac{2}{7} \times 2\frac{1}{10}$

12 $3\frac{5}{7} \times 1\frac{1}{13}$

17 $6\frac{1}{4} \times 1\frac{3}{5}$

13 $8\frac{1}{3} \times 3\frac{3}{5}$

18 $5\frac{1}{2} \times 1\frac{9}{11}$

14 $2\frac{1}{10} \times 7\frac{6}{7}$

19 $8\frac{3}{4} \times 2\frac{2}{7}$

15 $6\frac{3}{10} \times 1\frac{4}{21}$

20 $16\frac{1}{2} \times 3\frac{7}{11}$

MULTIPLYING BY A WHOLE NUMBER

We can use the rule for multiplying fractions when we have to find the product of a fraction and a whole number; we treat the whole number as a fraction,

e.g.   we write 2 as $\frac{2}{1}$

EXERCISE 8D

Calculate $\frac{3}{4} \times 5$

$\frac{3}{4} \times 5 = \frac{3}{4} \times \frac{5}{1}$

$= \frac{15}{4} = 3\frac{3}{4}$

FIRST WRITE 5 AS THE FRACTION $\frac{5}{1}$ THEN USE THE RULE FOR MULTIPLYING FRACTIONS.

Find

1 $\frac{3}{5} \times 6$

4 $\frac{7}{9} \times 12$

7 $\frac{3}{8} \times 24$

2 $\frac{4}{7} \times 14$

5 $20 \times \frac{3}{5}$

8 $27 \times \frac{5}{18}$

3 $5 \times \frac{2}{3}$

6 $8 \times \frac{5}{16}$

9 $\frac{3}{10} \times 50$

Calculate $6 \times 7\frac{1}{3}$

$6 \times 7\frac{1}{3} = \frac{\cancel{6}^{2}}{1} \times \frac{22}{\cancel{3}_{1}}$

$= \frac{44}{1} = 44$

Cancelling top and bottom by 3.

Calculate

10 $5 \times 4\frac{3}{5}$

14 $18 \times 6\frac{1}{9}$

18 $5\frac{5}{7} \times 21$

11 $2\frac{1}{7} \times 14$

15 $4 \times 3\frac{3}{8}$

19 $3 \times 6\frac{1}{9}$

12 $3\frac{1}{8} \times 4$

16 $3\frac{3}{5} \times 10$

20 $1\frac{3}{4} \times 8$

13 $4\frac{1}{6} \times 9$

17 $2\frac{5}{6} \times 3$

21 $28 \times 1\frac{4}{7}$

FRACTIONS OF A QUANTITY

Frequently in everyday life we need to find a fraction of a quantity. Maybe we see a rail of clothes in a sale with a notice

One-third off all coats on this rail

or we want half a pint of milk, or wish to measure three-quarters of the length of a piece of wood.

Suppose Margot was given £20 in cash for her birthday and that she was persuaded to put $\frac{3}{5}$ of it into a savings account. To find out how much she is to put in a savings account Margot needs to find $\frac{3}{5}$ of £20.

We can do this by first dividing 20 by 5 to find the size of $\frac{1}{5}$ of £20,

i.e. $\quad \frac{1}{5}$ of £20 = £20 ÷ 5 = £4

then $\quad \frac{3}{5}$ of £20 = £4 × 3 = £12

We can also find $\frac{3}{5}$ of £20 directly by multiplication as we know that

$\frac{3}{5}$ of £20 means $\frac{3}{5} \times £20$

i.e. $\quad \frac{3}{5}$ of £20 $= £\frac{3}{5} \times 20 = £\frac{3}{5} \times \frac{20^4}{1} = £\frac{12}{1} = £12$

EXERCISE 8E

Find $\frac{2}{3}$ of £27.

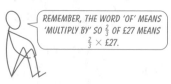

REMEMBER, THE WORD 'OF' MEANS 'MULTIPLY BY' SO $\frac{2}{3}$ OF £27 MEANS $\frac{2}{3} \times$ £27.

$\frac{2}{3}$ of £27 = £$\frac{2}{3}$ × 27

$$= £\frac{2}{\cancel{3}} \times \frac{\cancel{27}^9}{1} = £\frac{18}{1} = £18$$

Find

1 $\frac{1}{3}$ of 12

2 $\frac{2}{5}$ of 45

3 $\frac{3}{4}$ of £84

4 $\frac{7}{10}$ of 50 litres

5 $\frac{3}{5}$ of £1

6 $\frac{3}{8}$ of 64 miles

7 $\frac{1}{6}$ of 42

8 $\frac{3}{7}$ of 42

9 $\frac{1}{3}$ of £18

10 $\frac{2}{5}$ of 25 gallons **11** $\frac{2}{3}$ of 25 millilitres **12** $\frac{2}{5}$ of 100 milligrams

13 David gives $\frac{1}{3}$ of the biscuits in this packet to Sue and $\frac{1}{2}$ of them to Lorna. How many biscuits

a does Sue get?

b does Lorna get?

c are left for David?

14 The milkman removes this crate of milk from his float. He delivers $\frac{1}{4}$ of the bottles to the Smiths and $\frac{2}{5}$ of them to the Baghdadis. How many bottles of milk

a do the Smiths get

b do the Baghdadis get

c are left in the crate?

15 Find

a $\frac{3}{5}$ of 30 metres   **d** $\frac{3}{7}$ of 21 miles   **g** $\frac{3}{5}$ of 25 p

b $\frac{3}{4}$ of £20   **e** $\frac{5}{8}$ of 32 km   **h** $\frac{3}{8}$ of 40 miles

c $\frac{1}{2}$ of 120 litres   **f** $\frac{2}{7}$ of 1 week   **i** $\frac{5}{8}$ of 16 gallons

16 Find

a $\frac{2}{5}$ of £125   **f** $\frac{3}{8}$ of 104 mm

b $\frac{5}{8}$ of 600 litres   **g** $\frac{5}{9}$ of 675 dollars

c $\frac{3}{4}$ of 224 km   **h** $\frac{2}{7}$ of 392 francs

d $\frac{7}{8}$ of 112 miles   **i** $\frac{5}{12}$ of 324 days

e $\frac{4}{7}$ of 161 cm   **j** $\frac{4}{9}$ of 189 hours

Find $\frac{2}{5}$ of £3

$\frac{2}{5}$ of £3 $= \frac{2}{5}$ of 300 pence   We change £3 to 300 pence, as it is not easy to work with fractions of £1.

$$= \frac{2}{{}_{1}\cancel{5}} \times \frac{\cancel{300}^{60}}{1} \text{ pence}$$

$$= 120 \text{ pence} = £1.20$$

---

17 In this question give your answer in the unit in brackets.

a $\frac{3}{4}$ of £2 (pence)   **f** $\frac{5}{12}$ of a year (months)

b $\frac{4}{5}$ of 3 metres (cm)   **g** $\frac{7}{10}$ of a metre (cm)

c $\frac{3}{5}$ of £1 (pence)   **h** $\frac{3}{8}$ of 4 cm (mm)

d $\frac{2}{3}$ of 1 hour (minutes)   **i** $\frac{5}{7}$ of 1 week (days)

e $\frac{2}{5}$ of half an hour (minutes)   **j** $\frac{5}{8}$ of 1 m (cm)

18 A bag of flour weighs $1\frac{1}{2}$ kg. What is the weight of 20 bags?

19 Three and a half sacks of sand are added to a cement mix. Each sack of sand weighs 26 kg. What weight of sand is added to the cement?

20 The area of a garden is $40 \, \text{m}^2$. Two fifths of the area is used for growing soft fruit. How many square metres are used for growing soft fruit?

21 If $\frac{19}{20}$ of my body weight is water and I weigh $52\frac{1}{2}$ kg, how much of my weight is water?

**ONE QUANTITY
AS A FRACTION
OF ANOTHER**

Anne took a Geography test and scored 38 marks out of 50. Julia took a different Geography test and obtained 45 marks out of 60.

- Julia asserted that she had scored a higher mark than Anne. This is true when the raw marks are considered, but it is not a fair way to compare the performance of the two girls as these marks are out of different totals.
  A more reasonable method is to compare the fraction of the total mark obtained by each girl.

Anne scored 38 out of 50, i.e. $\frac{38}{50}$ of the total marks available.

Julia scored 45 out of 60, i.e. $\frac{45}{60}$ of the total marks available.

Now we can compare these fractions by changing them to equivalent fractions with denominators of 100:

$$\frac{38}{50} = \frac{76}{100} \quad \text{and} \quad \frac{45}{60} = \frac{3}{4} = \frac{75}{100}$$

so Anne performed marginally better than Julia.

Many quantities can be divided into equal parts. For instance, there are seven days in a week, so one day is $\frac{1}{7}$ of a week and 5 days is $\frac{5}{7}$ of a week.

Similarly, 30 minutes can be expressed as a fraction of $2\frac{1}{2}$ hours.

There are 150 minutes in $2\frac{1}{2}$ hours

so 30 minutes is $\frac{30}{150}$, i.e. $\frac{1}{5}$ of $2\frac{1}{2}$ hours.

> To express one quantity as a fraction of another,
> first express both quantities in the same unit
> and then put the first quantity over the second quantity.

EXERCISE 8F

Express the first quantity as a fraction of the second quantity.

a 15 cm, 75 cm   **b** 680 g, 2 kg

a 15 cm as a fraction of 75 cm is $\dfrac{\cancel{15}^{1}}{_{5}\cancel{75}} = \dfrac{1}{5}$

b

> Both quantities must be in the same unit so we change the larger unit to the smaller unit.

$$2\,kg = 2 \times 1000\,g$$
$$= 2000\,g$$

Then 680 g as a fraction of 2 kg $= \dfrac{680^{17}}{_{50}2000} = \dfrac{17}{50}$

In questions **1** to **18** express the first quantity as a fraction of the second quantity.

1 15 minutes, 45 minutes

2 35 seconds, 120 seconds

3 70 cm, 200 cm

4 £2, £5

5 35 g, 80 g

6 8 in, 18 in

7 3 litres, 12 litres

8 45 km, 150 km

9 20 hours, 60 hours

10 25 ml, 150 ml

11 20 minutes, 2 hours

12 25 cm, 400 mm

13 12 minutes, 2 hours

14 55 p, £2.25

15 500 m, 3 km

16 60 cm, 2 m

17 12 mm, 5 cm

18 5.6 cm, 12 cm

19 Sally's journey to school costs 55 p on one bus and 35 p on another bus.

    a Find the total cost of her journey

    b What fraction of the total cost arises from each bus?

20 Andrew has a 25 acre field. He plants 15 acres with wheat. What fraction of the field does he plant with wheat?

21   Simon gets £2.40 a week pocket money. If he spends £1.35, what fraction of his pocket money is left?

22   When she left home, Carol's school bag weighed $3\frac{1}{4}$ kg. When she got to school, she took out her maths text book. Her school bag then weighed $2\frac{1}{2}$ kg. What was the weight of her maths book as a fraction of the weight of her bag when she left home?

23   This pumpkin weighed $5\frac{1}{2}$ kg before it was carved.

It now weighs $1\frac{1}{2}$ kg.

What fraction of its weight has been removed?

MIXED EXERCISE

EXERCISE 8G

1   Find, without using a calculator

  a $\frac{1}{4}$ of 28   **b** $\frac{3}{5}$ of 40   **c** $\frac{5}{7}$ of 63

2   Find, using a calculator if necessary

  a $\frac{7}{12}$ of 432 litres   **b** $\frac{5}{8}$ of £384

3   Find

  a $\frac{2}{3} \times 33$ **b** $52 \times \frac{7}{13}$ **c** $\frac{7}{21} \times 35$ **d** $39 \times \frac{5}{9}$

4   Calculate

  a $\frac{1}{4} \times \frac{3}{8}$ **b** $\frac{3}{5} \times \frac{3}{5}$ **c** $\frac{4}{9} \times \frac{7}{12}$ **d** $\frac{6}{7} \times \frac{21}{22}$

5   One-fifth of the cars in a park are red and one-sixth of the red cars were made in France. What fraction of the cars in the park were red and were made in France?

6   On a farm $\frac{3}{7}$ of the land is used for growing cereals and $\frac{7}{12}$ of the land that is used for growing cereals is planted with maize. What fraction of the acreage of the farm is planted with maize?

7   Each week, Jon saved 75 p from his £2 pocket money. What fraction of his pocket money did he save?

8   Peter scored 20 out of 80 on Section A of a quiz and 54 out of 60 on Section B. What fraction of the total score did Peter get?

PUZZLES

1 In the Silcox family, Joe, who is in his nineties, is George's father and Harry is George's son. George is $\frac{1}{2}$ of his father's age and Harry is $\frac{1}{6}$ of his grandfather's age. The total of their ages is 160 years.

By trying different ages, find the age of each.

2 Solve this cross-fraction puzzle by trying different fractions for a, b, c and d.

Each letter stands for a simple fraction that is smaller than 1 and

$a + b = \frac{3}{4}$

$a \times c = \frac{1}{8}$

$d = 3 \times b$

$a \times d = \frac{3}{8}$

a	b
c	d

INVESTIGATION

In each part of this investigation use each digit from 2 to 9 once and only once.

a Write down four fractions so that their product is as small as possible.

b Find two fractions, each with two digits in the numerator and two digits in the denominator, that multiply together to give the smallest possible value. Is it possible to get this smallest value by multiplying a different pair of fractions together? Justify your answer.

c Write down a fraction with two digits in the numerator and two digits in the denominator, together with two fractions each of which has one digit in the top and one digit in the bottom, such that the value of the product of all three fractions is as small as possible. Can this be done in more than one way? Justify your answer.

REFLECTIONS, TRANSLATIONS AND ROTATIONS

In Book 7B, Chapter 5, we saw that if an object is reflected in a mirror line the image is identical in size and shape to the object

Keith has bought a new panelled hardwood door for the lounge. He rests it against the wall ready to hang it. A large mirror is fixed to a perpendicular wall.
The image of the door in the mirror is a *reflection*.
When he moves the door along the wall and fits it, the door is being *translated*.
When the door is hung it *rotates* about a vertical line through the hinges.
In all three cases: reflection, translation and rotation, the size and shape of the door remains unchanged. All that changes is its position.

EXERCISE 9A   Which kind of movement is suggested by each of the descriptions in questions **1** to **7** – a reflection, a translation or a rotation ?

1 A car travelling along a straight road.

2 A car travelling round a roundabout.

3 Pushing a coin across the counter to pay for a magazine.

4 Turning a page of this book.

5 Looking at yourself in the bathroom mirror.

6 Comparing the two sides of the soundbox of a violin.

7 Riding on a fairground roundabout.

8 Can you think of everyday situations/happenings that can be described as

a a reflection   **b** a translation   **c** a rotation?

Try to think of at least three of each type.

REFLECTIONS

Consider a piece of paper, with a drawing on it, lying on a table. Stand a mirror upright on the paper and the reflection can be seen as in the picture.

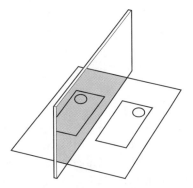

If we did not know about such things as mirrors, we might imagine that there were two pieces of paper lying on the table like this:

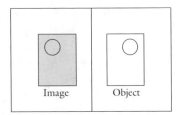

The *object* and the *image* together form a symmetrical shape and the *mirror line* is the axis of symmetry.

EXERCISE 9B

In this exercise it may be helpful to use a small rectangular mirror, or you can use tracing paper to trace the object and turn the tracing paper over, to find the image.

Copy the objects and mirror lines (indicated by dotted lines) onto squared paper and draw the image of each object.

1

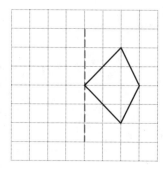

3

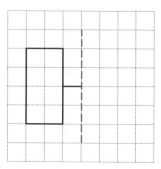

2

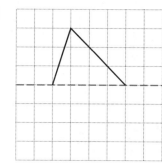

4

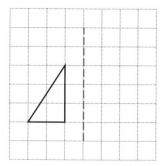

Copy triangle ABC and the mirror line onto squared paper. Draw the image. Label the corresponding vertices (corners) of the image A′, B′, C′.

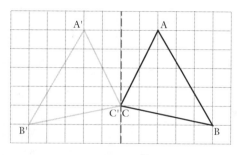

In this case C and C′ are the same point.

In questions **5** to **14** copy the object and the mirror line on to squared paper. Draw the image. Label the vertices of the object A, B, C, etc. and label the corresponding vertices of the image A′, B′, C′, etc.

5
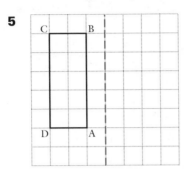

6
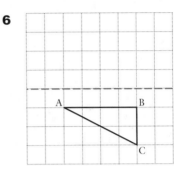

7
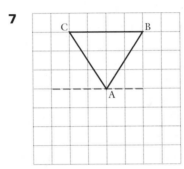

In mathematical reflection, though not in real life, the object can cross the mirror line.

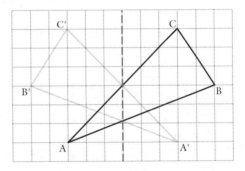

8
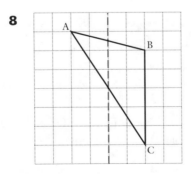

9
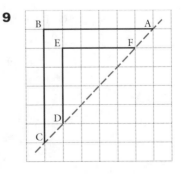

10
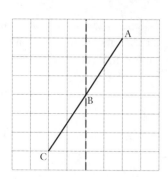

12
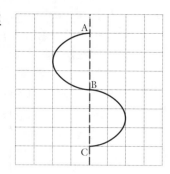

11
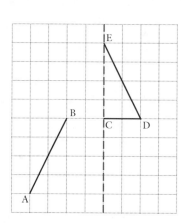

13
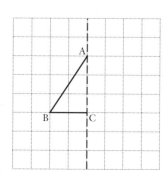

14
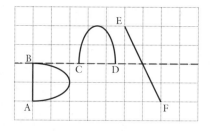

15 Which points in questions **5** to **14** are labelled with two letters? What is special about their positions?

16 In the diagram for question **10**, join A and A′.

   a Measure the distances of A and A′ from the mirror line. What do you notice?

   b At what angle does the line AA′ cut the mirror line?

17 Repeat question **16** on other suitable diagrams, in each case joining each object point to its image point. What conclusions do you draw?

In questions **18** and **19** use 1 cm to 1 unit.

18 Draw axes, for x from -5 to 5 and for y from 0 to 5. Draw triangle ABC by plotting A(1, 2), B(3, 2) and C(3, 5). Draw the image A′B′C′ when ABC is reflected in the y-axis.

19 Draw axes, for x from 0 to 5 and for y from -2 to 2. Draw triangle PQR where P is (1, -1), Q is (5, -1) and R is (4, 0). Draw the image P′Q′R′ when △PQR is reflected in the x-axis.

In questions **20** and **21** use squared paper and draw axes for x and y from -5 to 5.

20 Draw square PQRS: P(1, 1), Q(4, 1), R(4, 4), S(1, 4). Draw square P′Q′R′S′: P′(-2, 1), Q′(-5, 1), R′(-5, 4), S′(-2, 4). Draw the mirror line so that P′Q′R′S′ is the reflection of PQRS and describe the mirror line.

21 Draw lines AB and PQ: A(2, -1), B(4, 4), P(-2, -1), Q(-5, 4). Is PQ a reflection of AB? If it is, draw the mirror line. If not, give a reason.

TRANSFORMATIONS

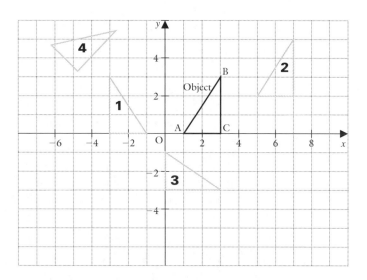

Imagine a triangle ABC cut out of card and lying in the position shown. We can reflect △ABC in the y-axis by picking up the card, turning it over and putting it down again in position 1.

Starting again from its original position, we can change its position by sliding the card over the surface of the paper to position 2, 3 or 4. Some of these movements can be described in a simple way, some are more complicated. They are all called *transformations* of the object.

TRANSLATIONS   Consider the movements in the diagram:

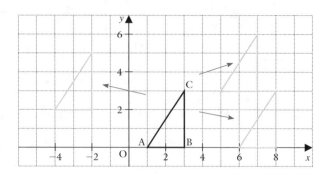

All these movements are of the same type. The side AB remains parallel to the *x*-axis in each case and the triangle continues to face in the same direction. This type of movement is called a *translation*.

Although not a reflection we still use the words *object* and *image*.

EXERCISE 9C   **1** In the following diagram, which images of △ABC are given by translations?

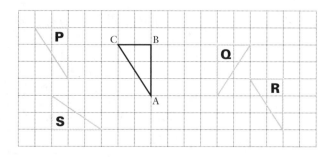

2 In the following diagram, which images of △ABC are given by a translation, which by a reflection and which by neither?

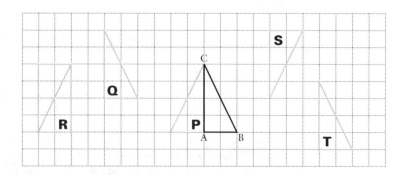

3 Repeat question **2** with the diagram on page 171.

Draw sketches to illustrate the following translations.
(Choose a simple object such as a square or a triangle.)

4 An object is translated 6 cm to the left.

5 An object is translated 4 units parallel to the *x*-axis to the right.

6 An object is translated 3 m due north.

7 An object is translated 5 km south-east.

8 An object is translated 3 units parallel to the *x*-axis to the right and then 4 units parallel to the *y*-axis upwards.

9

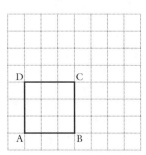

a Square ABCD is translated parallel to AB a distance equal to AB. Sketch the diagram and draw the image of ABCD.

b Square ABCD is translated parallel to AC a distance equal to AC. Sketch the diagram and draw the image of ABCD.

10 Draw sketches to illustrate the following translations of the rectangle ABCD. In each case give the coordinates of the point to which A has been translated.

  a 6 units to the right followed by 3 units up. Mark it P.

  b 6 units to the left followed by 3 units down. Mark it Q.

  c 5 units down followed by 3 units to the left. Mark it R.

  d 2 units up followed by 6 units to the left. Mark it S.

  e Describe, in words, how to translate **i** Q to R **ii** P to Q.

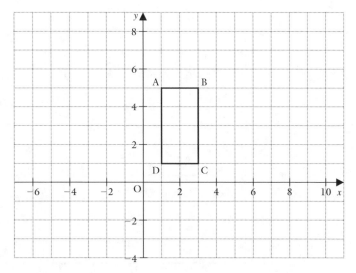

11 Draw axes for x and y from 0 to 12. Draw $\triangle$ABC with A(5, 0),
B(4, 3), C(2, 2) and $\triangle$A′B′C′ with A′(11, 2), B′(10, 5),
C′(8, 4).
Is $\triangle$A′B′C′ the image of $\triangle$ABC under a translation? If so, describe
the translation using the method given in the previous question.
Join AA′, BB′ and CC′. What type of quadrilateral is AA′B′B? Give
reasons for your answer.

**ORDER OF
ROTATIONAL
SYMMETRY**

A shape has rotational symmetry when it can be rotated, or turned, about
a centre point and still look the same.

If a shape needs to be turned through a
third of a complete turn to look the
same, then it will need two more such
turns to return to its original position.
Therefore, starting from its original
position, it takes three turns, each
one-third of a revolution, to return to
its starting point.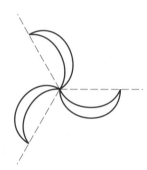

It has *rotational symmetry of order 3*.

EXERCISE 9D

Give the order of rotational symmetry of the following shape.

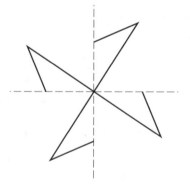

> The smallest angle turned through to fit over its original position is a right angle or
> one-quarter of a complete turn.

The shape has rotational symmetry of order 4.

1 Give the order of rotational symmetry for each shape.

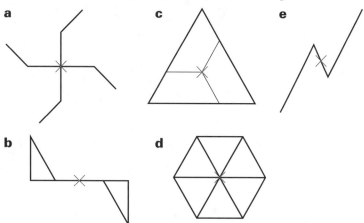

The point about which the shape is turned is called the *centre of rotation*.

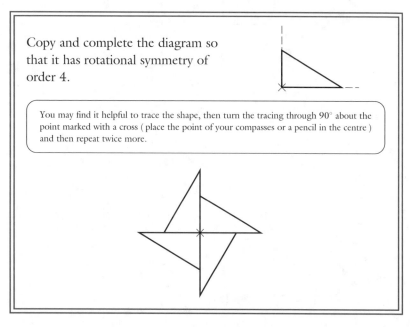

Copy and complete the diagram so that it has rotational symmetry of order 4.

You may find it helpful to trace the shape, then turn the tracing through 90° about the point marked with a cross (place the point of your compasses or a pencil in the centre) and then repeat twice more.

Each of the diagrams in questions **2** to **7** has rotational symmetry of the order given and × marks the centre of rotation.
Copy and complete the diagrams. (Tracing paper may be helpful.)

2

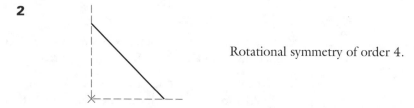

Rotational symmetry of order 4.

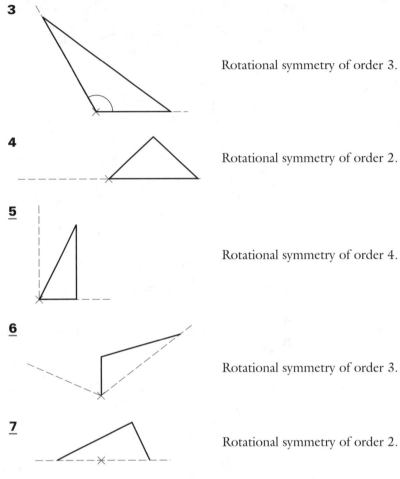

3

Rotational symmetry of order 3.

4

Rotational symmetry of order 2.

5

Rotational symmetry of order 4.

6

Rotational symmetry of order 3.

7

Rotational symmetry of order 2.

8 In questions **2** to **7**, give the size of the angle, in degrees, through which each shape is turned.

ROTATIONS

A 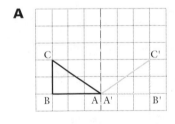   **B** 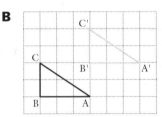   **C**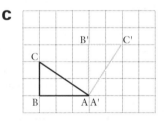

So far in transforming an object we have used reflections, as in **A**, and translations, as in **B**, but for **C** we need a rotation.

In this case we are rotating △ABC about A through 90° clockwise (↻). We could also say △ABC was rotated through 270° anticlockwise (↺).

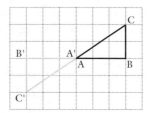

For a rotation of 180° we do
not need to say whether it is
clockwise or anticlockwise.

EXERCISE 9E

Give the angle of rotation when △ABC is mapped to △A′B′C′.

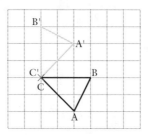

If you cannot 'see' the angle of rotation, trace △ABC. Without moving the tracing paper push a pin through the tracing paper into the point marked with a ✕. Next rotate the tracing paper until △ABC lies exactly over △A′B′C′. The angle of rotation is the angle turned through by any side of △ABC that passes through ✕ (extended if necessary). In this case ∠BCB′ is 90°.

The angle of rotation is 90° anticlockwise.

In questions **1** to **4**, give the angle of rotation when △ABC is mapped to △A′B′C′. If the angle is not obvious you may find using tracing paper helps.

1

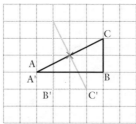

3

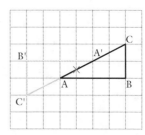

2

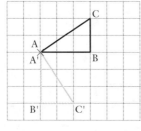

4

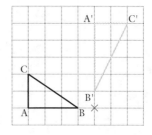

Copy the diagrams in questions **5** to **10**, using 1 cm to 1 unit.
Draw the images of the given shapes if each shape is rotated about the
point marked ✕ through the angle indicated.

Using tracing paper may help.

5

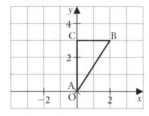

Angle of rotation 90° anticlockwise

6

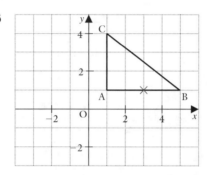

Angle of rotation 180°.

7

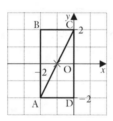

Angle of rotation 180°.

8

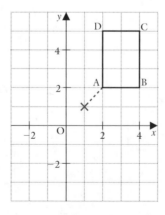

Angle of rotation 180°.

(As the centre of rotation
is not a point on the
object, join it to A first.)

9

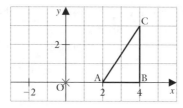

Angle of rotation
90° anticlockwise

10

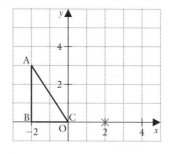

Angle of rotation 90° clockwise

11

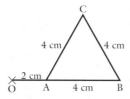

Draw the diagram accurately. Then draw accurately, using a protractor, the image of △ABC under a rotation of 60° anticlockwise about O.

CONGRUENCE

The diagram below was drawn on a computer. Triangle A was drawn first. The other triangles were obtained by transforming A in various ways, including turning it over (reflection) and round (rotation). All the triangles are exactly the same shape and size. If they were cut out, they would fit exactly over each other.

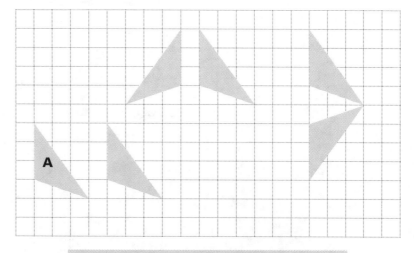

Any two figures that are exactly the same shape
and size are called *congruent* figures.

EXERCISE 9F   In each of the following questions, state whether or not the two figures are congruent. If you are not sure, trace one figure and see if the tracing will fit over the other figure. If necessary, turn the tracing over.

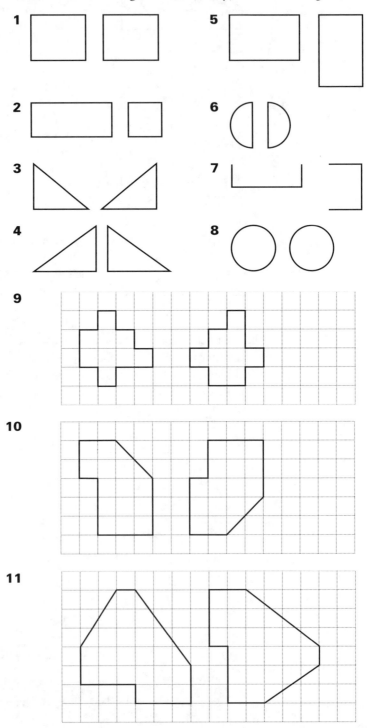

**PRACTICAL
WORK**

a Make a tracing of the flower on a wild strawberry plant as shown below.

Although not perfectly symmetrical, this flower has approximate rotational symmetry (and approximate line symmetry).

How many petals does it have?

Put your tracing on top of the flower. Push a pin through the centre of your traced flower and rotate your tracing until it fits almost exactly over the original flower again.

Repeat this until your tracing returns to its starting position. In how many different positions did you place your tracing, including the original position? What is the order of rotational symmetry for this flower?

b Look carefully at each of the drawings given below. Give the order of rotational symmetry for each flower.

For each flower compare the number of petals with the order of rotational symmetry.

c Which, if any, of the above flowers have rotational symmetry but not line symmetry?

d Use a book about wild flowers to investigate the possible number of petals that different wild flowers have. Can you name different wild flowers that have any number of petals from 1 to 12? How is the order of symmetry of a flower connected with the number of petals it has?

Copy, and as far as possible complete, the following table for up to 12 petals.

Include the flowers given above as well as the ones you find yourself.

Number of petals	Number of different flowers found with this number of petals
1	
2	
3	
4	
5	
6	
7	

Can you find at least one flower to go in each line?

How many petals are **i** most common **ii** least common?

e Compare your findings with those of another member of the class.

INVESTIGATION

a On squared paper draw x- and y-axes and scale each axis from 0 to 10. Plot the points A(3, 3), B(2, 6), C(3, 10), D(4, 9), E(6, 8) and F(5, 6). Join the points in order and join F to A.

b Plot the points (2, 2), (4, 4), (10, 10) and draw a straight line through them.

c Use this line as a mirror line to find a reflection of the shape ABCDEF. Label the reflection A′B′C′D′E′F′, where A′ is the reflection of A, B′ the reflection of B, and so on.

d Copy and complete the following table.

Coordinates of original point	A(3, 3)	B(2, 6)			
Coordinates of reflected point	A′( )	B′( )			

e What rule can you give to find the coordinates of the reflected point if you are given the coordinates of a starting point?

PERCENTAGES, FRACTIONS AND DECIMALS

We often refer to parts of a whole in different ways: $\frac{3}{4}$ of the pupils in my class have a pet; 60% of provisional drivers fail their driving test first time; I live 0.9 km from the school.
In this chapter we consider the relationships between these three different ways of describing parts of a whole and learn how to change from one form to another.

CHANGING PERCENTAGES TO FRACTIONS

We know that if 40% of an audience are men this means that $\frac{40}{100}$ of the audience are men. Now $\frac{40}{100}$ can be simplified.

Dividing the top and the bottom by 20 gives $\dfrac{40^2}{_5100} = \dfrac{2}{5}$

Similarly $45\% = \dfrac{45}{100}$

$\qquad\qquad = \dfrac{9}{20}$

EXERCISE 10A

A company increased its turnover last year by 130%.
What fraction is this?

$\qquad 130\% = \dfrac{130}{100}$

$\qquad\qquad\quad = \dfrac{13}{10} = 1\dfrac{3}{10}$

In questions **1** to **30** express each percentage as a fraction in its lowest terms.

1 30%	**5** 48%	**9** 170%	**13** 450%	**17** 375%
2 12%	**6** 56%	**10** 250%	**14** 232%	**18** 166%
3 65%	**7** 64%	**11** 140%	**15** 175%	**19** 184%
4 32%	**8** 83%	**12** 354%	**16** 648%	**20** 225%

In the town of Calham $12\frac{1}{2}\%$ of the population are under 5. What fraction is this?

$12\frac{1}{2}\% = 12.5\% = \dfrac{12.5}{100}$

> Change a percentage to a fraction by dividing by 100.

$= \dfrac{125}{1000}$

> Get rid of the decimal point by multiplying the top and the bottom of 10.

$= \dfrac{1}{8}$

> Divide top and bottom by 25 and then by 5.

21 $37\frac{1}{2}\%$ **23** $62\frac{1}{2}\%$ **25** $5\frac{1}{2}\%$ **27** $11\frac{3}{4}\%$ **29** $3\frac{5}{8}\%$

22 $2\frac{1}{2}\%$ **24** $3\frac{1}{4}\%$ **26** $4\frac{3}{4}\%$ **28** $3\frac{1}{8}\%$ **30** $14\frac{7}{10}\%$

31 Forty-four per cent of the students in a college are females. What fraction is this?

32 Thirty-eight per cent of the houses in a village were built before 1914. What fraction is this?

33 In Mayland 95% of homes have a telephone. What fraction is this?

34 In Bilchester 28% of the population attend church at least once a month. What fraction is this?

CHANGING FRACTIONS TO DECIMALS

In Chapter 6 we saw that

> to change a fraction to a decimal, divide the top by the bottom.

Reminder: some equivalent fractions and decimals are in frequent use and should be remembered.

In particular $\quad \frac{1}{2} = 0.5, \qquad \frac{1}{4} = 0.25, \qquad \frac{3}{4} = 0.75$

and $\frac{1}{10} = 0.1$ from which we can find $\frac{2}{10}, \frac{3}{10}, \ldots$ as a decimal.

EXERCISE 10B

Express as a decimal   **a** $\frac{3}{4}$ **b** $\frac{21}{40}$

a $\frac{3}{4} = 3 \div 4 = 0.75$

$$\begin{array}{r} 0.75 \\ 4\overline{)3.00} \end{array}$$

b $\frac{21}{40} = 21 \div 40$ (Divide 21 first by 10.)

$= 2.1 \div 4$

$= 0.525$

$$\begin{array}{r} 0.525 \\ 4\overline{)2.100} \end{array}$$

Express the following fractions as decimals without using a calculator.

1 $\frac{1}{4}$ **4** $\frac{5}{8}$ **7** $\frac{12}{25}$ **10** $\frac{17}{40}$

2 $\frac{1}{25}$ **5** $\frac{27}{40}$ **8** $\frac{9}{16}$ **11** $\frac{67}{125}$

3 $\frac{17}{20}$ **6** $\frac{11}{20}$ **9** $\frac{13}{40}$ **12** $\frac{39}{400}$

Express as a decimal   **a** $1\frac{2}{25}$ **b** $3\frac{3}{8}$

a $1\frac{2}{25} = 1 + 2 \div 25$

$= 1 + 0.08$

$= 1.08$

$$\begin{array}{r} 0.08 \\ 25\overline{)2.00} \\ 200 \end{array}$$

b $3\frac{3}{8} = 3 + 3 \div 8$

$= 3.375$

$$\begin{array}{r} 0.375 \\ 8\overline{)3.000} \\ \underline{24} \\ 60 \\ \underline{56} \\ 40 \\ \underline{40} \end{array}$$

Express as a decimal, without using a calculator

13 $5\frac{1}{4}$ **15** $6\frac{3}{20}$ **17** $14\frac{17}{40}$ **19** $3\frac{23}{80}$

14 $10\frac{3}{4}$ **16** $12\frac{17}{40}$ **18** $7\frac{12}{125}$ **20** $9\frac{19}{20}$

In questions **21** to **26** express each fraction as a decimal.

21 Everybody in the class sat a test and $\frac{7}{8}$ of the pupils passed.

22 A large crowd gathered to watch the opening of the new supermarket; $\frac{3}{4}$ of the crowd were women.

23 Hank inspected a delivery of apples. He found that $\frac{1}{16}$ of them were bruised.

24 During one cold night last winter, $\frac{1}{8}$ of Kim's geraniums were killed by the frost.

25 Edna's weekly pay is $3\frac{1}{2}$ times more than it used to be 20 years ago.

26 Amberley Computers increased sales last year by the fraction $\frac{13}{4}$.

Sometimes when we divide the top number of a fraction by the bottom number we do not get an exact value.

For example, $\frac{2}{3} = 2 \div 3$

$$= 0.666\,66\ldots$$

When the value is not exact we usually give a fraction as a decimal correct to a given number of decimal places.

For example, $\frac{2}{3} = 0.67$ (correct to 2 d.p.)

Note that it is important to say that the decimal has been corrected, because $\frac{2}{3}$ is not exactly 0.67.

EXERCISE 10C

Express $\frac{5}{7}$ as a decimal correct to 2 decimal places.

$\frac{5}{7} = 5 \div 7$

$\phantom{\frac{5}{7}} = 0.714$

$\phantom{\frac{5}{7}} = 0.71$ (correct to 2 d.p.)

$$\begin{array}{r} 0.714 \\ 7{\overline{)5.000}} \\ 49 \\ \overline{10} \\ 7 \\ \overline{30} \\ 28 \end{array}$$

In questions **1** to **12** express each fraction as a decimal correct to 2 decimal places. Do not use a calculator.

1 $\frac{1}{3}$ **4** $\frac{5}{7}$ **7** $\frac{4}{9}$ **10** $\frac{3}{7}$

2 $\frac{6}{7}$ **5** $\frac{2}{9}$ **8** $\frac{3}{11}$ **11** $\frac{7}{9}$

3 $\frac{4}{11}$ **6** $\frac{5}{12}$ **9** $\frac{5}{9}$ **12** $\frac{1}{7}$

In questions **13** to **24** express each fraction as a decimal correct to 2 decimal places.

13 $\frac{2}{3}$ **15** $\frac{5}{41}$ **17** $\frac{11}{28}$ **19** $\frac{14}{31}$ **21** $\frac{35}{72}$ **23** $\frac{16}{19}$

14 $\frac{82}{87}$ **16** $\frac{4}{17}$ **18** $\frac{7}{60}$ **20** $\frac{11}{13}$ **22** $\frac{13}{23}$ **24** $\frac{63}{80}$

25

A Youth Club has 63 members, 37 of whom are females.

a Find the fraction of the members that are female.

b Express this fraction as a decimal correct to 2 decimal places.

26 The rules of the Sackville Dancing Club state that at least 40% of the members must be men. At present the membership stands at 34 women and 22 men.

a What is the total membership?

b Find the fraction of the membership that are women.

c Express the fraction found in part **b** as a decimal correct to 2 decimal places.

d Is the rule satisfied?

27 An alloy of copper and zinc must contain at least $37\frac{1}{2}$% zinc. A manufacturer makes some alloy by mixing 218 kg copper with 132.5 kg zinc. Will the composition of the alloy be satisfactory?

CHANGING A PERCENTAGE TO A DECIMAL

We have already seen how to express a percentage as a fraction.

For example, $30\% = \frac{30}{100}$

But $\frac{30}{100}$ means $30 \div 100$ and to divide by 100 we move the decimal point two places to the left,

i.e. $30\% = 30 \div 100 = 0.3$

To change a percentage to a decimal, divide by 100.

EXERCISE 10D

Express 45% as a decimal.

$$45\% = \frac{45}{100} = 0.45$$

THIS STEP DOES NOT HAVE TO BE WRITTEN BECAUSE I CAN DIVIDE BY 100 IN MY HEAD, SO I CAN WRITE 45% = 0.45.

In questions **1** to **12** express each percentage as a decimal. Do not use a calculator.

1 60%	**4** 25%	**7** 65%	**10** 87%
2 95%	**5** 36%	**8** 19%	**11** 8%
3 12%	**6** 5%	**9** 85%	**12** 33%

Express $2\frac{1}{2}\%$ as a decimal.

$2\frac{1}{2}\% = 2.5\%$ First write $\frac{1}{2}$ as a decimal.

$2.5\% = 0.025$ Now divide 2.5% by 100.

In questions **13** to **18** express each percentage as a decimal. Do not use a calculator.

13 $5\frac{1}{2}\%$	**15** $3\frac{3}{4}\%$	**17** $6\frac{3}{5}\%$
14 $15\frac{1}{4}\%$	**16** $28\frac{2}{5}\%$	**18** $5\frac{4}{5}\%$

Express 137% as a decimal.

$137\% = 1.37$

137% IS 100% + 37%, SO THE DECIMAL IS MORE THAN 1.

In questions **19** to **30** express each percentage as a decimal.

19 124%   **23** 365%   **27** $235\frac{3}{4}$%

20 185%   **24** 138%   **28** $163\frac{7}{10}$%

21 166%   **25** $112\frac{1}{2}$%   **29** 2345%

22 235%   **26** $188\frac{3}{5}$%   **30** 5920%

Sometimes a percentage does not give an exact decimal.

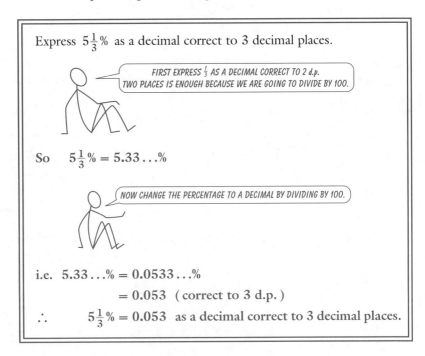

Express $5\frac{1}{3}$% as a decimal correct to 3 decimal places.

FIRST EXPRESS $\frac{1}{3}$ AS A DECIMAL CORRECT TO 2 d.p.
TWO PLACES IS ENOUGH BECAUSE WE ARE GOING TO DIVIDE BY 100.

So $5\frac{1}{3}$% = 5.33...%

NOW CHANGE THE PERCENTAGE TO A DECIMAL BY DIVIDING BY 100.

i.e. 5.33...% = 0.0533...%
              = 0.053 (correct to 3 d.p.)
∴ $5\frac{1}{3}$% = 0.053 as a decimal correct to 3 decimal places.

In questions **31** to **42** express each percentage as a decimal correct to 3 decimal places. Use a calculator if you need to.

31 $7\frac{2}{3}$%   **34** $1\frac{2}{7}$%   **37** $4\frac{4}{9}$%   **40** $15\frac{5}{12}$%

32 $5\frac{7}{9}$%   **35** $6\frac{21}{23}$%   **38** $24\frac{3}{19}$%   **41** $10\frac{7}{11}$%

33 $28\frac{4}{7}$%   **36** $12\frac{9}{11}$%   **39** $8\frac{6}{7}$%   **42** $3\frac{15}{19}$%

43 A bank lowers its lending rate from $9\frac{7}{32}$% to $8\frac{27}{32}$%. Express each rate as a decimal correct to 3 decimal places. Give, as a percentage correct to 2 decimal places, the decrease in the lending rate.

44 Last year the population of Benstable increased by $2\frac{3}{8}$% while the population of the nearby village of Forton increased by $5\frac{2}{3}$%.

  a Express each percentage as a decimal correct to 2 decimal places.

  b By what percentage, correct to 2 decimal places, did the rate of increase of the population in Forton exceed the rate of increase of the population in Benstable?

  c When all the available information had been studied it was found that the actual population of Benstable had increased by more than the actual population of Forton. Explain this apparent contradiction.

CHANGING DECIMALS TO PERCENTAGES

> To convert a decimal to a percentage multiply by 100.

For example, $0.25 = 0.25 \times 100\% = 25\%$

To multiply by 100 move the decimal point 2 places to the right.

Similarly $\qquad 1.63 = 1.63 \times 100\% = 163\%$

EXERCISE 10E

> Express each decimal as a percentage.   **a** 0.54   **b** 0.073
>
> **a** $0.54 = 0.54 \times 100\% = 54\%$
> **b** $0.073 = 0.073 \times 100\% = 7.3\%$

Express each decimal as a percentage.

1 0.3	**6** 0.45	**11** 0.09	**16** 1.24
2 0.62	**7** 0.75	**12** 0.08	**17** 3.46
3 0.95	**8** 0.925	**13** 0.183	**18** 0.055
4 0.07	**9** 0.005	**14** 0.76	**19** 0.333
5 1.25	**10** 2.62	**15** 1.455	**20** 3.927

CHANGING FRACTIONS TO PERCENTAGES

To convert a fraction to a percentage, first change the fraction to a decimal, then multiply by 100.

For example, $\frac{17}{20} = 0.85$

$$= 0.85 \times 100\% = 85\%$$

$17 \div 20 = 1.7 \div 2$
$= 0.85$

$1\frac{5}{8} = 1.625$

$$= 1.625 \times 100\% = 162.5\%$$

$\frac{5}{8} = 0.625$

and $\frac{13}{19} = 0.68421\ldots$

$$= 0.68421.. \times 100\% = 68.42\% \quad (\text{correct to 2 d.p.})$$

EXERCISE 10F

Express each fraction or mixed number as a percentage.

a $\frac{37}{40}$ **b** $5\frac{9}{20}$ **c** $\frac{5}{9}$

Give answers that are not exact correct to 2 decimal places.

a $\frac{37}{40} = 0.925 = 0.925 \times 100\% = 92.5\%$

b $\frac{9}{20} = 0.45$

so $5\frac{9}{20} = 5.45 = 5.45 \times 100\% = 545\%$

c $\frac{5}{9} = 0.55555\ldots = 0.55555\ldots \times 100\% = 55.56\%$

$(\text{correct to 2 d.p.})$

Express each fraction or mixed number as a percentage. Give answers that are not exact correct to 2 decimal places.

1 $\frac{4}{5}$ **5** $\frac{13}{20}$ **9** $\frac{19}{21}$ **13** $\frac{13}{18}$

2 $\frac{7}{20}$ **6** $\frac{3}{7}$ **10** $\frac{7}{8}$ **14** $\frac{29}{4}$

3 $4\frac{1}{4}$ **7** $5\frac{2}{3}$ **11** $\frac{15}{40}$ **15** $17\frac{7}{8}$

4 $1\frac{5}{9}$ **8** $\frac{13}{14}$ **12** $3\frac{11}{17}$ **16** $\frac{21}{31}$

CHANGING DECIMALS TO FRACTIONS

In Book 7B we studied place value in decimals.

As a result we know that $0.4 = 4$ tenths

24.07 is 2 tens, 4 units, no tenths and 7 hundredths

and   5.36 is 5 units, 3 tenths and 6 hundredths.

Now $0.56 = 5$ tenths and 6 hundredths

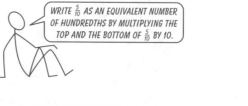

$$= \frac{5}{10} + \frac{6}{100}$$

$$= \frac{50}{100} + \frac{6}{100}$$

$$= \frac{56}{100}$$

$$= \frac{14}{25}$$

EXERCISE 10G

Write as a fraction or as a mixed number in its lowest terms

  a 0.6   **b** 12.04

  a $0.6 = \dfrac{\cancel{6}^{3}}{{}_{5}\cancel{10}}$

          $= \dfrac{3}{5}$

  b $12.04 = 12\dfrac{\cancel{4}^{1}}{{}_{25}\cancel{100}}$

          $= 12\dfrac{1}{25}$

In questions **1** to **12** write each decimal as a fraction in its lowest terms, using mixed numbers where necessary.

1 0.2	**4** 0.001	**7** 1.8	**10** 15.5
2 0.06	**5** 1.7	**8** 0.007	**11** 2.01
3 0.6	**6** 10.07	**9** 1.04	**12** 3.005

Write, as a fraction in its lowest terms   **a** 0.36   **b** 0.425

a $0.36 = \frac{36}{100} = \frac{9}{25}$

b $0.425 = \frac{4}{10} + \frac{2}{100} + \frac{5}{1000}$

WRITE EACH FRACTION IN THOUSANDTHS.

$\quad = \frac{400}{1000} + \frac{20}{1000} + \frac{5}{1000}$

$\quad = \frac{425}{1000}$

NOW THAT I UNDERSTAND, I CAN WRITE 0.425 AS $\frac{425}{1000}$ STRAIGHT AWAY NEXT TIME.

$\quad = \frac{17}{40}$

In questions **13** to **24** write each decimal as a fraction in its lowest terms, using mixed numbers where necessary.

13 0.45	**16** 0.664	**19** 0.64	**22** 3.92
14 0.245	**17** 0.88	**20** 2.35	**23** 1.375
15 2.95	**18** 0.468	**21** 1.56	**24** 5.44

In each statement from **25** to **28** write the decimal as a fraction in its lowest terms.

25 It is estimated that 0.86 of the families in Northgate Street own a car.

26 In a wood 0.68 of the trees lose their leaves in the winter.

27 George observed that 0.48 of the cars that passed him carried only the driver.

28 There were 360 seats on the aircraft and only 0.05 of them were vacant.

MIXED EXERCISE

EXERCISE 10H

In this exercise give any answers that are not exact correct to 2 decimal places.

In questions **1** to **8** convert each percentage into

a a fraction in its lowest terms   **b** a decimal.

1 35%	**3** 76%	**5** $8\frac{1}{2}\%$	**7** 144%
2 4%	**4** 330%	**6** $66\frac{2}{3}\%$	**8** $8\frac{2}{7}\%$

In questions **9** to **16** give each fraction as

a a decimal   **b** a percentage

9 $\frac{1}{4}$ **11** $\frac{3}{10}$ **13** $\frac{4}{25}$ **15** $\frac{37}{50}$

10 $\frac{13}{16}$ **12** $\frac{23}{48}$ **14** $\frac{16}{3}$ **16** $\frac{27}{7}$

In questions **17** to **24** give each decimal as

a a percentage   **b** a fraction in its lowest terms.

17 0.4   **19** 0.03   **21** 1.24   **23** 2.95

18 0.08   **20** 1.08   **22** 1.55   **24** 0.72

Copy and complete the following table.

	Percentage	Decimal	Fraction
25	38%		
26		0.05	
27			$1\frac{1}{2}$
28		0.45	
29	15%		
30		0.85	

	Percentage	Decimal	Fraction
31			$\frac{9}{10}$
32	$17\frac{1}{2}\%$		
33			$1\frac{2}{5}$
34	125%		
35		1.6	
36	250%		

FINDING A PERCENTAGE OF A QUANTITY

The contents of certain foods are often given as percentages. For example, suppose a joint of meat is 25% fat or a cake is 15% sugar. To find out the weight of fat in the meat or the weight of sugar in the cake we need to be able to calculate the percentage of a quantity.

This is part of the list of ingredients found in a packet of cereal.

Carbohydrate	67.8%
Protein	11.8%
Fibre	10.1%
Fat	2.8%

Other examples occur when we want to buy items on credit. A deposit is usually required and this may be given as a percentage of the price. If the deposit is 20% then to find the cash amount of the deposit, we must work out 20% of the marked price.

Kate earns £260 a week. If Kate wants to know the money value of a 4.5% pay rise, she needs to find 4.5% of £260.

Now $4.5\% = \frac{4.5}{100} = 0.045$

so 4.5% of £260 $= 0.045 \times £260$

> Remember that 'of' means '×'.

$= £0.045 \times 260$

$= £11.70$

> To find a percentage of a quantity, change the percentage to a decimal and multiply by the quantity.

EXERCISE 10I

> A joint of meat, weighing 1600 grams, contains 15% fat. What weight of fat is there in the joint?
>
> The weight of fat is 15% of 1600 g
> $$15\% = 0.15$$
> and 15% of $1600\,\text{g} = 0.15 \times 1600\,\text{g}$
> $$= 240\,\text{g}$$
> $\therefore$ the amount of fat in the meat is 240 g.
>
> REMEMBER THAT 'OF' MEANS '×'.

Find the value of

1 40% of £800

6 6% of 3500 millimetres

2 15% of 100 metres

7 30% of 500 litres

3 33% of 600 kilograms

8 86% of 110 grams

4 74% of 200 litres

9 30% of £4200

5 60% of £48

10 25% of £60

> A metal casting weighs 65 kg and is 7.4% zinc. How much zinc is there in the casting?
>
> $7.4\% = 0.074$
>
> so 7.4% of $65 \text{ kg} = 0.074 \times 65 \text{ kg}$
>
> $\qquad\qquad\qquad\qquad = 4.81 \text{ kg}$
>
> The casting therefore contains 4.81 kg of zinc.

Find the value of

11 5.5% of £560

12 9.75% of 80 m

13 15.8% of 5 litres

14 2.75% of 344 m

15 18.6% of 440 g

16 7.25% of £35.30

17 4.5% of 45 m^2

18 67% of 316 cm^2

19 44.4% of 8.5 kg

20 2.5% of 6 km

21 If 8% of a crowd of 24 500 at a football match were females, how many females attended?

22 By the end of the month a distributor had sold 74% of the 1250 washing machines he had in stock at the beginning of the month. How many washing machines had he sold?

23 Jim Benton is employed in a factory that produces cars. At present he earns £340 a week. He is due to receive a 3.5% increase in his pay. How much will this be?

24 The number of TV sets produced by a factory each week is set to rise by 12.5% from its present figure of 22 400. How many extra TV sets do they expect to produce each week?

If 54% of the 1800 pupils in a school are boys, how many girls are there in the school?

> First find the number of boys.

Number of boys = $\dfrac{54}{100}$ × 1800

$0.54 \times 1800 = 972$

Number of girls = $1800 - 972$

$= 828$ Check: $972 + 828 = 1800$

25 There are 80 houses in my street and 65% of them have a telephone. How many houses

    a have a telephone   **b** do not have a telephone?

26

In my class there are 30 pupils and 40% of them have a bicycle. How many pupils

    a have a bicycle   **b** do not have a bicycle?

27 Yesterday, of the 240 flights leaving London Airport, 15% were bound for North America. How many of these flights

    a flew to North America   **b** did not fly to North America?

28 In a particular year, 64% of the 16 000 Jewish immigrants entering Israel came from Eastern Europe. How many of the immigrants did not come from Eastern Europe?

29 There are 120 shops in the High Street, 35% of which sell food. How many High Street shops do not sell food?

30 Alex earns £18 000 a year. Deductions amount to 22.4% of his salary. Find

    a his total deductions   **b** his earnings after deductions.

31 Gary bought a car for £16 000. After 5 years it was worth 38% of the purchase price. Find its value after 5 years.

32 Sim's insurance premium for house contents is 0.9% of the value of the goods insured. How much must he pay if he estimates the value of the contents of his home to be £22 500?

33 Lena invests £450 in the Blackweir Building Society for one year. The building society pays interest of 5.66% on the sum invested each year. How much interest will she receive?

34 Tony's taxable income is £3400. How much tax does he have to pay if it is charged at 20%?

35 Eve has a taxable income of £17 000. She has to pay tax on the first £4000 at 20% and tax on the remainder at 24%.

   a How much tax does she pay on the first £4000?

   b On how much is she taxed at 24%?

   c How much tax does she pay at this higher rate?

   d How much tax does she pay altogether?

36 Bianca's season ticket for the train costs £345.60 a quarter. Fares are to rise by 5.6% of their present cost. How much more will her season ticket cost?

37 Last year the amount I paid for insurance was £520.50. This year my insurance premium will increase by 12% of what I paid last year. Find the increase.

38 A mathematics book has 320 pages, 40% of which are on algebra, 25% on geometry and the remainder on arithmetic.

   a What percentage of the pages are on arithmetic?

   b How many pages of arithmetic are there?

The price of a dining table is given as £860 plus VAT.
If the rate of VAT is $17\frac{1}{2}$%, find the price that a customer must pay for the table.

The value of the VAT is 17.5% of £860

$$= £0.175 \times 860$$
$$= £150.50$$

The customer pays   £860 + £150.50
$$= £1010.50$$

In questions **39** to **41** find the total purchase price of the item. Take the rate of VAT as $17\frac{1}{2}\%$.

39 An electric cooker marked £626 + VAT.

40 A calculator costing £9.60 + VAT.

41 A van marked £5640 + VAT.

42 The price tag on a television set is marked £289 plus VAT at 15%. What does the customer have to pay?

43 Harrison buys the following goods in a hardware store:
1 tool box: £8.50, 1 aluminium-framed tool case: £18.70,
1 set of screwdrivers: £14.65, 1 37-piece socket and bit set: £19.50.
To all prices, VAT at $17\frac{1}{2}\%$ must be added. Write out a bill.

How much must he pay?

MIXED EXERCISE

EXERCISE 10J

1 Express as a decimal

    a 85%   **c** 136%   **e** $5\frac{7}{20}\%$ **g** $124\frac{2}{5}\%$

    b $\frac{7}{40}$ **d** $\frac{31}{40}$ **f** $7\frac{1}{4}\%$ **h** $3\frac{17}{25}$

2 Express as a percentage

    a 0.03   **c** 0.005   **e** $\frac{2}{5}$ **g** $\frac{33}{40}$

    b 0.64   **d** 0.36   **f** $\frac{19}{20}$ **h** $\frac{25}{80}$

3 Express as a fraction in its lowest terms

    a 36%   **c** 176%   **e** 0.625   **g** 5.85

    b 0.16   **d** 0.63   **f** 1.84   **h** 284%

4 Express as a decimal correct to 3 decimal places

    a $\frac{7}{11}$ **b** $\frac{16}{31}$ **c** $6\frac{2}{3}\%$ **d** $8\frac{11}{32}\%$

5 Express as a percentage correct to 2 decimal places

    a $\frac{5}{11}$ **b** $\frac{23}{31}$ **c** $\frac{23}{6}$ **d** $4\frac{7}{13}$

6 Find the value of

    a 42% of 12 m   **c** 7.24% of 8.4 kg

    b 16% of 54 kg   **d** 15.3% of 550 g

7   The marked price of a video recorder is £164.50 plus VAT at $17\frac{1}{2}$%. How much will it cost me? Give your answer correct to the nearest penny.

8   Jo earned £364.50 last week. Deductions amounted to 24.8% of her earnings.
Find   **a** Jo's deductions   **b** her take-home pay.

**PRACTICAL
WORK**

a Visit some shops during the sales. Which shops, if any, give their reductions in   **i** percentages   **ii** fractions   **iii** decimals?

b Which is the most common way of stating a reduction? Do you think that it is the easiest to understand?

c Do different types of businesses use different ways of stating reductions?

d Given below are extracts from two catalogues. The extract from the second catalogue shows that prices exclude VAT, whereas the extract from the first catalogue shows that VAT is included in the listed price. Compare the prices of the articles that appear in both extracts. Which method of pricing do you prefer? Why do you think one catalogue gives prices excluding VAT?

These prices *include* VAT.

These prices *exclude* VAT.

These prices date from August 1996.

Summary 3

Multiplying and dividing decimals by 10, 100, 1000, ...

To multiply a decimal by 10, 100, 1000, ..., we move the point 1, 2, 3, ... places to the right,

e.g. $2.56 \times 10 = 25.6$,   and $2.56 \times 1000 = 2560$

To divide a decimal by 10, 100, 1000, ..., we move the point 1, 2, 3, ... places to the left,

e.g. $2.56 \div 10 = 0.256$,   and $2.56 \div 1000 = 0.002\,56$

Multiplying decimals

To multiply decimals without using a calculator, first ignore the decimal point and multiply the numbers. Then add together the decimal places in each of the decimals being multiplied; this gives the number of decimal places in the answer,

e.g. $2.5 \times 0.4 = 1.00 = 1$ $(25 \times 4 = 100)$

$$[(1)+(1) = (2)]$$

Dividing by a decimal

To divide by a decimal, we move the point in *both* numbers to the right until the number we are dividing by is a whole number,

e.g. $2.56 \div 0.4 = 25.6 \div 4$

Now we can use ordinary division, keeping the decimal point in the same place,

e.g. $25.6 \div 4 = 6.4$ $4\overline{)25.6}^{\,6.4}$

Correcting decimals

To round (that is, to correct) a number to a specified number of decimal places, look at the figure in the next decimal place: if it is 5 or more, add 1 to the previous figure, otherwise leave the previous figure as it is,

e.g. to write 2.564 correct to 2 decimal places, we have

$$2.564 = 2.56 \ (\text{correct to 2 decimal places}),$$

and to write 2.564 correct to 1 decimal place, we have

$$2.564 = 2.6 \ (\text{correct to 1 decimal place})$$

FRACTIONS

Multiplying fractions

To multiply one fraction by another fraction, we multiply together their numerators and multiply together their denominators,

e.g. $\quad \frac{1}{2} \times \frac{5}{3} = \frac{1 \times 5}{2 \times 3} = \frac{5}{6}$

Mixed numbers must be changed into improper fractions before they can be multiplied,

e.g. $\quad 1\frac{1}{2} \times \frac{3}{5} = \frac{3}{2} \times \frac{3}{5} = \frac{3 \times 3}{2 \times 5} = \frac{9}{10}$

To multiply by a whole number, treat it as a fraction by writing it over 1,

e.g. $\quad 4 \times \frac{3}{8} = \frac{4}{1} \times \frac{3}{8} = \frac{3}{2} = 1\frac{1}{2}$

Fractions of a quantity

To find a fraction of a quantity, multiply the fraction by the quantity,

e.g. $\quad \frac{3}{8}$ of £20 $= £\left(\frac{3}{8} \times 20\right) = £\left(\frac{3}{8} \times \frac{20}{1}\right)$

One quantity as a fraction of another

To express one quantity as a fraction of another, first express both quantities in the same unit and then place the first quantity over the second,

e.g. $\quad$ 25 p as a fraction of £3 is equal to $\frac{25}{300} = \frac{1}{12}$,

or, to put it another way, 25 p is $\frac{1}{12}$ of £3.

PERCENTAGES

'Per cent' means 'out of one hundred'.

INTERCHANGING PERCENTAGES, FRACTIONS AND DECIMALS

Changing a fraction to a decimal

Fractions can be changed to decimal notation by dividing the bottom number into the top number,

e.g. $\quad \frac{3}{8} = 3 \div 8 = 0.375$

Changing a decimal to a fraction

A decimal can be expressed as a fraction by placing the numbers after the decimal point over 1, together with a number of zeros equal to the number of decimal places,

e.g. $\quad 0.15 = \frac{15}{100}, \ 0.7 = \frac{7}{10}, \ 0.137 = \frac{137}{1000}, \ 1.25 = 1\frac{25}{100}$

Changing between percentages and fractions

A percentage can be expressed as a fraction by placing the percentage over 100,

e.g. $33\% = \frac{33}{100}$

Reversing the process, a fraction can be expressed as a percentage by multiplying the fraction by 100,

e.g. $\frac{2}{5} = \frac{2}{5} \times 100\% = \frac{2}{5} \times \frac{100}{1}\% = 40\%$

Changing between percentages and decimals

A percentage can be expressed as a decimal by dividing the percentage by 100, i.e. by moving the decimal point two places to the left,

e.g. $33\% = 0.33$

and a decimal can be expressed as a percentage by multiplying the decimal by 100, i.e. by moving the decimal point two places to the right.

For example, $0.325 = 32.5\%$

TRANSFORMATIONS

Reflection in a mirror line

When an object is reflected in a mirror line, the object and its image form a symmetrical shape with the mirror line as the axis of symmetry.

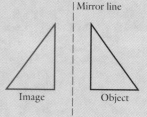

Translation

When an object is translated it moves without being turned or reflected to form an image.

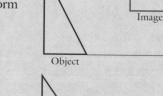

Rotation

When an object is rotated about a point to form an image, the point about which it is rotated is called the *centre of rotation* and the angle it is turned through is called the *angle of rotation*.

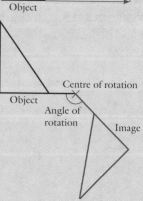

Congruence

When two figures are congruent they are exactly the same shape and size.
(They can be turned over
  compared with one another.)

These two triangles are congruent.

**REVISION
EXERCISE 3.1
(Chapters 6, 7
and 8)**

Do not use a calculator for questions **1** to **3**.

1 Find

  a 6.3×10 **c** $0.78 \div 100$

  b 4.82×100 **d** $5.26 \div 1000$

2 Find the value of

  a $0.27 \div 3$ **c** 0.07×0.4 **e** $3.2 \div 0.08$

  b $1.08 \div 8$ **d** 47×0.26 **f** 0.87×500

3 a Find the cost of 500 books at £9.95 each.

  b A pad of paper containing 400 sheets is 12.8 mm thick. What is
    the thickness of one sheet?

4 Give

  a 16.7 correct to the nearest whole number

  b 37.249 correct to 1 decimal place

  c 5.0946 correct to 2 decimal places.

5 Give the following numbers correct to the number of decimal places
indicated in the brackets.

  a 62.493 (1)   **c** 51.099 (2)

  b 17.086 (2)   **d** 0.0423 (2)

6 a Which is the larger and by how much:
    $29.4 \div 0.7$ or 23.2×1.8 ?

  b Which is the smaller and by how much:
    3.92×0.85 or $1.404 \div 0.72$?

7 Find

  a $\frac{1}{2}$ of 12   **c** $\frac{2}{3}$ of 27   **e** $\frac{5}{9}$ of 162

  b $\frac{3}{4}$ of 24   **d** $\frac{5}{6}$ of 72   **f** $\frac{3}{7}$ of 105

8 Find

    a $\frac{3}{5}$ of 40 miles   **c** $\frac{3}{8}$ of 56 litres

    b $\frac{3}{7}$ of 2 weeks   **d** $\frac{3}{4}$ of £24

9 Find

    a $\frac{3}{8}$ of £2 in pence   **c** $\frac{5}{9}$ of 153 francs

    b $\frac{3}{10}$ of 2 m in centimetres   **d** $\frac{4}{7}$ of 413 hours

10 a Find, as an improper fraction

    i $\frac{7}{12} \times 30$ **ii** $33 \times \frac{4}{9}$ **iii** $\frac{3}{10} \times 35$

    b Which is the larger: $\frac{3}{4}$ of $\frac{2}{5}$ or $\frac{1}{3} \times \frac{6}{7}$?

11 a Find 36 p as a fraction of £2.

    b There are 12 girls in a class of 28. What fraction of the pupils in the class are girls?

REVISION EXERCISE 3.2 (Chapters 9 and 10)

1 Which of these shapes have both line and rotational symmetry?

a

c

b

d

2 State whether or not these pairs of figures are congruent.

a

b

c

3 Copy each diagram on to squared paper using 1 cm as 1 unit. Draw the image of the given shape if it is rotated about the point marked through the angle given.

a 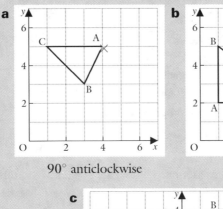   **b**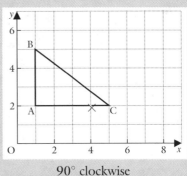

90° anticlockwise   90° clockwise

c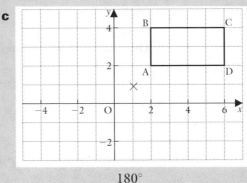

180°

4 Copy the diagram for question **3** part **a** and extend the x-axis back to -5. On your new copy draw the image of $\triangle ABC$ when it is reflected in the y-axis.

5 Copy the diagram for question **3** part **c**. On your copy draw the image of ABCD when it is translated 2 units down and 5 units to the left.

6 a Express each percentage as a fraction in its lowest terms.

  i 75%   **ii** 76%   **iii** 125%   **iv** 35.5%

  b Express each percentage as a decimal.

  i 40%   **ii** 58%   **iii** $6\frac{1}{4}\%$ **iv** 142%

7 a Express each fraction as a decimal.

  i $\frac{3}{4}$ **ii** $\frac{16}{25}$ **iii** $\frac{7}{40}$ **iv** $\frac{13}{50}$

  b Express each fraction as a decimal correct to 2 decimal places.

  i $\frac{5}{9}$ **ii** $\frac{6}{7}$ **iii** $\frac{11}{12}$ **iv** $\frac{24}{29}$

8 a Express each decimal as a percentage.

    i 0.7   **ii** 0.08   **iii** 0.725   **iv** 0.044

  b Express each fraction or mixed number as a percentage. Give answers that are not exact correct to 2 decimal places.

    i $\frac{2}{5}$ **ii** $\frac{12}{5}$ **iii** $\frac{25}{4}$ **iv** $3\frac{4}{9}$

9 a Write each decimal as a fraction in its lowest terms, using mixed numbers where necessary.

    i 0.4   **ii** 0.003   **iii** 1.6   **iv** 8.04

  b Find   **i** $2\frac{1}{2}\%$ of £44.80   **ii** $37\frac{1}{2}\%$ of 64 m

10 a A commercial traveller is paid 5% commission on sales over £3000. How much commission will he receive if he sells goods to the value of £10 500 ?

  b The marked price of a camera is £86.65 plus value added tax at $17\frac{1}{2}\%$. How much must I pay for this camera? Give your answer correct to the nearest penny.

REVISION EXERCISE 3.3 (Chapters 6 to 10)

Do not use a calculator for questions **1** and **2**.

1 Find

    a 4×0.003 **c** 420×0.07 **e** $6.3 \div 0.03$

    b 5.2×1.8 **d** 0.6×0.1 **f** $4.8 \div 800$

2 a Express each fraction as a decimal.

    i $\frac{3}{10}$ **ii** $\frac{5}{8}$ **iii** $\frac{17}{20}$ **iv** $\frac{17}{25}$ **v** $\frac{7}{16}$

  b Multiply 5.07 by 100 and divide the result by 1000.

3 Use your calculator to find, correct to 2 decimal places

    a $0.063 + 0.412 \times 0.057$ **c** $8.07 \times (2.983 - 0.884)$

    b $47 \times 0.0793 - 0.734$ **d** $(1.17 + 0.829) \times 3.23$

4 a Find, correct to 3 decimal places

    i 0.203×3.873 **ii** $41.8 \div 6$

  b Use a calculator to find, correct to 2 decimal places

    i $0.68 \div 12$ **ii** 0.738×15.6 **iii** 1.42^2 **iv** 0.73^3

5 Find

    a $\frac{4}{9}$ of 45 mm   **c** $\frac{3}{5}$ of 75 cm

    b $\frac{9}{10}$ of £440   **d** $\frac{5}{12}$ of 372 days

6 a Find

    i $\frac{2}{3} \times \frac{3}{4}$ **ii** $\frac{2}{5} \times \frac{3}{5}$ **iii** $\frac{3}{7} \times \frac{7}{12}$ **iv** $\frac{5}{7} \times \frac{11}{20}$

    b Which is the smaller: $\frac{2}{3} \times \frac{9}{11}$ or $\frac{4}{5}$ of $\frac{5}{8}$?

    c Find 10 cm as a fraction of 1 metre.

7 Copy the objects and the mirror lines (indicated by broken lines) onto squared paper and draw the image of each object.

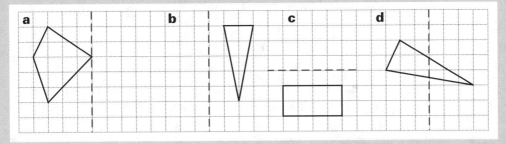

8 Which of the shapes are congruent with the coloured shape ?

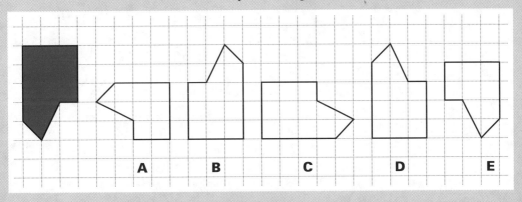

9 a Express as a fraction in its lowest terms

    i 64%   **ii** 0.45   **iii** 172%   **iv** 0.325

    b Express as a percentage

    i 0.55   **ii** $\frac{7}{12}$ **iii** 1.84   **iv** 1.335

10 a Express as a decimal

    i 63%   **ii** $\frac{17}{40}$ **iii** $\frac{35}{8}$ **iv** $16\frac{3}{4}\%$

    b A joint of beef weighs 6.4 kg and is $12\frac{1}{2}$% bone. Find the weight of bone in the joint.

**REVISION
EXERCISE 3.4
(Chapters 1 to 10)**

1 Find, without using a calculator

   a $(3+4) \times 7$ **c** $15 \times 2 \div 5 - 2 + 3$

   b 350×532 **d** $48 \div 3 - 15 \div 5 \times 2$

2 Write down the size of each angle marked with a letter.

  a 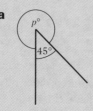   **b** 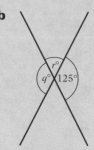   **c**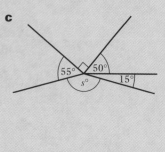

3 a Find $8321 \div 36$, giving the remainder if there is one.

  b Kate bought 4 grapefruit at 37 p each and 7 kg of potatoes at 19 p per kilogram. She paid with a £5 note. How much change did she get? Give your answer in pence.

4 Find

  a $\frac{31}{100} + \frac{19}{100}$ **c** $3\frac{2}{7} + 6\frac{1}{3}$

  b $\frac{1}{3} + \frac{1}{9} + \frac{1}{12}$ **d** $8\frac{7}{12} - 3\frac{3}{8}$

5 In the following diagram, which images of $\triangle ABC$ are given by

  a a translation   **c** neither a translation nor a reflection?

  b a reflection

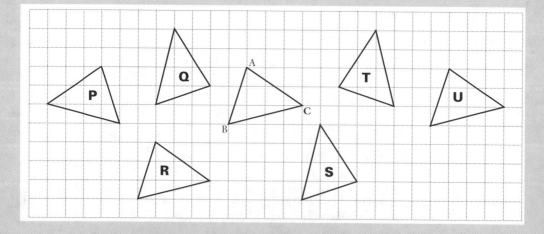

6 Find, without using a calculator

    a 0.08×12 **c** 0.09×0.9 **e** $1.75 \div 50$

    b $0.546 \div 5$ **d** $0.279 \div 9$ **f** 0.042×70

7 Use a calculator to find, correct to 2 decimal places, the value of

    a $0.724 \div 3$ **c** $3.42 \div 0.973$

    b $7.392 \div 6$ **d** 0.245×1.672

8 Find

    a $\frac{5}{6}$ of 72 ft   **c** $39 \times \frac{5}{13}$ **e** $\frac{3}{5}$ of half an hour in minutes

    b $\frac{6}{7}$ of 168 cm   **d** $56 \times \frac{5}{7}$ **f** 24 p as a fraction of £2

9 Find the size of each marked angle.

    a 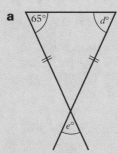 **b** 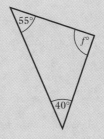 **c**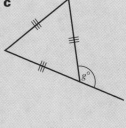

10 a Express as a fraction in its lowest terms

      i 82%   **ii** 0.15   **iii** 118%

    b Due to a reduction in orders the workforce at a factory was reduced by 8%. What fraction is this?

REVISION EXERCISE 3.5 (Chapters 1 to 10)

1 Find, without using a calculator

    a $3 \times 6 \times 7 \times 3$ **c** $12 \div 3 + 2 \times 4$

    b $38 \times (42 - 12)$ **d** 374×303

2 The hand of a clock starts at 12. Which number is it pointing to when it has turned through an angle of

    a $270°$ **b** $120°$ **c** $30°$ **d** $540°$?

3 a Find the missing digits in the following products

      i $\square \times 8 \times 3 = 144$ **ii** $128 \div \square = 16$

    b Divide 3714 by 14 giving the remainder if there is one.

4 Find

  a $\frac{5}{12} - \frac{1}{3} + \frac{1}{6}$ **c** $3\frac{2}{7} + 6\frac{1}{3}$

  b $\frac{2}{3} + \frac{1}{4} - \frac{7}{12}$ **d** $8\frac{1}{4} - 3\frac{7}{8}$

5 Which of the following shapes have rotational symmetry?

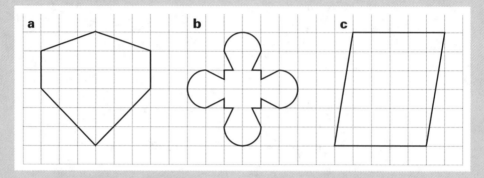

6 Find, without using a calculator

  a 0.642×0.3 **c** $0.8 \div 4$ **e** $0.45 \div 0.006$

  b 4×0.18 **d** $0.392 \div 7$ **f** $60 \div 0.08$

7 Give the following quantities correct to the number of decimal places indicated in the brackets.

  a $84.36\,\text{cm}$ (1)   **d** $65.493\,\text{kg}$ (2)

  b $0.774\,\text{g}$ (2)   **e** 0.1245t (3)

  c 35.062 seconds (1)   **f** $9.0527\,\text{km}$ (2)

8 a Find, as an improper fraction **i** $\frac{7}{12} \times 36$ **ii** $33 \times \frac{4}{9}$

  b Which is the larger: $\frac{3}{5}$ of $\frac{4}{9}$ or $\frac{2}{3}$ of $\frac{9}{10}$?

9 Construct a triangle PQR in which $PQ = 9.5\,\text{cm}$, $\widehat{P} = 63°$ and $\widehat{Q} = 72°$.

10 a Express as a percentage

  i $\frac{11}{40}$ **ii** 0.666 **iii** $\frac{13}{4}$ **iv** 1.05

  b Express as a decimal, correct to 3 decimal places if necessary

  i 38% **ii** $\frac{35}{9}\%$ **iii** $\frac{7}{24}$ **iv** $1\frac{8}{9}$

  c In a golf club $\frac{4}{5}$ of the members are men.

   i What percentage is this?

   ii If there are 450 members, how many of them are men?

11 Give the order of rotational symmetry for each shape.

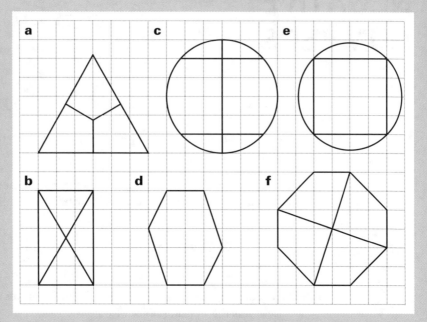

NEGATIVE NUMBERS

Negative numbers are written with a minus sign in front, for example, we write negative 2 as −2.

One of the most familiar uses of negative numbers is on temperature scales; a temperature of 2° Celsius below freezing is marked as −2°.

The reading on this thermometer is −4° and it means 4° below 0; 0° Celsius is the freezing point of water.
Negative numbers can be used to describe any quantity that is below a natural zero level, for example distance below sea level, time before blast-off.

Negative numbers are also used for other purposes.
This is an extract from the financial pages of the *London Evening Standard*.

Abbey National	647	+3
BAA	494	−5
British Airways	564	+8
British Gas	$236\frac{1}{2}$	−3
BT	372	−10
Rolls-Royce	178	−3

It shows the closing prices (in pence) of some shares. The column of positive and negative numbers show how those prices have changed from the previous day. In this case, positive and negative numbers are being used to describe gains and losses in prices.

EXERCISE 11A   Discuss what the numbers are describing in these examples.

1   Gilts closing prices.

Trea	10%	01	£$112\frac{11}{16}$	$-\frac{1}{8}$
Trea	$9\frac{3}{4}$%	02	£$113\frac{1}{16}$	$+\frac{3}{32}$
Trea	10%	03	£$116\frac{11}{32}$	$-\frac{5}{32}$
Trea	$11\frac{1}{2}$%	01-04	£$118\frac{21}{32}$	$+\frac{1}{8}$

2

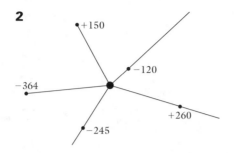

This is the display on a monitor showing the movement of aircraft in and out of an airport.

DIRECTED NUMBERS

We can see that negative numbers are used in a variety of ways, so we need to know how to work with them.

Positive and negative numbers are together known as *directed numbers*.

THE NUMBER LINE

In Book 7B we used numbers in the context of temperatures with a scale on a thermometer.

If we draw the scale only, all we have is a line with numbers marked on it. It is called a *number line*.

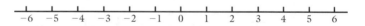

On this number line,	5 is to the *right* of 3
and we say that	5 is *greater* than 3
which we write as	5 > 3

Also	−2 is to the *right* of −4
and we say that	−2 is *greater* than −4
i.e.	−2 > −4

So 'greater' means 'higher up the scale'.
(A temperature of −2 °C is higher than a temperature of
  −4 °C.)

Now	2 is to the *left* of 6
and we say that	2 is *less* than 6
i.e.	2 < 6

Also	−3 is to the *left* of −1
and we say that	−3 is *less* than −1
i.e.	−3 < −1

So 'less than' means 'lower down the scale'.

EXERCISE 11B   In questions **1** to **12** write either > or < between the two numbers.

1 3   2   **5** 1   −2   **9** −3   −9

2 5   1   **6** −4   1   **10** −7   3

3 −1   −4   **7** 3   −2   **11** −1   0

4 −3   −1   **8** 5   −10   **12** 1   −1

In questions **13** to **24** write down the next two numbers in the sequence.

13 4, 6, 8   **17** 9, 6, 3   **21** 36, 31, 26

14 −4, −6, −8   **18** −4, −1, 2   **22** −10, −8, −6

15 4, 2, 0   **19** 5, 1, −3   **23** −1, −2, −4, −8

16 −4, −2, 0   **20** 2, 4, 8, 16   **24** 1, 0, −1

25 Starting with 6, what number is given by

   a an increase of 8   **b** a decrease of 8?

26 Starting with −3, what number is given by

   a a decrease of 5   **b** an increase of 3?

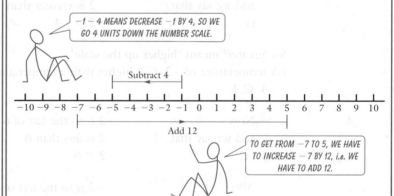

Copy each statement and fill in the missing numbers

a −1 − 4 = □   **b** −7 + □ = 5   **c** −3 − 5 + 7 = □

−1 − 4 MEANS DECREASE −1 BY 4, SO WE GO 4 UNITS DOWN THE NUMBER SCALE.

Subtract 4

−10 −9 −8 −7 −6 −5 −4 −3 −2 −1 0 1 2 3 4 5 6 7 8 9 10

Add 12

TO GET FROM −7 TO 5, WE HAVE TO INCREASE −7 BY 12, i.e. WE HAVE TO ADD 12.

a −1 − 4 = −5   **b** −7 + 12 = 5   **c** −3 − 5 + 7 = −8 + 7
                                                          = −1

Copy each statement and fill in the missing number.

27 $7 - 9 = \square$ **29** $4 - \square = -2$ **31** $-1 + \square = 4$

28 $3 - 5 = \square$ **30** $\square + 4 = 2$ **32** $\square - 3 = 2$

Find

33 $7 - 9 + 4$ **35** $10 - 4 - 9$ **37** $-2 - 3 + 9$

34 $-5 - 11 + 3$ **36** $-3 - 4 + 2$ **38** $-4 + 2 + 5$

ADDITION AND SUBTRACTION OF POSITIVE NUMBERS

We do not always place a plus sign in front of a positive number, i.e. we normally write $2 - (+3)$ as $2 - 3$, so $-(+3)$ means 'subtract 3'.
We would also write $2 + (+3)$ as $2 + 3$, so $+(+3)$ means 'add 3'.

ADDITION AND SUBTRACTION OF NEGATIVE NUMBERS

The extract from the London Evening Standard at the beginning of this chapter had this entry.

BT   372 -10

This means that, at the end of that day, BT shares were priced at 372 pence and that this was 10 pence less than their price at the close of business the day before.
To get back to the price of the previous day, this 10 pence loss has to be removed, i.e. we have to subtract -10 pence from 372 pence.
This can be written as $372 - (-10)$
The loss is actually taken away when 372 pence *gains* 10 pence.
This can be written as $372 + 10$

Since $372 - (-10)$ and $372 + 10$ achieve the same result, we conclude that *taking away a negative number is the same as adding a positive number.*

If the share price falls again the next day by another 10 pence, we have to add this loss to 372 pence.
This can be written as $372 + (-10)$
The further drop in share price is found by starting with 372 pence and taking away 10 pence.
This can be written as $372 - 10$

Because $372 + (-10)$ and $372 - 10$ have the same result, we see that *adding a negative number is the same as subtracting a positive number.*

The conclusions about adding and subtracting directed numbers can be summarised in this simple rule.

> If the signs are the *same*, the result is *positive*,
> if the signs are *different*, the result is *negative*.

EXERCISE 11C

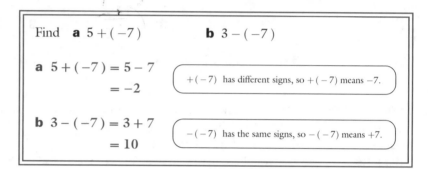

Find   **a** $5 + (-7)$ **b** $3 - (-7)$

a $5 + (-7) = 5 - 7$

            $= -2$

> $+(-7)$ has different signs, so $+(-7)$ means -7.

b $3 - (-7) = 3 + 7$

            $= 10$

> $-(-7)$ has the same signs, so $-(-7)$ means $+7$.

Find, without using a calculator

1 $3 + (-1)$	**8** $-3 - (-9)$	**15** $3 + (-3)$
2 $5 + (-8)$	**9** $-4 + (-10)$	**16** $3 + (-2)$
3 $4 - (-3)$	**10** $2 - (-8)$	**17** $-3 - (+2)$
4 $-1 - (-4)$	**11** $-7 + (-7)$	**18** $6 - (-3)$
5 $-2 + (-7)$	**12** $-3 - (-3)$	**19** $4 + (+4)$
6 $-2 - (-5)$	**13** $+4 + (-4)$	**20** $-5 + (-7)$
7 $5 + (-7)$	**14** $+2 - (-4)$	**21** $9 - (+2)$

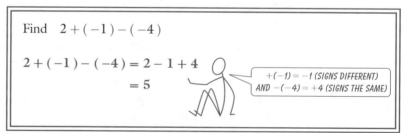

Find $2 + (-1) - (-4)$

$2 + (-1) - (-4) = 2 - 1 + 4$

               $= 5$

> $+(-1) = -1$ (SIGNS DIFFERENT)
> AND $-(-4) = +4$ (SIGNS THE SAME)

Find, without using a calculator

22 $5 + (-1) - (-3)$ **23** $(-1) + (-1) + (-1)$

24 $4-(-2)+(-4)$

31 $9+(-12)-(-4)$

25 $-2-(-2)+(-4)$

32 $7+(-3)-(+5)$

26 $6-(-7)+(-8)$

33 $2-(-4)+(-6)$

27 $9+(-5)-(-9)$

34 $5+(-2)-(+1)$

28 $8-(-7)+(-2)$

35 $8-(-3)+(+5)$

29 $10+(-9)+(-7)$

36 $7+(-4)-(-2)$

30 $12+(-8)-(-4)$

37 $8-(-2)-(-1)$

Find $\quad -8-(4-7)$

$-8-(4-7)=-8-(-3)$
$\qquad\qquad\quad =-8+3$
$\qquad\qquad\quad =-5$

WORK OUT INSIDE THE BRACKET FIRST.

Find, without using a calculator

38 $3-(4-3)$

41 $-3-(7-10)$

39 $5+(7-9)$

42 $6+(8-15)$

40 $4+(8-12)$

43 $(3-5)+2$

44 $5-(6-10)$

48 $(7+4)-15$

45 $(4-9)-2$

49 $8+(3-8)$

46 $(3-8)-(9-4)$

50 $(7-12)-(6-9)$

47 $(3-1)+(5-10)$

51 $(4-8)-(10-15)$

52 Add $(+7)$ to (-5).

55 Add -5 to $+3$.

53 Subtract 7 from -5.

56 Find the sum of -3 and $+4$.

54 Subtract (-2) from 1.

57 Find the sum of -8 and $+10$.

58 Subtract positive 8 from negative 7.

59 Find the sum of -3 and -3 and -3.

60 Find the value of twice negative 3.

61 Find the value of four times -2.

62 At the start of the last round in a competition the scores stood at

Alf 37, Tanita, 24, Colin 35 and Jean 42.

Each competitor gains points for correct answers but loses them for wrong answers.
During the last round Alf gained 24 points and lost 15,
Tanita gained 16 and lost 21,
Colin gained 8 and lost 29,
while Jean gained 26 and lost 14.

Who won the competition?
Who came second, third and last?

63 Newtown is 5 miles from Menton and 3 miles from Leek. All three villages lie on a stretch of the B3840. How far is it from Menton to Leek if they are on opposite sides of Newton?

64 Frank sat an examination with 10 questions. For each question, five possible answers were given and Frank had to tick the answer he thought was correct.

For each answer he got correct he scored 2 points. For each answer he got wrong he scored -1 point. He scored nothing for each question that he did not answer.

a What was the highest possible score in this examination?

b What was the lowest possible score in this examination?

c Frank got 6 questions correct, 2 wrong and he did not answer the rest. What did Frank score in this examination?

65 The time in Florida is   UK time $-$ 6 hours.
The time in Athens is   UK time $+$ 2 hours.

a When it is 2 p.m. in the UK, what time is it in
  i Florida   **ii** Athens?

b Freda catches a plane in Florida at 6 p.m. local time and flies direct to Athens. The journey takes 9 hours. When Freda arrives, she telephones her mother in the UK. What is the time in the UK when Freda rings?

NUMBER
PUZZLES

1 a The numbers in a sequence are formed by adding together the previous two numbers.
Starting with $-10, 2$, the next number is $-10 + 2 = -8$, so the first three terms are $-10, 2, -8, \ldots$
Write down the next six numbers in the sequence.

b The next number in a sequence is found by taking the last number from the one before it.
Starting with $-10, 2$, the next number is $-10 - 2 = -12$, and the number after this is $2 - (-12) = 14$,
so the first four numbers are $-10, 2, -12, 14$.
Write down the next six numbers in the sequence.

2 The numbers in this triangular pattern are formed by adding together the two numbers above.

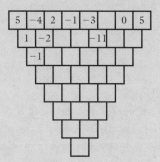

Copy and complete the triangular array.

3 The numbers in this triangular pattern are obtained by finding the *difference* (i.e. the larger – the smaller) between the two numbers above.

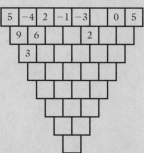

Copy and complete the pattern. Is there more than one way in which it can be completed?

FORMULAS

USING LETTERS FOR UNKNOWN NUMBERS

A formula is a general instruction for finding one quantity from other quantities.

For example, to find the number of biscuits each pupil in a class gets when a box containing 60 biscuits is shared out among them, we need to work out 60 divided by the number of pupils in the class.

We can use symbols to write the formula more briefly, i.e.

number of biscuits each pupil gets $=$ 60 $\div$ number of pupils in the class

This is still not very brief because it contains a lot of words, so we need a shorter way of giving the same information.

We are always looking for shorter ways of giving the same amount of information. Letters are often used as abbreviations for words. For example, on a score sheet you sometimes see o.g. which is short for 'own goal', we use p to stand for pence, EU for European Union and PO for Post Office. Things are no different in mathematics.

- We use a letter for an unknown number; this means that we can write a formula in a shorter way.

Using n for the number of biscuits each pupil gets and x for the number of pupils in the class, we can write the formula

number of biscuits each pupil gets $=$ 60 $\div$ number of pupils in the class

as
$$n = 60 \div x$$

This is a simple example of a formula using letters.

LEAVING OUT MULTIPLICATION AND DIVISION SIGNS

In the search for even shorter ways of writing formulas, we use the fact that $\frac{2}{3}$ and $2 \div 3$ mean the same, so we write $60 \div x$ as $\dfrac{60}{x}$.

$60 \div x$ means the same as $\dfrac{60}{x}$

For an expression such as $2 \times w$, we omit the multiplication sign and write $2w$.

$2w$ means $2 \times w$

Notice that the order in which we multiply numbers does not matter, so

$$2 \times w = w \times 2 = 2w.$$

However, we cannot omit $+$ and $-$ signs, i.e.

there is no shorter way of writing $2 + w$
or of wrting $x - y$

EXERCISE 12A

1 Write each of the following formulas in an alternative form using $\times$ and/or $\div$ signs.

a $x = 5y$

e $p = \dfrac{4q}{7}$

b $t = 3s$

f $R = \dfrac{9x}{5}$

c $A = \dfrac{v}{5}$

g $H = \dfrac{2x}{3}$

d $w = \dfrac{3}{n}$

h $y = \dfrac{5}{2x}$

2 Write each of the following formulas in a shorter form.

a $P = 4 \times a$

e $y = x \div 3$

b $Q = p \times 3$

f $P = m \div 5$

c $y = 6 \times x$

g $t = 2 \div x$

d $M = y \times 2$

h $y = 10 \div x$

3 Write each of the following formulas in a shorter form.

a $w = 3 \times m \div 4$

d $A = 2 \times v \div d$

b $y = 2 \times x \div 7$

e $P = Q \times 2 \div R$

c $T = R \times 3 \div t$

f $L = 5 \times A \div r$

4 Explain why the multiplication sign in 2×3 cannot be left out.

Write a formula in letters and symbols that connects the cost ($£C$) of a number (n) of kilograms of cheese when the cost of 1 kilogram is £2.

IT IS EASIER FIRST TO WRITE THE FORMULA IN WORDS.

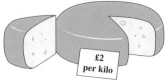

£2 per kilo

The number of pounds ($£$) = 2 times the number of kilograms

$$C = 2 \times n$$
$$C = 2n$$

In each question from **5** to **9** write down a formula, in letters and symbols, that connects the two given letters.

5 The number, s, of stones that a person weighs is the number, w, of pounds the person weighs divided by 14.

6 The number, P, of inches round the edge of a square is four times the number, x, of inches along the length of one side.

7 The distance, k kilometres, between two villages is found by multiplying the distance between them, m miles, by 1.61.

8 The number, n, of eggs in a box is the number, t, of trays in the box multiplied by 48.

9 The number, N, of components taken out of stock is 10 more than the number, n, of units to be assembled.

Sometimes we have to choose the letters ourselves.

The total number of plastic extrusions produced by a machine is found by multiplying the number of hours for which the machine operates by 15.
Choose your own letters to represent the unknown numbers and use the letters to write down a formula connecting them.

Let the total number of extrusions be N when the machine operates for t hours.

Total number of extrusions = number of hours $\times$ 15

$$N = t \times 15$$
$$N = 15t$$

In questions **10** to **13** choose your own letters to represent the unknown numbers that can vary. State clearly the meaning you give to each letter. Write down the resulting formula.

10 The profit made by a business is equal to its income minus its fixed costs of £12 000 each week.

11 The perimeter of a square is found by quadrupling the length of one side.

12 The number of cans of lemonade delivered to a store is found by multiplying the number of boxes delivered by 48.

13 The displacement of an engine is found by multiplying the capacity of one cylinder by four.

USING FORMULAS

When a formula is given that connects two related quantities we can find the value of one quantity corresponding to any given value of the other.

EXERCISE 12B

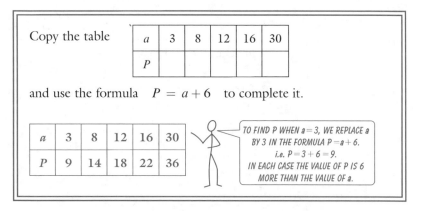

Copy the table

a	3	8	12	16	30
P					

and use the formula $P = a + 6$ to complete it.

a	3	8	12	16	30
P	9	14	18	22	36

TO FIND P WHEN a = 3, WE REPLACE a BY 3 IN THE FORMULA P = a + 6. i.e. P = 3 + 6 = 9. IN EACH CASE THE VALUE OF P IS 6 MORE THAN THE VALUE OF a.

In questions **1** to **7** copy the table and use the given formula to complete it.

1 $a = b + 7$

b	1	2	3	4	5	6
a						

2 $P = 6a$

Remember that $6a$ means $6 \times a$

a	1	3	6	8	10	12
P						

3 $M = m - 4$

m	6	8	10	13	17
M					

4 $b = 2.5 + c$

c	2	5	5.6	5.8	6.3
b					

5 $p = 12.5 - q$

q	3	5	6.5	7.2	8.9
p					

6 $y = 3.5x$

x	2	4	5	5.6	7.2
y					

7 $p = \dfrac{36}{v}$

v	1	2	3	4	5	8
p						

8

N	1	2	3	4	5	6	7
Nth term $= 2N - 1$	1	3	5	7			

a Copy and complete this table which gives the first 7 terms of a sequence.

b Write down the 50th term of this sequence.

9 Copy and complete the table to give the first 8 terms of a sequence.

N	1	2	3	4	5	6	7	8
Nth term $= 4 - 3N$								

10

N	1	2	3	4	5	6	7
Nth term $= \dfrac{2}{N}$							

a Copy and complete the table, giving the terms, where necessary, as decimals correct to 2 decimal places.

b Find the 100th term of this sequence, correct to 2 decimal places if necessary.

Joy is 9 years older than Carol.

a Write down a formula that expresses Joy's age (p years) in terms of Carol's age (q years).

b Use your formula to find Joy's age when Carol is 18 years old.

a In words, Joy's age is equal to Carol's age plus 9 years. As a formula, using the letters given in the question, this becomes

$$p = q + 9$$

b $p = 18 + 9$

$= 27$

IF CAROL IS 18 WE REPLACE q BY 18 IN THE FORMULA.

i.e. Joy is 27 when Carol is 18.

11 With the formula $t = 20w$, we can work out how long it takes to bake a loaf of bread. The number of pounds that the uncooked loaf weighs is w and t is the number of minutes it takes to bake the loaf.

    a How many minutes are needed to bake a loaf weighing 2 lb ?

    b How long should a loaf weighing 3 lb take to bake ?

    c If a loaf weighs $2\frac{1}{4}$ lb how long will it take to bake ?

12 When tyres are bought for a car assembly line, the formula $t = 5c$ is used where c is the number of cars to be assembled and t is the number of tyres needed.

    a How many tyres are needed to assemble one car ?

    b They plan to assemble 2500 cars next week. How many tyres are needed ?

    c The last delivery of tyres was an order for 2500. How many cars will this supply ?

13 Tim is 5 years older than Linda.

    a If Tim is T years old and Linda is x years old, write down a formula connecting their ages.

    b How old is Linda if Tim is 15 ?

    c How old will each person be in 6 years time ?

    d Will the same formula hold in 6 years time ? Justify your answer.

14 A number y is always 13 less than a number x.

   a Write down the formula connecting x and y.

   b Find y when x is **i** 16   **ii** 4

15 Richard is 28 years younger than his father.

   a Write down a formula for Richard's age, N years, in terms of his father's age, m years.

   b Richard's father is 38 now.
     How old is Richard?

   c How old will Richard be when his father is 60?

16 The charge to send a parcel by special delivery is £2 per kilogram plus a fixed fee of £2.50.
Construct a formula that connects the total cost with the weight of the parcel.
Choose your own letters for this question but remember to give the exact meaning of each one.

17 A father is three times as old as his son.

   a If the father's age is H years and the son's age is x years write down a formula connecting H and x.

   b Use your formula to find the father's age if the son is 12 years old.

   c Will the same formula hold in 12 years time?
     If not suggest what the formula will be in 12 years time.

18 One packet of crisps costs 35 p.
Construct a formula that gives the cost of a number of packets of crisps. Choose your own letters for the unknown values and give the meaning of each one.

FORMULAS WITH TWO OPERATIONS

A printer quotes a fixed cost of £500 plus £3 per copy to print a quantity of local history books. To work out the cost he uses the formula

$$C = 500 + 3n$$

where C is the number of £s it costs to print n books.

To find the value of C when $n = 2000$, two operations are necessary. First we must multiply 3 by 2000, and secondly we must add the result to 500.

If $n = 2000$, $C = 500 + 3 \times 2000$
$$= 500 + 6000$$
$$= 6500$$

> Remember, with mixed operations, we do multiplication and division before addition and subtraction.

Using this formula, the cost for printing 2000 books is £6500.

EXERCISE 12C

The number of drawing pins (N) needed to pin up q paintings is given by the formula $N = 2q + 2$.
How many pins are needed to pin up 5 paintings?

$$N = 2q + 2$$
If $q = 5$, $\quad N = 2 \times 5 + 2$
$$= 10 + 2$$
$$= 12$$

> $2q$ is short for $2 \times q$

12 pins are needed to pin up 5 paintings.

To answer questions **1** to **4** use the formula $N = 2q + 2$, which gives the number of pins needed to hold up q paintings.

1 How many pins are needed to put up 8 paintings?

2 If 13 paintings are put up, how many pins are used?

3 How many pins are used to put up a single painting?

4 a If $q = 6$, what is N? **b** What is N when $q = 11$?

Sari is making a matchstick pattern. If she completes n squares she needs M matchsticks where $M = 4n + 1$.
Use this formula to answer questions **5** to **7**.

5 How many matchsticks does she need to complete 6 squares?

6 She completes 9 squares. How many matchsticks does she use?

7 a Find M if $n = 4$. **b** When $n = 12$, what is M?

8 The formula for C in terms of n is $C = 3n + 4$.
Copy the table and complete it.

n	1	4	9	12
C				

9 p and q are connected by the formula $q = 5p - 4$.
Copy the table and complete it.

p	2	5	7	11	15
q					

10 A bicycle manufacturer buys in tyres and uses the formula

$$N = 2a + 10$$

to calculate the number of tyres to order when a is the number of bicycles to be assembled.

a How many tyres should be ordered if 50 bicycles are to be assembled?

b Why do you think 10 has been added to $2a$ in the formula?

FORMULAS WITH TWO SUBSTITUTIONS   In the previous exercise we had to substitute a value for the letter on the right-hand side to find the value of the letter on the left-hand side. In the next exercise two substitutions are required on the right-hand side.

EXERCISE 12D

Use the formula $A = l \times b$, where A cm^2 is the area of a rectangle of length l cm and breadth b cm, to find the area of a rectangle that is 8 cm long and 5 cm wide.

$$A = l \times b$$
If $l = 8$ and $b = 5$, $A = 8 \times 5$
$$= 40$$

The area of the rectangle is 40 cm^2.

Use the formula $A = l \times b$ to find A when

1 $l = 5$ and $b = 3$ **3** $l = 8$ and $b = 3.5$

2 $l = 8$ and $b = 6$ **4** $l = 4.4$ and $b = 2.7$

5 A rectangle is 12 cm long and 6 cm wide.
Find its area.

6 Find the area of a rectangle measuring 20 mm by 15 mm.

If $c = 5a - 2b$, find c when $a = 3$ and $b = 4$.

If $a = 3$ and $b = 4$,
$$c = 5 \times 3 - 2 \times 4$$

Remember, do multiplication first.

$$= 15 - 8$$
$$= 7$$

---

7 If $P = 2l + 2b$ find P when

a $l = 7.5$ and $b = 2.4$ **b** $l = 5.6$ and $b = 2.8$

8 Given that $I = m \times v$ find I when

a $m = 2.5$ and $v = 4$ **b** $m = 1.8$ and $v = 6.5$

9 Use the formula $v = u + 10t$ to find v when

a $u = 3$ and $t = 8$ **b** $u = 8$ and $t = 3$

10 If $p = \dfrac{48}{v}$ find p when

a $v = 4$ **b** $v = 12$ **c** $v = 16$

11 A printer uses the formula $P = a + 3b$ to work out the cost ($£P$) of printing b books when the set-up costs are $£a$.

a Can you attach a meaning to the '3' in the formula?
b Find the cost of printing 1500 books if the set-up costs are £800.
c Find the value of P when $a = 750$ and $b = 3500$.

12 A caterer uses the formula $C = a + 20n$ to work out the cost, $£C$, of providing a wedding reception for n guests.

a What meaning can you attach to
i to '20' in the formula **ii** a?
b Find the value of C if $a = 425$ and $n = 84$.
c Find the cost of a reception for 120 people if the fixed overheads are £350.

MULTIPLYING AND DIVIDING WITH DIRECTED NUMBERS

The formula $y = 3 - 2x$ relates the x- and y-coordinates of some points. The x-coordinate of a point can be negative so we may need to find y when $x = -3$.

This involves working out the value of $-2 \times (-3)$.

In other cases we may need to find $3 \div (-3)$, or $(-2) \div 2$

To find the rules for multiplying and dividing with directed numbers, we use some facts we already know.

From Chapter 11, we know that $(-2) + (-2) = -4$,

we also know that 2×3 is the same as $3 + 3$.

This means that $2 \times (-4)$ is the same as $(-4) + (-4)$

and $\qquad\qquad\qquad\qquad\qquad\qquad (-4) + (-4) = -8$

therefore $\qquad 2 \times (-4) = -8$

As numbers can be multiplied in any order, it follows that

$$(-4) \times 2 = -8$$

This reasoning applies to any numbers, so *when a positive and a negative number are multiplied, the answer is negative.*

From Chapter 11 again, we know that $-(-2) = +2$

so $\qquad -2 \times (-4) = -[2 \times (-4)]$

$$= -[-8]$$

$$= +8$$

Therefore *when two negative numbers are multiplied, the answer is positive.*

Now division is the reverse of multiplication,

i.e. as $(-4) \times 2 = -8$, $(-8) \div (-4) = 2$

So, *a negative number divided by a negative number gives a positive answer.*

$$(-4) \times 2 = -8 \quad \text{also gives} \quad (-8) \div 2 = -4$$

i.e. *a negative number divided by a positive number gives a negative answer.*

Lastly, as $-2 \times -4 = 8$, $8 \div (-2) = -4$

Hence *a positive number divided by a negative number also gives a negative answer.*

We can summarise these results as follows.

> When directed numbers are multiplied or divided,
> both signs the SAME gives a POSITIVE answer,
> DIFFERENT signs gives a NEGATIVE answer.

EXERCISE 12E Do not use a calculator.

Find the value of **a** $5 \times (-6)$ **b** $(-3) \times 7$ **c** $\dfrac{(-14)}{7}$

a $5 \times (-6) = -30$

b $(-3) \times 7 = -21$ ⟨ $(-3) \times 7$ is the same as $7 \times (-3)$ ⟩

c $\dfrac{(-14)}{7} = -2$

Find the value of

1 $3 \times (-5)$ **3** $4 \times (-8)$ **5** $(-5) \times 4$ **7** $(-6) \times 6$

2 $6 \times (-8)$ **4** $(-3) \times 9$ **6** $(-8) \times 3$ **8** $4 \times (-6)$

9 $\dfrac{(-6)}{3}$ **11** $\dfrac{(-24)}{6}$ **13** $\dfrac{(-26)}{2}$ **15** $\dfrac{(-36)}{6}$

10 $\dfrac{(-18)}{9}$ **12** $\dfrac{(-24)}{8}$ **14** $\dfrac{(-48)}{8}$ **16** $\dfrac{(-36)}{12}$

Calculate   **a** $(-5) \times (-2)$ **c** $-5 \div (-4)$
          b $3 \div (-4)$ **d** $-5(-4)$

a $(-5) \times (-2) = 10$ ⟨ The same signs gives a positive answer. ⟩

b $3 \div (-4) = -\dfrac{3}{4}$ ⟨ Remember, if a number does not have a positive or negative sign given, it is positive. Different signs give a negative answer. ⟩

c $-5 \div (-4) = \dfrac{5}{4} = 1\frac{1}{4}$ ⟨ The same signs give a positive answer. ⟩

d $-5(-4) = 20$ ⟨ $-5(-4)$ means $-5 \times (-4)$ ⟩

Calculate

17 $(-3) \times (+5)$ **21** $(-6) \times (-7)$ **25** $(+5) \div (-1)$

18 $(+4) \div (-2)$ **22** $(-4) \times (-3)$ **26** $(-6) \times (-3)$

19 $(-7) \times (-2)$ **23** $(-6) \div (+3)$ **27** $(-3) \times (-9)$

20 $(+4) \div (+1)$ **24** $(-8) \div (-2)$ **28** $(-8) \div (-2)$

29 $7 \times (-5)$ **33** $-6(4)$ **37** $3(-2)$

30 $-6(-4)$ **34** $-2(-4)$ **38** 5×3

31 $\frac{-4}{2}$ **35** $-(-3)$ **39** $\frac{6}{-3}$

32 $18 \div (-9)$ **36** $\frac{36}{-6}$ **40** $-5(-4)$

41 $6 \times (-\frac{1}{2})$ **44** $(+\frac{2}{3}) \times (+9)$ **47** $\frac{3}{4}(-4)$

42 $-3(+\frac{3}{4})$ **45** $-\frac{3}{8} \times \frac{2}{3}$ **48** $(-\frac{1}{4}) \times (-\frac{2}{3})$

43 $(-3.6) \div (-1.8)$ **46** $0.5 \div (-0.25)$ **49** $(-1.2) \div 0.3$

FORMULAS THAT INVOLVE DIRECTED NUMBERS

Many formulas involve negative numbers. One of these is the formula
$$c = \tfrac{5}{9}(f - 32)$$
which converts temperature from f degrees Fahrenheit to c degrees Celsius.

EXERCISE 12F

Use the formula $c = \tfrac{5}{9}(f - 32)$ to convert $14\,°F$ to $°C$.

If $f = 14,\ c = \tfrac{5}{9}(14 - 32)$

$\quad\quad = \tfrac{5}{9} \times (-18)$

$\quad\quad = 5 \times (-18) \div 9$

$\quad\quad = -10$

$\therefore\ 14\,°F$ is equivalent to $-10\,°C$

In questions **1** to **8** use the formula $c = \tfrac{5}{9}(f - 32)$ to convert the following temperatures into $°C$.

1 $5\,°F$ **3** $32\,°F$ **5** $-13\,°F$ **7** $10.4\,°F$

2 $23\,°F$ **4** $-4\,°F$ **6** $24.8\,°F$ **8** $-12.5\,°F$

9 If $v = u + 5t$ find v when

     a $u = -10$ and $t = 1$ **b** $u = -15$ and $t = 0.5$

10 Given that $P = q + 2r,$ find P when

    a $q = -4$ and $r = 3$ **c** $q = -3$ and $r = -2$

    b $q = 6$ and $r = -4$ **d** $q = 8$ and $r = -4$

11 If $y = 5x - c$ find y when

    a $x = 4$ and $c = -5$ **c** $x = -3$ and $c = -9$

    b $x = -3$ and $c = 5$ **d** $x = 2$ and $c = -10$

12 Given that $A = 5b - 2c$ find A when

    a $b = -3$ and $c = 9$ **c** $b = -7$ and $c = 4$

    b $b = 2$ and $c = -6$ **d** $b = -0.05$ and $c = -1.5$

13 Given that $P = 3q - 2r$ find P when

    a $q = 0.7$ and $r = -3.5$ **b** $q = -0.55$ and $r = 3.4$

MIXED EXERCISES

EXERCISE 12G

1 Each pack delivered to an electronics company by Modcomp Ltd contains 48 components.

    a Write down a formula that connects the total number (N) of components delivered with the number (n) of packs delivered.

    b Use your formula to find the number of components in 12 packs.

2 The formula connecting p, q and r is $r = 5p - 2q$.
Find the value of r when

    a $p = 4$ and $q = 3$ **b** $p = 4.7$ and $q = 1.3$

3 Find

    a -2×4 **b** $-(-5)$ **c** $-10 \div 5$

4 Find

    a $4 - (-5)$ **b** $3 - 2 \times 5$ **c** $\frac{24}{-8}$

5 If $y = 3x + c,$ find the value of y when

    a $x = -2$ and $c = 8$ **b** $x = 4$ and $c = -7$

EXERCISE 12H

1 60 watt electric light bulbs are sold in packs of six.

    a Write down a formula that gives the total number (N) of bulbs in terms of the number (n) of packs bought.

    b Anne buys 6 packs. How many bulbs has she bought?

2 Given that $E = Ri$ find E when

    a $R = 8$ and $i = 2$ **b** $R = 4.5$ and $i = 0.6$

    Remember that Ri means $R \times i$.

3 Find

    a $(-5) - (-5)$ **b** $3 + (5 - 8)$ **c** $-2 - (4 - 9)$

4 Calculate

    a $-2(-6)$ **b** $15 \div (-3)$ **c** $\frac{-25}{5}$

5 Given that $P = 12 - 5q$ find P when

    a $q = 5$ **b** $q = -6$

INVESTIGATION

Try this on a group of pupils or friends.

Think of a number between 1 and 10.
Add 4.
Multiply the result by 5.
Double your answer.
Divide the result by 10.
Take away the number you first thought of.
Write down your answer.

However many times you try this the answer is 4.
Investigate what happens when you use numbers other than whole numbers between 1 and 10. Try, for example, larger whole numbers, decimals, negative whole numbers, fractions.
Is the answer always 4?
Try to use the algebra you have learned in this chapter to explain your conclusion.

UNITS

From the information on the box, Julia can work out that 10 boxes weigh 122 400 grams.

To compare the weight of 10 boxes of tiles with the load she can put in her car, Julia needs both weights in the same unit.

Julia can

- either change 250 kg to grams, but this involves very large numbers and they are not easy to compare

- or change 122 400 grams into kilograms which will be a far smaller number. This will immediately show her whether 10 boxes is a safe load for her car.

EXERCISE 13A

Discuss whether in these situations it is more sensible to express the quantities in large or in small units.

1 A table-tennis top measures 276.5 cm by 160 cm. Can I use it indoors?

2 The maximum load recommended for this trolley is 70 kg. Will it be overloaded if I use it to carry 250 of these 750 gram tins?

3 Each bottle holds 350 ml of water. Can I empty 10 of these bottles into a jug that holds 2 litres?

CHANGING FROM SMALL UNITS TO LARGE UNITS

The examples above show that we need to be able to change from one unit to another.

The units that are usually used for measuring length are the kilometre, metre, centimetre and millimetre; and the relationships between them are

$$10 \, \text{mm} = 1 \, \text{cm} \qquad 100 \, \text{cm} = 1 \, \text{m} \qquad 1000 \, \text{m} = 1 \, \text{km}$$

The common units for measuring weight are the gram and the kilogram. For very heavy objects, the tonne (t) is also used, and for very light objects we use the milligram (mg). The relationships between these units are

$$1000 \, \text{mg} = 1 \, \text{g} \qquad 1000 \, \text{g} = 1 \, \text{kg} \qquad 1000 \, \text{kg} = 1 \, \text{t}$$

Note that the units for measuring weight are called *units of mass*.

The common units for measuring capacity are the litre (l) and the millilitre (ml) where

$$1000 \, \text{ml} = 1 \, \text{litre}$$

In Book 7B we saw that when we change from a large unit to a smaller unit, we multiply.

For example, to give 2 m in cm, we multiply 2 by 100 cm,

i.e. $2\,m = 2 \times 100\,cm$

$= 200\,cm$

However if we want to change from centimetres to metres, we know that a metre is longer than a centimetre, so there are fewer metres than centimetres in a given length. This means that when we change 450 cm to metres, we divide by 100,

i.e. $450\,cm = 450 \div 100\,m$

$= 4.5\,m$

Whenever we change from a small unit to a large one, we divide.

EXERCISE 13B

1 Which unit would you choose to use for

   a the length of your bedroom

   b the weight of a sack of potatoes

   c the distance from Exeter to Bristol

   d the weight of a lorry loaded with bricks

   e the length of your fingernail

   f the weight of one egg

   g the weight of pure aspirin in one pill

   h the width of a dining table

   i the capacity of a spoon

   j the capacity of a wheelbarrow?

Change 5600 g to kilograms.

$5600\,g = 5600 \div 1000\,kg$

$= 5.6\,kg$

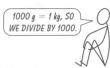

1000 g = 1 kg, SO WE DIVIDE BY 1000.

2 Express the given quantity in the unit in brackets.

   a 300 mm (cm)   **d** 5840 mg (g)   **g** 1560 ml (l)

   b 2000 m (km)   **e** 7000 kg (t)   **h** 7650 m (km)

   c 250 cm (m)   **f** 2590 g (kg)   **i** 2133 mm (cm)

Express 45 ml in litres.

$45 \text{ ml} = 45 \div 1000 \text{ litres}$
$= 0.045 \text{ litres}$

1000 ml = 1 litre, so we divide by 1000.

3 Express the given quantity in the unit in brackets.

a 72 m (km)   **d** 86 kg (t)   **g** 28 mg (g)

b 12 cm (m)   **e** 560 g (kg)   **h** 790 ml (litres)

c 150 ml (litres)   **f** 88 mm (cm)   **i** 86 g (kg)

4 A table is 200 cm long. How many metres is this?

5 Find the perimeter of this triangle
in metres.

290 cm   430 cm

520 cm

6 Find the total weight of these
jars of jam in

a grams   **b** kilograms.

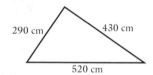

500g   850g   450g   600g

7 The weight of each parcel is written
on it. What is the total weight in

a grams   **b** kilograms?

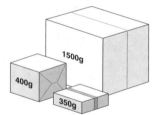

1500g

400g

350g

8 A full sack of potatoes weighs 14 kg. Two people each help
themselves to 700 g of potatoes.
What is the weight of the potatoes left in the sack?

9

320 cm   132 cm   400 cm   285 cm

Which of these vehicles can go under a bridge with this sign on it?

3.5 m

10 Each side of a square is 45 cm long. What is the perimeter of the square in metres?

11 There is a limit of 1 tonne on the weight a lift can carry. If an average adult weighs 70 kg, can the lift carry 20 adults?

12 A girl's journey to school starts with a walk of 500 m to the bus stop. She then travels 2.5 km by bus and still has a walk of 100 m to school. What distance in kilometres does the girl have to travel?

13 Which is heavier, a locomotive weighing 86 tonnes or a loaded lorry weighing 39 800 kg?

14 Put these weights in order of size with the lightest first.

3 t   900 kg   279 000 kg   279 000 g

15 Put these weights in order of size with the heaviest first.

7900 mg   2.5 g   0.25 kg   79 g

WORKING WITH UNITS

In some problems, we have to change from large units to smaller ones. There are more smaller units than larger units in a given quantity so when changing to a smaller unit, we multiply.

When we have to change to a larger unit, we divide.

ADDING AND SUBTRACTING METRIC QUANTITIES

Jane has several items to carry home. To find out the total weight of these items, she must add their weights.

Before we can add or subtract *any* two quantities, they must both be expressed in the same unit.

It does not matter whether we choose to find the total weight in grams or in kilograms, but as most people know what they feel like to carry, we will choose kilograms.

Now 250 g = 0.25 kg and 454 g = 0.454 kg,

so Jane has to carry (0.25 + 1.5 + 0.454) kg, i.e. 2.204 kg

EXERCISE 13C

1 a Find the perimeter of this carpet in metres.

b Is 10 m of carpet edging enough to go all round the edge of this carpet?

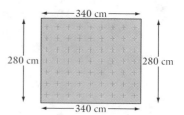

2 a What is the total weight of these groceries?

b Alan reckons that he can carry 15 kg of shopping. Will he be able to carry this load?

3 One tin of baked beans weighs 220 g. Fifty of these tins fill a box. What weight, in kilograms, should be written on the box?

4 One fence post is 130 cm long. What length of wood, in metres, is needed to make ten of these posts?

5 A lorry is loaded with bricks. The weight of the bricks is 2.5 tonnes. The weight of the lorry when empty is 2500 kg. What is the weight of the loaded lorry?

Find the sum of 5 m, 4 cm and 97 mm in

a metres   **b** centimetres.

a $4 \text{ cm} = 4 \div 100 \text{ m}$

$= 0.04 \text{ m}$

and $97 \text{ mm} = 97 \div 1000 \text{ m}$

$= 0.097 \text{ m}$

$\therefore$ $5 \text{ m} + 4 \text{ cm} + 97 \text{ mm} = (5 + 0.04 + 0.097) \text{ m}$

$= 5.137 \text{ m}$

b $5 \text{ m} = 5 \times 100 \text{ cm}$

$= 500 \text{ cm}$

and $97 \text{ mm} = 97 \div 10 \text{ cm} = 9.7 \text{ cm}$

$\therefore$ $5 \text{ m} + 4 \text{ cm} + 97 \text{ mm}$

$= (500 + 4 + 9.7) \text{ cm}$

$= 513.7 \text{ cm}$

IF I HAD THOUGHT, I COULD HAVE MULTIPLIED THE ANSWER TO PART **a** BY 100

Find, expressing your answer in the unit given in brackets

6 4 litres − 900 ml (ml)

13 20 g − 150 mg (g)

7 52 mm + 87 cm (m)

14 36 kg − 7580 g (kg)

8 1.3 kg − 150 g (g)

15 1.5 t − 590 kg (kg)

9 1.3 m − 564 mm (cm)

16 3.9 m + 582 mm (cm)

10 2.05 t + 592 kg (kg)

17 0.3 m − 29.5 cm (mm)

11 3.7 litres + 872 ml (litres)

18 790 g + 1.5 kg + 370 g (kg)

12 390 cm + 2 m + 1730 mm (cm)

19 0.55 kg + 50 g + 892 mg (g)

20 Subtract 52 kg from 0.8 t, giving your answer in kilograms.

21 Find the difference, in grams, between 5 g and 890 mg.

22 Find the total length, in millimetres, of a piece of wood 282 cm long and another piece of wood 1260 mm long.

23 Find the total weight, in kilograms, of 250 g of butter, 2.5 kg of potatoes and 1.5 kg of flour.

24 One tin of cherries weighs 240 g. What is the weight, in kilograms, of ten of these tins?

25 One fence post is 150 cm long. What length of wood, in metres, is needed to make 40 such fence posts?

For questions **26** to **32**, choose the most suitable unit for your answer.

26 A wooden vegetable crate and its contents weigh 6.5 kg. If the crate weighs 1.2 kg what is the weight of its contents?

27 A girl travels to school by walking 450 m to the bus stop and then travelling 1.65 km by bus. The distance she walks after getting off the bus is 130 m. What total distance does she travel?

28 A man takes three parcels to the Post Office and has them weighed. One parcel weighs 4 kg 37 g, the weight of the second is 3 kg 982 g and the third one weighs 1 kg 173 g. What is their total weight?

29 A rectangular field is 947 m long and 581 m wide. What is the perimeter of the field? What length of fencing would be needed to go round the field, leaving space for two gates each 3 m wide?

30 A freight train has five trucks. Two of them are carrying 15 t 880 kg each. Another has a load of 14 t 700 kg and the last two are each loaded with 24 t 600 kg. What is the total weight of the contents of the five trucks? If the weight of each truck is 5 t 260 kg, what is the combined weight of the trucks and their contents?

31 A wall is 3.5 m high and a damp patch starts at the bottom of the wall. The damp patch rises up the wall by 5 cm every night and recedes by 3 cm during the day. If it carries on like this, how many days will it be before the damp patch reaches the top of the wall?

32 A bucket that will hold 5 litres of water is placed underneath a drip from the ceiling. Two drips are falling each second and each drip is 2 ml of water.
How long will it take for the bucket to fill?

IMPERIAL UNITS

Most measurements in the United Kingdom are given in metric units but some Imperial units are still used. For instance, distances on road signs are usually given in miles whereas signposts on footpaths often use kilometres for distances. We need to cope with a mixture of metric and Imperial units.

Consider this situation.
David found instructions in a book for making papier-mâché. Among other things, he needed $1\frac{1}{2}$ lb of flour. He had a 1.5 kg bag of flour and a set of digital scales that weigh in pounds and ounces. David needs to know

- how many ounces there are in one pound so that he can read the scales
- whether he has enough flour, that is if 1.5 kg is heavier than $1\frac{1}{2}$ pounds.

To be able to cope with similar situations, we need to be familiar with the Imperial units still in use and to know their approximate values in metric units, and vice-versa.

UNITS OF LENGTH

Miles, yards, feet and inches are Imperial units of length that are still used. The relationships between them are

12 inches (in) = 1 foot (ft)   3 feet = 1 yard (yd)
1760 yards = 1 mile

EXERCISE 13D

Express 2 ft 5 in in inches.

$$2 \text{ ft} = 2 \times 12 \text{ in}$$
$$= 24 \text{ in}$$
$$\therefore \quad 2 \text{ ft } 5 \text{ in} = 24 \text{ in} + 5 \text{ in}$$
$$= 29 \text{ in}$$

> 2 feet 5 inches is sometimes written as 2′ 5″

Express the given quantity in the unit in brackets.

1 5 ft 8 in (in)

2 4 yd 2 ft (ft)

3 2 ft 11 in (in)

4 8 ft 4 in (in)

5 5 yd 2 ft (ft)

6 10 ft 3 in (in)

7 9 yd 1 ft (ft)

8 9 ft 10 in (in)

Express 52″ in feet and inches.

$$52″ = 52 \div 12 \text{ ft}$$
$$= 4′ 4″$$

> There are 4 twelves in 52 with 4 left over.

Express the given quantity in the units in brackets.

9 36 in (ft)

10 29 in (ft and in)

11 86 in (ft and in)

12 9 ft (yd)

13 13 ft (yd and ft)

14 75 in (ft and in)

15 100 ft (yd and ft)

16 120 in (ft and in)

17 How many yards are there in

a $1\frac{1}{2}$ miles   **b** $\frac{1}{4}$ mile   **c** $\frac{1}{8}$ mile ?

18 Andy walks to school along a main road. At the start of his journey, a road sign tells him it is $\frac{3}{4}$ mile to the junction where his school is. How many yards does he have to walk ?

19 Josh has four cork tiles.
Each tile is 14 inches square.
He arranges them in a row to
make a notice board.
How long, in feet and inches,
is the board?

20 Jane has a liquorice lace that is 2 feet long. She cuts it into 6 equal lengths.
How long is each length?

21 Gold coloured chain is sold from a street stall at £1.50 per 4 inches.
How much will 2 feet of this chain cost?

22 I passed a sign on a motorway saying 'Road works – 1 mile ahead'.
The next sign I passed said 'Road works – 800 yards ahead'.
How far apart are the two signs?

23 One lane on a motorway is closed by cones for a distance of 1 mile.
The cones are placed 4 feet apart.
How many cones are used?

UNITS OF MASS   Imperial units for weighing that are still used are stones, pounds and ounces. Other units of mass that you may still see are hundredweights and tons (not to be confused with tonnes).

The relationships between them are

16 ounces (oz) = 1 pound (lb)   14 pounds = 1 stone
112 pounds = 1 hundredweight (cwt)
20 hundredweight = 1 ton

EXERCISE 13E   Express the given quantity in terms of the units given in brackets.

1 2 lb 6 oz (oz)

2 1 lb 12 oz (oz)

3 4 lb 3 oz (oz)

4 2 stone 3 lb (lb)

5 7 stone 6 lb (lb)

6 24 oz (lb and oz)

7 18 oz (lb and oz)

8 36 oz (lb and oz)

9 57 lb (stones and lb)

10 106 lb (stones and lb)

11 3 tons 4 cwt (cwt)

12 1 cwt 50 lb (lb)

13 30 cwt (tons and cwt)

14 120 lb (cwt and lb)

15 A recipe for Bolognaise sauce needs 12 oz of minced beef for
3 portions of sauce. Amy wants to make 12 portions.
What weight of minced beef should she buy?

16 James went on a diet. Before he started, he weighed 10 stone 6 lb.
How much did he weigh after losing 10 lb?

17 Joseph bought two bags of bait for fishing. One bag weighed 12 oz
and the other bag weighed 9 oz.
What is the total weight of this bait in pounds and ounces?

18 The owner of a corner shop buys a 12 lb bag of mint humbugs from
which he makes up 32 smaller bags each containing the same weight
of humbugs.
What is the weight of humbugs in each of these bags?

19 Apples are sold at 64 p per lb. What is the cost of an apple weighing
3 ounces?

20 Anthea bought a 56 lb sack of potatoes. She weighed out half of
this quantity on her bathroom scales which measure in stones and
pounds.
What weight should show on the scales?

21 'Pick your own' strawberries are being sold at 64 p per pound. A
family picks 8 lb 12 oz of strawberries.
How much will they have to pay for them?

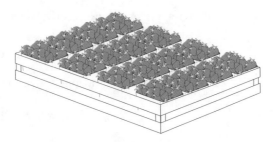

22 A lorry loaded with rubble weighs 12 tons. It delivers 30 cwt of
rubble to one site and then 50 cwt of rubble to another site. The
tare (empty) weight of the lorry is 5 tons.
What weight of rubble is still in the lorry?

ROUGH EQUIVALENCE BETWEEN METRIC AND IMPERIAL UNITS

When you shop you will find that nearly all prepacked goods (tinned foods, sugar, biscuits, prepacked fruit, etc.) are sold in grams or kilograms and some loose produce (vegetables, fruit, cheese from the delicatessen counter, etc.) is sold in pounds and ounces. It is often useful to be able to convert, roughly, pounds into kilograms and grams into pounds.

Earlier in this chapter, David needed to know if 1.5 kg was heavier than $1\frac{1}{2}$ lb. A rough conversion is good enough to answer this question:

| 1 kg is about 2 lb | so that | 1 lb is about 500 g |

Now we can see that 1.5 kg is more than $1\frac{1}{2}$ lb, so David had enough flour.

Rough conversions between metric and Imperial units of length are

1 metre is about 1 yd, i.e. 3 feet

1 mile is about $1\frac{1}{2}$ km   so   1 km is about $\frac{2}{3}$ mile

These rough approximations are good enough for most purposes but there are situations when more accurate conversions are required. For example, if we need to replace a $\frac{1}{2}''$ water pipe, we find that water pipes are now sold with diameters given in millimetres. So that we can decide which is nearest to $\frac{1}{2}''$, it is useful to know that 1 inch $\approx$ 2.5 cm, i.e 25 mm, so $\frac{1}{2}''$ is about 12.5 mm.

This is easier to remember as

4 inches $\approx$ 10 cm

Remember that the symbol $\approx$ means 'is approximately equal to'.

Better approximations for other units are

1 metre $\approx$ 39 inches

so one metre is slightly longer than one yard

5 miles $\approx$ 8 kilometres

so 1 mile is less than 2 km

1 kg $\approx$ 2.2 lb

so 1 kg is a bit more than 2 lb.

EXERCISE 13F   In questions **1** to **15**, write the first unit very roughly in terms of the unit in brackets.

1 3 kg (lb)   **6** 5 m (ft)   <u>**11**</u> 20 ft (m)

2 2 m (ft)   **7** 3.5 kg (lb)   <u>**12**</u> 800 g (lb)

3 4 lb (kg)   **8** 8 ft (m)   <u>**13**</u> 9 lb (kg)

4 9 ft (m)   **9** 250 g (oz)   <u>**14**</u> 50 m (ft)

5 1.5 kg (lb)   **10** 500 g (lb)   <u>**15**</u> 12 kg (lb)

Use the approximation 5 miles $\approx$ 8 km to convert 60 miles into an approximate number of kilometres.

If 5 miles $\approx$ 8 km,
then 60 miles = 5 x 12 miles
$\approx$ 8 x 12 km = 96 km

In questions **16** to **21** use the approximation 5 miles $\approx$ 8 km to convert the given number of miles into an approximate number of kilometres.

16 10 miles   **18** 15 miles   **20** 75 miles

17 20 miles   **19** 100 miles   **21** 40 miles

22 I buy a 5 lb bag of potatoes and two 1.5 kg bags of flour.
What weight, roughly, in pounds do I have to carry ?

23 A window is 6 ft high. Roughly, what is its height in metres ?

24 I have a picture which measures 2 ft by 1 ft. Wood for framing it is sold by the metre.
Roughly, what length of framing, in metres, should I buy ?

25 In the supermarket I buy a 4 kg packet of sugar and a 5 lb bag of potatoes.
Which is heavier ?

26 The distance between London and Dover is about 70 miles. The distance between Calais and Paris is about 270 kilometres.
Which is the greater distance ?

27 A recipe requires 250 grams of flour.
Roughly, how many ounces is this?

28 An instruction in an old knitting pattern says knit 6 inches. Mary
has a tape measure marked only in centimetres.
How many centimetres should she knit?

29 The instructions for repotting a plant say that it should go into a
10 cm pot. The flower pots that Tom has in his shed are marked
3 in, 4 in and 5 in. Which one should he use?

30 Peter Stuart wishes to extend his central heating which was installed
several years ago using 1 in and $\frac{1}{2}$ in diameter copper tubing. The
only new piping he can buy has diameters of 10 mm, 15 mm, 20 mm
or 25 mm.
Use the approximation 1 in $\approx$ 2.5 cm to determine which piping
would be nearest to

a the 1 in pipes   **b** the $\frac{1}{2}$ in pipes.

31 A carpenter wishes to replace a 6 in floorboard. The only sizes
available are metric and have widths of 12 cm, 15 cm, 18 cm and
20 cm. Which one should he buy?

32 Eddy knows his height is 4 ft 5 in. He needs to fill in a passport
application form and has to give his height in metres.
What should he enter for his height?

33 In one catalogue a table-cloth is described as measuring 4 ft by 8 ft.
In another catalogue a different table-cloth is described as
measuring 1 m by 2 m.
Which one covers the larger area?

34 The doctor tells Mr Brown that he needs to lose 10 kilograms in
weight. Mr Brown's scales at home show his weight now as
15 stone 6 lb.
What will his scales show when he has lost the required weight?

35 A shop sells material at £10.50 per metre while the same material is
sold in the local market at £9 per yard. Which is cheaper?

36 Arrange these weights in order of size with the lightest first.

2 oz,   50 g,   0.04 kg, $\frac{1}{5}$ lb

37 Arrange these lengths in order of size with the longest first.

25 cm,   8 inches,   25 mm, $1\frac{1}{8}$ inches

PRACTICAL WORK

This is a group exercise.

A group of Year 8 pupils were asked to write down their heights and weights on sheets of paper which were then gathered in.

This is a list of *exactly* what was written down.

Height	Weight
141 cm	35 kg
138 cm	4 stones
1.8 m	6.26 stones
4 feet 5 inches	4 kg
52 feet	6 stones
5 foot 4	8 stones
1 metre 53	$7\frac{1}{2}$ stones
1 metre 41 cm	28.0 kg
141 cm	5 stones 4 pounds
4 feet 7 inches	32 kg

a This group of children used a mixture of units. Some of the entries are unbelievable.

Which are they?

Discuss what the reasons might be for these unbelievable entries.

b Find out how your group know their heights and weights; each of you write down your own height and weight on a piece of paper.

Use whatever unit you know them in, and do not write your name on it.

Collect in the pieces of paper and write out a list like the one above.

c What official forms do you know about that ask for height?

What unit is required?

d Write down your own height and weight in both metric and Imperial units.

INVESTIGATIONS

1 There are other Imperial units that have specialised uses; for example,

furlongs are used to measure distances in horse racing,

hands are used to measure the heights of horses,

fathoms are used to measure the depth of sea water.

a Use reference materials to find out the relationships between these units and the more common Imperial units of length.

b Find out as much as you can about other Imperial units of distance and weight.

c Nautical miles are used to measure distances at sea.

Find out what you can about nautical miles, including the rough equivalence of 1 nautical mile in miles and in kilometres.

2 Suppose that you want to measure the length of the table you are sitting at.

● You could measure it with a ruler.

● You could measure it with a tape measure marked in centimetres and millimetres.

● You could measure it with a precision instrument that will read lengths to tenths of a millimetre, or even hundredths of a millimetre.

● You could measure the length in several different places.

Write a short report, with reasons for your conclusions, on

a how accurately the length can be measured using each of the methods described above

b whether it is possible to find the length exactly

c whether you think it is possible to give any measurement exactly.

SUMMARISING AND COMPARING DATA

Aisha would like to have a personal cassette player and decides to save up to buy one. However she has no idea about the likely cost, so she needs some information. A detailed price list of all available models can be confusing and some sort of summary of the prices could be more useful. For instance, it might help Aisha if she is told that

- prices vary from about £8 to £120
- the most common cost is around £20
- a middle-of-the-range one costs about £30
- average price is £35.

EXERCISE 14A

In each of the following situations, discuss which would be more useful to you: to have detailed figures or some form of summary.

1 You are going on holiday and want to know what weather to expect.

2 You need to buy some soft drinks for an end-of-term party for your class.

3 You want to know if there are more people taller than you than there are shorter than you.

4 You want to know how much you would have to pay for a new multimedia computer.

**RANGE AND
CENTRAL
TENDENCY**

We often need to represent a set of numbers by one representative number which gives an indication of the middle of the set. It is also useful to have an indication of the spread of the numbers.

The first bullet point at the beginning of this chapter about the cost of personal cassette players gives an idea of the spread of prices.

We can give an indication of the spread of a list of values by giving their *range*.

> The range is the difference between the largest and smallest values.

The range of prices for the cassette players is £120 − £8 = £112.

253

Each of the last three bullet points at the start of this chapter about the cost of a personal cassette player illustrates one way of indicating a central price.

Figures which give an indication of the middle of a set are called *measures of central tendency*. There are three of these: the mode, the median and the mean.

The price given at the second bullet point is the mode because, as we saw in Book 7B, the *mode* is the value that occurs most often.
The information at the third bullet point tells us the *median* price.
As we saw in Book 7B, the *median* is the middle value when the values have been placed in order of size.
The last piece of information gives the mean price and we will now look at this in more detail.

MEAN VALUE

The most commonly used central figure is the arithmetic average or *mean*. This is the figure that results from sharing out the different values equally.

For example,

Jan

Raj

Sara

Jan, Raj and Sara searched for some pebbles to use for skimming on water.   Jan found 9 pebbles, Raj found 4 and Sara found 5 pebbles. They decided to put the pebbles into one pile and divide them up equally.

There are 18 pebbles in total to be shared among the three of them, so this gives 6 pebbles each; 6 is called the *mean* of 9, 4 and 5.

To find the mean we add up all the values and divide by the number of values.

$$\text{Mean} = \frac{\text{Sum of all the values}}{\text{Number of values}}$$

The mean is not always a whole number, or even a quantity that can exist.

For example, if Jan has 2 cats, Raj has 1 cat and Sara has 1 cat, then this gives 4 cats in total.
If they could be shared equally each of the three children would have $\frac{4}{3} = 1\frac{1}{3}$ cats, and this is clearly impossible.

But $1\frac{1}{3}$ *is* the mean of the *numbers* 2, 1 and 1.

In five tests, Alan received marks of 7, 8, 7, 9 and 4.

a What is his mean mark?

b What is the range of his marks?

a Total marks scored $= 7 + 8 + 7 + 9 + 4$

$$= 35$$

There are 5 marks.

Mean mark $= 35 \div 5$

$$= 7$$

b The highest mark is 9 and the lowest mark is 4.

The range of the marks is $9 - 4 = 5$

1 Six pupils got the following marks in a test: 5, 7, 8, 4, 8, 4.
What is the mean mark?

2 In three different shops, the price of a can of cola is 27 p, 25 p and 23 p.

   a What is the mean price?

   b What is the range of the prices?

3 Five people decided to pool their money. They put in the following amounts:

$$£10, £5, £6, £7 \text{ and } £12.$$

   a How much was in the pool?

   b If the five people had contributed equally to this total, how much would each have given?

   c What was the mean amount contributed to the pool?

4 The ages of the children in a swimming club are

$$9, 10, 8, 10, 11, 8, 12, 9, 10, 11, 10, 12$$

Find the mean age and the range of ages.

5 Find the mean and range of

   a 2, 4, 8, 4, 7, 1, 7, 6, 5, 6

   b 12, 15, 13, 10, 24, 16

   c 24, 35, 44, 28, 34

   d 1.2, 1.5, 1.3, 1.2

   e 12.4, 16.5, 27.9, 3.5, 26.1

6 These amounts of money were spent in the school canteen by each of the 30 pupils in Class 8S on Monday.

$$£2.10, \quad £1.75, \quad £1.44, \quad £0.56, \quad £2.30, \quad £1.50,$$
$$£0.45, \quad £1.25, \quad £1.75, \quad £0.30, \quad £1.20, \quad £0.36,$$
$$£1.27, \quad £1.20, \quad £1.84, \quad £1.44, \quad £1.60, \quad £0.25,$$
$$£2.50, \quad £1.75, \quad £1.66, \quad £1.50, \quad £1.75, \quad £0.45,$$
$$£1.20, \quad £1.25, \quad £0.45, \quad £0.36, \quad £2.30, \quad £1.75$$

a Find the mean amount spent.

b Find the range of the amounts spent.

7 The lengths, in centimetres correct to 1 decimal place, of twenty privet leaves taken from one bush are

$$2.5, \quad 1.4, \quad 1.6, \quad 2.3, \quad 3.2, \quad 2.8, \quad 2.6, \quad 2.9, \quad 1.7, \quad 3.1,$$
$$1.7, \quad 2.7, \quad 3.1, \quad 2.5, \quad 2.9, \quad 2.1, \quad 3.0, \quad 2.5, \quad 2.5, \quad 2.6$$

Find the mean length and the range of the lengths.

8 The numbers of chocolate-covered raisins in each of twenty 50 g boxes are

$$52, 49, 48, 49, 50, 45, 55, 53, 46, 44,$$
$$51, 50, 46, 50, 47, 47, 49, 48, 51, 49$$

a Find the mean number of sweets in one box.

b What is the range?

9 The buses that passed the school gate in four hours were counted. From this information it was found that the average number of buses per hour was 3.
How many buses were counted?

10 The 28 pupils in Class 8R took a maths test. The average mark was 15. Carlos was away on the day of the test and took it later. His mark was 24.

a Will Carlos's mark increase or decrease the average mark for the test?

b What is the total of the marks for all 27 children who took the test at the proper time?

c Find the new mean mark when Carlos's mark is added into the total.

FINDING THE MEAN FROM A FREQUENCY TABLE

This table shows the marks in a maths test.

Mark	Frequency
0	1
1	1
2	8
3	11
4	5
5	4
	Total: 30

From the figures in the table we can guess that the mean mark is about 3. To find the mean mark we first need to add up all the marks.

We could do this by listing each mark, but it is quicker to find the sum of the 0s, 1s, 2s, ... separately and then add these up. We can do this easily direct from the table.

For example, there are eight 2s, so the 2s add up to $8 \times 2 = 16$.

We add another column to the table so that we can keep track of what we are doing.

Mark	Frequency	Frequency × Mark
0	1	0
1	1	1
2	8	16
3	11	33
4	5	20
5	4	20
	Total: 30	Total: 90

Now we can see that there are 30 pupils and their marks add up to 90, so the mean mark is $90 \div 30 = 3$
(This agrees with our guess.)

EXERCISE 14C

1 The pupils in Class 8G gathered this information about themselves.

Number of children in each family	Frequency
1	8
2	12
3	4
4	2

a Guess the mean number of children per family.

b Find the mean number of children per family.

2 Josh tossed three coins several times and recorded the number of heads that showed at each toss. His results are shown in the table.

Number of heads obtained when three coins are tossed	Frequency
0	9
1	7
2	16
3	3

a Guess the value of the mean.

b Find the mean number of heads per toss.

3 Once every five minutes, Debbie counted the number of people queuing at a checkout and gave her results in this table.

Number of people queuing at a supermarket checkout	Frequency
0	4
1	6
2	5
3	2
4	2

a How many times did she count?

b What was the mean number of people queuing?

4 The children in Class 8P were asked to count the number of one pound coins that they had with them. The distribution of these coins is shown in the bar chart.

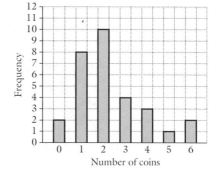

a How many children took part?

b What is the total value of the one pound coins?

c What is the range of the number of one pound coins?

d If the total sum of money represented here was shared out equally among the children, how much would each child have?

e What is the mean number of one pound coins per child?

5

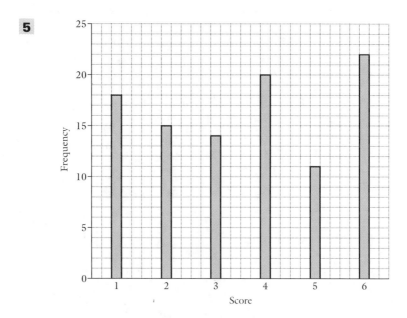

This bar chart illustrates the distribution of scores when an ordinary six-sided dice was thrown 100 times.

a Find the mean score.

b The dice was thrown 20 more times and the mean score from these 20 throws was 2.5. If these throws are combined with the first 100 throws and the mean score from all 120 throws is found, will this mean be larger or smaller than the mean score from the first 100 throws? Give a reason for your answer.

c Find the mean score of the 120 throws.

USING MEAN AND RANGE TO COMPARE TWO DISTRIBUTIONS

So far in this cricket season, Tom Batt has played five innings. His scores were 22, 53, 40, 35 and 25 so his mean score is 35. Reg Wicketaker has also completed five innings of 26, 90, 0, 52 and 17 so his mean score is 37.

There is little difference between the mean scores but
the range of Tom's scores is $53 - 22 = 31$
and the range of Reg's scores is $90 - 0 = 90$.

Comparing the two batsmen's scores indicates that, although Tom Batt has a slightly lower batting average, his scores are the more consistent of the two.

EXERCISE 14D

1 In the end-of-term tests, nine subjects were set and each one was marked out of 20. Sandra took eight subjects and her marks were

$$12, 16, 14, 9, 8, 20, 15 \text{ and } 10.$$

Karen took only five subjects and scored

$$10, 15, 11, 14 \text{ and } 10.$$

a On average, which girl did better?

b Which girl was more consistent in the standard she achieved?

2 These two bar charts illustrate the results of the same test given to Group 8A and Group 8B.

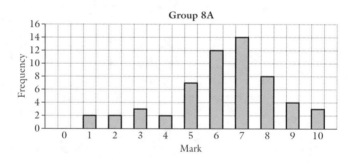

Group 8A

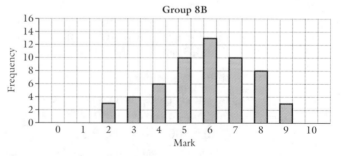

Group 8B

a Find the mean and range of each set of marks.

b Compare the two sets of marks.

3 Mr and Mrs Burton each made a batch of raisin cookies for a stall at the school fête. Out of curiosity they weighed each cookie and found that Mr Burton's weighed

20, 25, 16, 21, 24, 26, 13, 17, 22 and 16 grams.

Mrs Burton's weighed

22, 21, 18, 17, 20, 20, 21, 19, 20 and 22 grams.

Compare the means and ranges of the weights of the two batches and comment on them.

4 These two bar charts illustrate the distribution of the number of books borrowed from the school library by each pupil in Group 8A and by each pupil in Group 8B for the month of November.

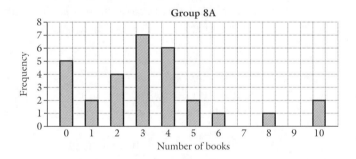

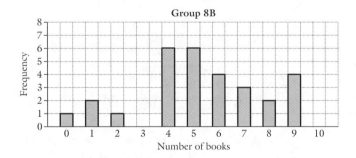

a Find the mean and range of each set of numbers of books borrowed.

b Compare the mean and range of each distribution.

c From the information you now have, is it reasonable to say that the pupils in Group 8B used the library more than the pupils in Group 8A?

WHICH MEASURE OF CENTRAL TENDENCY?

This chapter started with Aisha wanting to know about prices of personal cassette players. The central figures given are

- The average price is £35. This is the mean price.
- A middle range personal cassette player costs about £30. This is the median price.
- The most common cost is around £20. This is the modal price.

Now consider which summary is most useful to start with: the mean, the median or the mode?

The mean price involves adding up all the prices so its value takes account of the very expensive machines, and she would probably not be interested in these.

The median price shows that she has a choice of half the models available for a cost of £30 or less, so this is quite useful.

The modal price shows that there is more than one model costing about £20 so there is a choice of models at this price. It doesn't tell us how many models are priced at about £20; it could be only two or three, so this information is of limited use.

EXERCISE 14E

Discuss with the class the most useful way of summarising the information for the purpose given in each question.

1 You have a list of the heights of 100 twelve-year-old girls. You want to know if you are taller or shorter than most of these girls.

2 You have a list giving the numbers sold over the last term of each item stocked by the school tuck shop.

   a You need to buy more stock and do not want to run out of the most popular item.

   b You have to buy the same quantity of each item.

3 You have a list giving the maximum and minimum temperature in Cairo each day in February for the last five years. You need to decide what clothes to take with you for a 10-day trip to Cairo in February.

4 You have a list of all models of inkjet printers that will print colour on A4 paper. You want an idea of the price you would have to pay for one.

5 Which form of summary would be most useful for each situation given in **Exercise 14A**? Give a reason for your choice.

MIXED EXERCISE

EXERCISE 14F

1 In seven rounds of golf, a golfer returns scores of:

$$72, 87, 73, 72, 86, 72 \text{ and } 77$$

Find the mean, mode and median of these scores.

2 The heights (correct to the nearest centimetre) of a group of boys are

$$159, 155, 153, 154, 157, 162, 152, 160, 161, 157$$

Find   **a** their mean height   **c** their median height

       b their modal height   **d** the range of the heights.

3 The marks, out of 100, in a geography test for the members of a class were:

$$64, 50, 35, 85, 52, 47, 72, 31, 74,$$
$$49, 36, 44, 54, 48, 32, 52, 53, 48,$$
$$71, 52, 56, 49, 81, 45, 52, 80, 46$$

Find   **a** the mean mark   **c** the median mark

       b the modal mark   **d** the range of the marks.

4 The table shows how many pupils in a form were absent for various numbers of sessions during a certain school week.

Number of sessions absent	0	1	2	3	4	5	6	7	8	9	10
Frequency	20	2	4	0	2	0	1	2	0	0	1

Find   **a** the mode   **b** the median   **c** the mean.

5 The mean number of words in each sentence on the first page of *The Machine-Gunners* is 10 and the lengths of sentences range from one word to 25 words. For the first page of *Oliver Twist*, the mean length of the sentences is 68 words and they range from 34 words to 98 words.

Use this information to compare the sentences in each book.

6 The table shows the marks obtained by a group of children in a quiz.

Mark	1	2	3	4	5	6	7	8	9	10
Frequency	5	10	14	10	9	8	8	6	6	9

a How many children took part in the quiz?

b Find the mean, median and modal marks.

Which of the following statements are true?

c More than half the children got a score of 4 or more.

d A score of 3 is the most likely score.

e Jane got a score less than the mean, so more than half the group did better than Jane.

7 These frequency tables show the number of 20 p coins that ten children from two different classes had with them on one day.

Class 8T		Class 8R	
Number of 20 p coins	Frequency	Number of 20 p coins	Frequency
0	2	0	0
1	5	1	4
2	0	2	3
3	2	3	2
4	0	4	0
5	0	5	0
6	0	6	1

a Find the mean number of coins that each group had with them.

b Do you think that the mean is a good representative for each distribution?

c Find the median and the mode of each distribution.

d Which measure of central tendency would you use if you wanted to compare the two distributions? Explain your choice.

**PRACTICAL
WORK**

1 This information is from an Argos catalogue. It gives details of prices of personal cassette players.

a What is the cheapest player shown here?

b What is the range of prices? **c** Is there a mode?

d Find the median price and the mean price.

e Compare the information given here with the information at the start of this chapter.

2 If you throw a fair dice 60 times, then *in theory* you should get each score 10 times, i.e. a frequency table would look like this.

Score	1	2	3	4	5	6
Frequency	10	10	10	10	10	10

a Find the mean score of this theoretical distribution.

b If you throw a dice 60 times, you will be very unlikely indeed to get equal numbers of each score. But, if your dice is unbiased, and if you throw it fairly, you should get a mean score near to the theoretical mean. Throw a dice 60 times, record your results and find your mean score.

How does your mean compare with the theoretical mean? Can you say whether your dice is likely to be unbiased?

c Now repeat part **b** with an obviously biased dice. (You can make a biased dice by sticking a small piece of Blu-Tack on one face.)

AREAS AND VOLUMES

AREA

The amount of surface covered by a shape is called its *area*.

The usual way of measuring area is to find the number of squares that give the same amount of surface. So that other people understand what we mean, we use standard sized squares to describe areas.

The area covered by a square with sides 1 cm long is a standard unit of area, called one square centimetre. We write one square centimetre as 1 cm^2.

1 cm²

Other standard units of area are squares with sides 1 mm, 1 m, 1 km. They are called 1 mm^2, 1 m^2, 1 km^2.

To find an area we can place a grid of standard sized squares over the shape and count the number of squares inside. This is a good method for finding an approximation for the area of an irregular shape, such as a pond.

Consider this problem

Tom wants to cover a floor with a pattern made from these tiles.

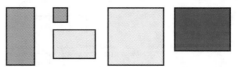

He knows the length and width of each tile in millimetres, but as part of his planning, he needs to find the area covered by each tile and also the area of his floor.

Tom could cover each tile with a centimetre grid and count the squares, but this would take a long time and would not give a very accurate answer. It would, in theory, be possible to use the same method to find the area of the floor, but it is not practical because it would take far too long.

- Rectangles and squares are common shapes and it is clear that we need a quick way to find their areas.

- A metre grid could be used to find the area of the floor, but we then have to convert the area measured in square metres to square centimetres in order to compare the areas of the tiles with the area they have to cover.

EXERCISE 15A

Discuss what you need to be able to do to solve these problems.

1 A manufacturer makes rectangular table mats measuring 20 cm by 30 cm.
How many square metres of material are needed to make 200 000 of these mats?

2 Frank wants to work out how much paint to buy to paint the walls of his house.

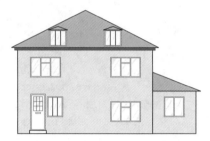

3 A printer wants to calculate the quantity of paper to buy in order to print 2500 books, each with 200 pages measuring 250 mm by 360 mm.

AREA OF A SQUARE

The discussion shows that we need a simple method for finding the areas of squares and rectangles.

A square is the simplest figure whose area can be found.

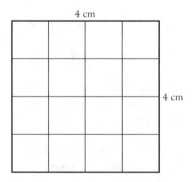

4 cm

4 cm

For this square, whose side is 4 cm long, it is easy to see that 4 rows of 4 squares, each of side 1 cm, will cover the square,

i.e. the area of a square of side 4 cm is $4 \times 4 \, \text{cm}^2 = 16 \, \text{cm}^2$

In general,

$$\text{area of a square} = (\text{length of side})^2$$

**AREA OF A
RECTANGLE**

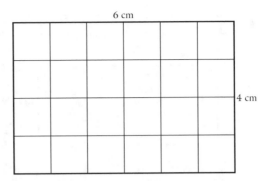

A rectangle measuring 6 cm by 4 cm is covered by 4 rows each containing 6 squares of side 1 cm,

i.e.   the area of the rectangle $= 6 \times 4 \, \text{cm}^2$

$$= 24 \, \text{cm}^2$$

A similar result can then be found for a rectangle of any size; for example, a rectangle of length 4 cm and breadth $2\frac{1}{2}$ cm has an area covered by $2\frac{1}{2}$ rows of 4 cm^2

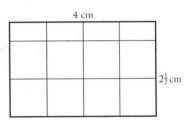

$$= 4 \times 2\frac{1}{2} \, \text{cm}^2$$

$$= 10 \, \text{cm}^2$$

In general, for any rectangle

$$\text{area} = \text{length} \times \text{breadth}$$

EXERCISE 15B

Find the area of each square, clearly stating the units involved.

1 A square of side 2 cm

3 A square of side 5 cm

2 A square of side 8 cm

4 A square of side 3 inches

Find the area of a square of side 2.3 cm

Area $= ($ length of side $)^2$

$\quad\quad = (2.3)^2 \, \text{cm}^2$

$\quad\quad = 5.29 \, \text{cm}^2$

PRESS **2** **.** **3** **x^2** **=**

Find the area of each square, clearly stating the units involved.

5 A square of side 1.5 cm

7 A square of side 0.7 m

6 A square of side 0.5 m

8 A square of side 2.5 mm

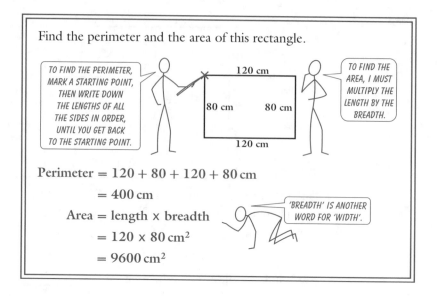

Find the perimeter and the area of this rectangle.

TO FIND THE PERIMETER, MARK A STARTING POINT, THEN WRITE DOWN THE LENGTHS OF ALL THE SIDES IN ORDER, UNTIL YOU GET BACK TO THE STARTING POINT.

120 cm

TO FIND THE AREA, I MUST MULTIPLY THE LENGTH BY THE BREADTH.

80 cm   80 cm

120 cm

Perimeter = 120 + 80 + 120 + 80 cm

$\qquad$ = 400 cm

Area = length × breadth

'BREADTH' IS ANOTHER WORD FOR 'WIDTH'.

$\qquad$ = 120 × 80 cm^2

$\qquad$ = 9600 cm^2

Find the perimeter and area of each rectangle, clearly stating the units involved.

9 A rectangle measuring 5 cm by 6 cm

10 A rectangle measuring 3 m by 9 m

11 A rectangle measuring 6 cm by 8 cm

12 A rectangle measuring 5 mm by 12 mm

13 A rectangle measuring 1.8 mm by 2.2 mm

14 A rectangle measuring 35 km by 42 km

15 A rectangle measuring 1.5 m by 1.9 m

16 A rectangle measuring 7.9 inches by 5.5 inches.

For each shape in questions **17–26** find **a** the perimeter **b** the area.

17

30 cm

18 cm

18

4.5 m

3.5 m

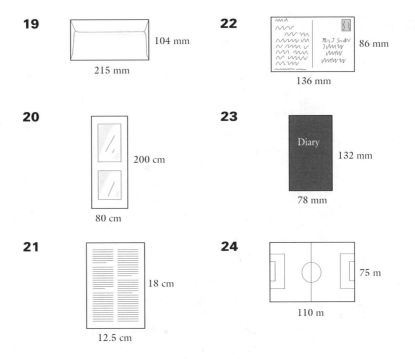

19 104 mm, 215 mm

20 200 cm, 80 cm

21 18 cm, 12.5 cm

22 Mrs J Smith, 86 mm, 136 mm

23 Diary, 132 mm, 78 mm

24 75 m, 110 m

25 A paving slab measuring 40 cm by 40 cm.

26 A rectangular table mat measuring 24 cm by 15 cm.

27 Find the area of

   a a soccer field measuring 110 m by 85 m

   b a rugby pitch measuring 100 m by 70 m

   c a tennis court measuring 26 m by 12 m.

28 A roll of wallpaper is 10 m long and 0.5 m wide.

   a Find the area, in square metres, of the wallpaper in the roll.

   b Is there enough paper in this roll to paper a wall measuring 2.7 m by 1.9 m? Give reasons for your answer.

29 The playing surface of a standard snooker table is a rectangle measuring 366 cm by 183 cm.

   a How far is it around the edge of the playing surface. Give your answer   **i** in cm   **ii** in metres.

   b Find, correct to 3 significant figures, the area of the playing surface   **i** in square centimetres   **ii** in square metres.

**COMPOUND
FIGURES**

It is often possible to find the area of a figure by dividing it into two or
more rectangles.

EXERCISE 15C

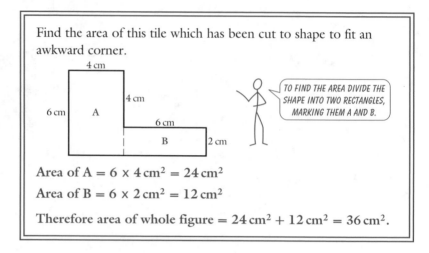

Find the area of this tile which has been cut to shape to fit an
awkward corner.

TO FIND THE AREA DIVIDE THE
SHAPE INTO TWO RECTANGLES,
MARKING THEM A AND B.

Area of A = 6 × 4 cm² = 24 cm²

Area of B = 6 × 2 cm² = 12 cm²

Therefore area of whole figure = 24 cm² + 12 cm² = 36 cm².

Find the areas of the following figures by dividing them into rectangles.
Make your own freehand drawing of each diagram.

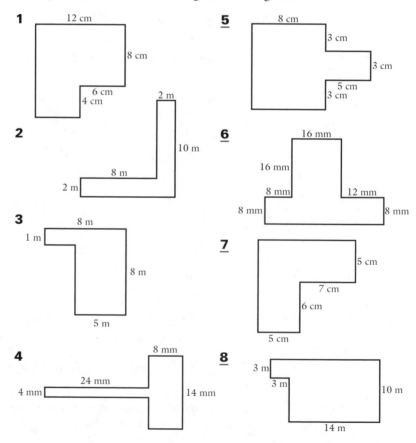

9 The diagram shows the pieces in a puzzle. Find the area of each piece.

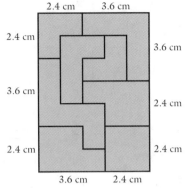

Find the area of the complete puzzle and use this to check your answers.

Find the area of this metal plate.

To find the area of this shape we need to cut away two rectangles.

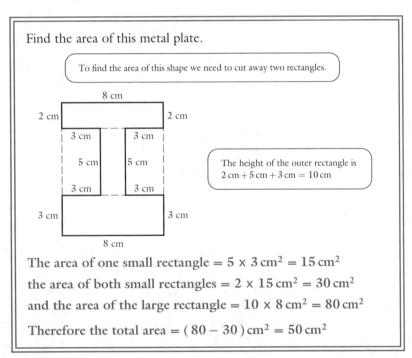

The height of the outer rectangle is $2\,cm + 5\,cm + 3\,cm = 10\,cm$

The area of one small rectangle = $5 \times 3\,cm^2 = 15\,cm^2$

the area of both small rectangles = $2 \times 15\,cm^2 = 30\,cm^2$

and the area of the large rectangle = $10 \times 8\,cm^2 = 80\,cm^2$

Therefore the total area = $(80 - 30)\,cm^2 = 50\,cm^2$

The following shapes are metal plates used to strengthen joints in wooden furniture. Find the area of each shape.

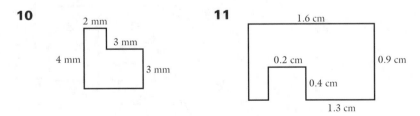

10

11

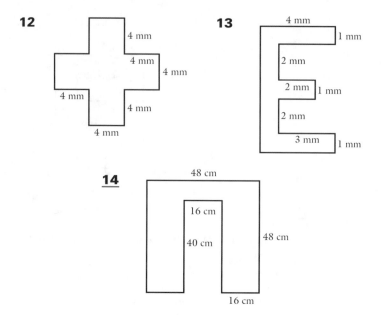

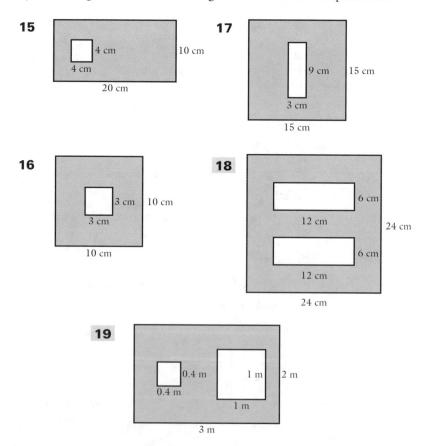

Find the shaded area of each gasket. *Hint*: you will find it easiest to do these by subtracting the area of the missing sections from the complete area.

The following table gives some of the measurements of various rectangles. Fill in the values that are missing.

	Length	Breadth	Perimeter	Area
20	4 cm		12 cm	
21	5 cm		14 cm	
22		3 m	16 m	
23		6 mm	30 mm	
24	6 cm			30 cm^2
25		10 m		120 m^2
26		4 km		36 km^2
27		7 mm		63 mm^2
28		5 cm	60 cm	
29	80 cm			1680 cm^2

CHANGING UNITS OF AREA

A square of side 1 cm may be divided into 100 squares of side 1 mm,

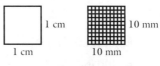

1 cm   10 mm

1 cm   10 mm

i.e.
$$1 \text{ cm}^2 = 100 \text{ mm}^2$$

Similarly, since 1 m = 100 cm,
    1 square metre = 100 × 100 square centimetres,

i.e.
$$1 \text{ m}^2 = 10\,000 \text{ cm}^2$$

and, as 1 km = 1000 m,
1 square kilometre = 1000 × 1000 square metres,

i.e.
$$1 \text{ km}^2 = 1\,000\,000 \text{ m}^2$$

When we convert from a unit of area that is large to a unit of area that is smaller, we must remember that the *number* of units will be bigger so we multiply,

e.g. $2\,\text{km}^2 = 2 \times 1\,000\,000\,\text{m}^2$
$\qquad\qquad = 2\,000\,000\,\text{m}^2$

but if we convert from a unit of area that is small into a larger unit of area, the number of units will be smaller so we divide,

e.g. $500\,\text{mm}^2 = 500 \div 100\,\text{cm}^2$
$\qquad\qquad\quad = 5\,\text{cm}^2$

EXERCISE 15D

Express $5.6\,\text{m}^2$ in cm^2.

As $1\,\text{m}^2 = 10\,000\,\text{cm}^2$,

$5.6\,\text{m}^2 = 5 \times 10\,000\,\text{cm}^2$

$\qquad\quad = 56\,000\,\text{cm}^2$

CHANGING LARGE UNITS TO SMALL UNITS MEANS I MUST MULTIPLY.

1 Express in cm^2

   a $3\,\text{m}^2$ **b** $12\,\text{m}^2$ **c** $7.5\,\text{m}^2$ **d** $82\,\text{m}^2$ **e** $0.5\,\text{m}^2$

2 Express in mm^2

   a $14\,\text{cm}^2$ **b** $3\,\text{cm}^2$ **c** $7.5\,\text{cm}^2$ **d** $26\,\text{cm}^2$ **e** $3.2\,\text{cm}^2$

3 Express $0.056\,\text{m}^2$ in cm^2.

4 Express in cm^2

   a $400\,\text{mm}^2$ **c** $50\,\text{mm}^2$ **e** $734\,\text{mm}^2$

   b $2500\,\text{mm}^2$ **d** $25\,\text{mm}^2$ **f** $1220\,\text{mm}^2$

5 Express in m^2

   a $5500\,\text{cm}^2$ **c** $760\,\text{cm}^2$ **e** $29\,700\,\text{cm}^2$

   b $140\,000\,\text{cm}^2$ **d** $18\,600\,\text{cm}^2$ **f** $192\,000\,\text{cm}^2$

6 Express in km^2

   a $7\,500\,000\,\text{m}^2$ **c** $50\,000\,\text{m}^2$ **e** $176\,\text{m}^2$

   b $430\,000\,\text{m}^2$ **d** $245\,000\,\text{m}^2$ **f** $750\,000\,\text{m}^2$

7 Use 5 miles $\approx 8\,\text{km}$ to find an approximate conversion from square miles to square kilometres.

In many problems involving finding the area of a rectangle, the length and breadth are given in different units. When this is the case we must change the units so that all the measurements are in the same units.

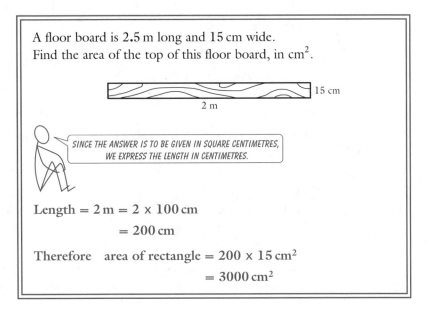

A floor board is **2.5 m** long and **15 cm** wide.
Find the area of the top of this floor board, in cm^2.

15 cm

2 m

SINCE THE ANSWER IS TO BE GIVEN IN SQUARE CENTIMETRES, WE EXPRESS THE LENGTH IN CENTIMETRES.

Length = 2 m = 2 × 100 cm
= 200 cm

Therefore area of rectangle = 200 × 15 cm²
= 3000 cm²

Find the area of each of the following rectangles, giving your answer in the unit in brackets.

	Length	Breadth	
8	10 m	50 cm	(cm^2)
9	6 cm	30 mm	(mm^2)
10	50 m	35 cm	(cm^2)
11	140 cm	1 m	(cm^2)
12	400 cm	200 cm	(m^2)
13	3 m	$\frac{1}{2}$ m	(cm^2)
14	1.2 cm	5 mm	(mm^2)
15	0.4 km	0.05 km	(m^2)
16	0.08 km	60 m	(m^2)

17 A roll of wallpaper is 12 m long and 55 cm wide. Find its area in square metres.

18 A plastic draft excluder is 3 m long and 15 cm wide. Find its area in square centimetres.

19 A school hall measuring 20 m by 15 m is to be covered with square floor tiles of side 50 cm.
How many tiles are required?

20 A rectangular carpet measures 4 m by 3 m.
Find its area.
What is the cost of cleaning this carpet at 75 p per square metre?

21 How many squares of side 50 cm may be cut from a roll of linen 25 m long and 1 m wide?

22 How many square concrete paving slabs, each of side 0.5 m, are required to pave a rectangular yard measuring 9 m by 6 m?

23 A patio that is 9 m square is to be covered with 450 mm square paving stones and edged, all the way round, with 250 mm long bricks.
How many paving stones are needed?
What extra information do you need in order to find the number of bricks needed?

24 A rectangular field measuring 40 m by 25 m is to be sown with grass seed so that 90 grams of seed is used to cover each square metre.
Each box of seeds holds 5 kg.
How many boxes are needed?

25 A rectangular lawn measuring 3 m by 4 m has a 1 m wide path round the outside edge.
Find the area of this path.

26 Diana is tiling a wall with square tiles of two different sizes. The smaller tile has sides 64 mm long. Four of these smaller tiles cover the same area as one larger tile. What is the length of a side of a larger tile?

VOLUME

The volume of a solid is the amount of space it occupies. As is the case with area, we need a standard unit for measuring volume. The most convenient unit is a cube.

A cube with a side of 1 cm has a volume of one cubic centimetre which is written $1\,cm^3$.

Similarly a cube with a side of 1 mm has a volume of $1\,mm^3$ and a cube with a side of 1 m has a volume of $1\,m^3$.

VOLUME OF A CUBOID

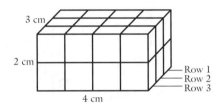

The diagram shows a cuboid measuring 4 cm by 3 cm by 2 cm.
To cover the area on which the block stands we need three rows of standard 1 cm cubes with four cubes in each row, i.e. 12 cubes.
A second layer of 12 cubes is needed to give the volume shown, so the volume of the block is 24 standard 1 cm cubes.

Therefore the volume of the solid is $24\,cm^3$.

This is also given when we calculate length $\times$ breadth $\times$ height,

i.e.   the volume of the block $= 4 \times 3 \times 2\,cm^3$

or   the volume of the cuboid $=$ length $\times$ breadth $\times$ height

EXERCISE 15E

1 Which unit would you use to give the volume of

a this book

b the room you are in

c one vitamin pill

d a lorry load of rubble

e a packet of cornflakes

f a 2 p coin

g a concrete building block?

Find the volume of a cuboid measuring 12 cm by 10 cm by 5 cm.

$$\text{Volume of cuboid} = \text{length} \times \text{breadth} \times \text{height}$$
$$= 12 \times 10 \times 5 \ \text{cm}^3$$

i.e. $\qquad\qquad\qquad \text{Volume} = 600 \ \text{cm}^3$

Find the volume of each of the following cuboids.

	Length	Breadth	Height
2	4 cm	4 cm	3 cm
3	20 mm	10 mm	8 mm
4	6.1 m	4 m	1.3 m
5	3.5 cm	2.5 cm	1.2 cm
6	4 m	3 m	2 m
7	8 m	5 m	4 m
8	8 cm	3 cm	$\frac{1}{2}$ cm
9	12 cm	1.2 cm	0.5 cm
10	4.5 m	1.2 m	0.8 m

When the lengths of the edges of a cuboid are given in different units, we must change some of them so that all measurements are given in the same unit.

A rectangular box is 25 cm long, 15 mm wide and 12 mm deep. Find the volume of the box in cubic centimetres.

25 cm   12 mm   15 mm

Width = $15 \div 10$ cm
$\qquad = 1.5$ cm

Depth = $12 \div 10$ cm
$\qquad = 1.2$ cm

Volume = length × breadth × depth
$\qquad = 25 \times 1.5 \times 1.2 \ \text{cm}^3$
$\qquad = 45 \ \text{cm}^3$

11 A rectangular block of concrete is 1 m long, 20 cm wide and 25 cm deep. Find the volume of the block in cubic centimetres.

12 A rectangular rod of aluminium measures 25 cm by 15 mm by 5 mm. Find its volume in cubic millimetres.

13 The shape of an outdoor aviary is a cuboid with measurements 2 m by 90 cm by 90 cm.
Find the volume of the aviary giving your answer in the most appropriate unit.

Find the volume of a cube with edge 6 cm.

> The edges of a cube are all the same length. So 'length × breadth × height' = (length of edge)^3

$$\text{Volume of cube} = (\text{ length of edge })^3$$
$$= 6^3$$
i.e. $$\text{Volume} = 216 \text{ cm}^3$$

Find the volume of a cube with the given side.

14 4 cm

15 5 cm

16 2 m

17 $\frac{1}{2}$ cm

18 2.5 cm

19 3 km

20 10 cm

21 $\frac{1}{4}$ m

22 3.4 m

23 A cuboid measures 4 cm by 8 cm by 4 cm. The same space is to be filled with smaller cubes.
How many cubes are needed if their sides are

a 1 cm **b** 2 cm **c** 4 cm?

24 Find the volume of air in a room measuring 4 m by 5 m which is 3 m high.

25 Find the volume, in cm^3, of a concrete block measuring 36 cm by 18 cm by 12 cm.

26 Find the volume of a school hall which is 30 m long and 24 m wide if the ceiling is 9 m high.

27 A classroom is 10 m long, 8 m wide and 3 m high. Find the largest number of pupils it should be used for if each pupil requires 5 m^3 of air space?

28 A kitchen worktop is 2 metres long, 60 cm deep and its underside is 90 cm above the floor. What is the volume of the space below the worktop?

29 An electric light bulb is sold in a box measuring 10 cm by 6 cm by 6 cm. If the shopkeeper receives them in a carton measuring 50 cm by 30 cm by 30 cm, how many bulbs would be packed in a carton?

30 How many rectangular packets, measuring 8 cm by 6 cm by 4 cm, can be packed in a rectangular cardboard box measuring 30 cm by 24 cm by 16 cm?

31 Rectangular blocks of stone measure 30 cm by 20 cm by 35 mm. How many of these blocks can be stored, in layers each 35 mm thick, in a cube-shaped crate whose edge is 1 metre?

32

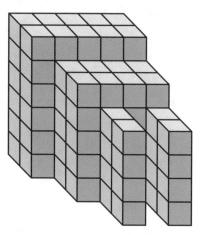

What is the least number of additional cubes that are needed to rearrange this loose stack of cubes into a single cube?

CHANGING UNITS OF VOLUME Consider a cube of side 1 cm. If each edge is divided into 10 mm the cube can be divided into 10 layers, each layer with 10×10 cubes of side 1 mm,

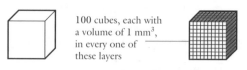

100 cubes, each with a volume of 1 mm³, in every one of these layers

i.e.
$$1 \text{ cm}^3 = 10 \times 10 \times 10 \text{ mm}^3$$
$$= 1000 \text{ mm}^3$$

Similarly, since $1\,\text{m} = 100\,\text{cm}$

$$1 \text{ cubic metre} = 100 \times 100 \times 100 \text{ cm}^3$$

i.e. $$= 1\,000\,000 \text{ cm}^3$$

EXERCISE 15F

Express $2.4\,\text{m}^3$ in cm^3.

Since $1\,\text{m}^3 = 100 \times 100 \times 100 \text{ cm}^3$

$2.4\,\text{m}^3 = 2.4 \times 100 \times 100 \times 100 \text{ cm}^3$

$= 2\,400\,000 \text{ cm}^3$

> We are changing to a smaller unit so we multiply.

Express in mm^3

1 $8\,\text{cm}^3$ **3** $6.2\,\text{cm}^3$ **5** $0.0092\,\text{m}^3$

2 $14\,\text{cm}^3$ **4** $0.43\,\text{cm}^3$ **6** $0.0004\,\text{cm}^3$

Express in cm^3

7 $3\,\text{m}^3$ **9** $0.42\,\text{m}^3$ **11** $22\,\text{mm}^3$

8 $2.5\,\text{m}^3$ **10** $0.0063\,\text{m}^3$ **12** $731\,\text{mm}^3$

CAPACITY

The capacity of a container is the volume of liquid that it can hold.

The most common unit of capacity in the metric system is the litre, where

$$1000 \text{ cm}^3 = 1 \text{ litre}$$

i.e. a litre is the volume of a cube of side $10\,\text{cm}$.

and $$1000 \text{ litres} = 1\,\text{m}^3$$

When the amount of liquid is small, such as a teaspoonful of water, the millilitre (ml) is used. A millilitre is a thousandth part of a litre, i.e.

$$1000 \text{ ml} = 1 \text{ litre} \quad \text{or} \quad 1 \text{ ml} = 1 \text{ cm}^3$$

EXERCISE 15G

Express 5.6 litres in cm^3.

$$1 \text{ litre} = 1000 \text{ cm}^3$$
$$5.6 \text{ litres} = 5.6 \times 1000 \text{ cm}^3$$
$$= 5600 \text{ cm}^3$$

Express in cm^3

1 2.5 litres   **3** 0.54 litres   **5** 35 litres

2 1.76 litres   **4** 0.0075 litres   **6** 0.028 litres

Express in litres

7 7000 cm^3 **9** 24 000 cm^3 **11** 12 m^3

8 4000 cm^3 **10** 5 m^3 **12** 4.6 cm^3

Find the capacity, in litres, of a water tank whose internal measurements are 2 m by 60 cm by 20 cm.

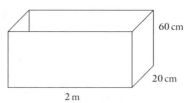

WE NEED TO FIND THE VOLUME OF THE TANK IN CUBIC CENTIMETRES. TO DO THIS, ALL THE MEASUREMENTS MUST BE IN CENTIMETRES SO FIRST CONVERT THE 2 m INTO CENTIMETRES.

Length of cuboid = 2 m = 2 × 100 cm = 200 cm

Volume of cuboid = length × breadth × height
$$= 200 \times 20 \times 60 \text{ cm}^3$$
$$= 240\,000 \text{ cm}^3$$

1000 cm^3 = 1 litre, so to convert cubic centimetres to litres, we divide by 1000.

Capacity of tank = 240 000 ÷ 1000 litres
$$= 240 \text{ litres.}$$

13 Find the capacity, in litres, of these cuboids.

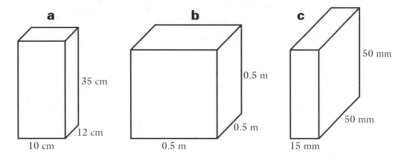

a

35 cm

12 cm

10 cm

b

0.5 m

0.5 m

0.5 m

c

50 mm

50 mm

15 mm

14 A metal block, measuring 25 cm by 10 cm by 10 cm is melted. How many litres of liquid metal are there?

15 A rectangular water storage tank is 3 m long, 2 m wide and 1 m deep. How many litres of water will it hold?

16 How many cubic metres of water are required to fill a rectangular swimming bath 15 m long and 10 m wide which is 2 m deep throughout? How many litres is this?

17 A rectangular fish tank is 1.5 metres long, 34 cm deep and 20 cm high. How many litres of water will it hold?

18 A rectangular carton of concentrated orange juice measures 5 cm by 10 cm by 4 cm. To make one glass of juice, 5 ml of this concentrate are needed. How many glasses of juice can be made from one full carton?

19 How many lead cubes, of side 2 cm, can be cast from 5 litres of liquid lead?

20

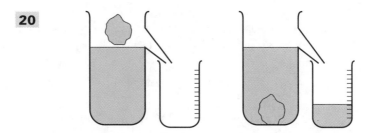

When a lump of metal has been lowered into the water, the reading on the small container is 250 ml. Find the volume of the lump in cubic centimetres.

IMPERIAL UNITS OF CAPACITY

Imperial units of capacity are still in use and the common ones are the pint and the gallon.

Milk is still sold in bottles holding 1 pint. Many cars give the capacity of the fuel tank in gallons. The relationship between pints and gallons is

1 gallon = 8 pints

Approximate conversions between metric and Imperial units of capacity can be made using

1 litre ≈ 1.75 pints   and   1 gallon ≈ 4.5 litres

EXERCISE 15H

1 Give, roughly, the number of pints equivalent to

   a 20 litres   **b** 12 litres   **c** 1.5 litres

2 Roughly, how many gallons is

   a 50 litres   **b** 30 litres   **c** 25 litres?

3 Give the approximate number of litres equivalent to

   a 4 pints   **b** $2\frac{1}{2}$ gallons   **c** 10 gallons

4 Arrange these containers in order of capacity, with the largest first.

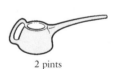

5 gallons   2 litres   2.5 gallons   4 pints   750 ml   2 pints

5 Liz fills her car up with petrol. The reading on the pump is 38 litres. How many gallons is this?

6 A recipe needs 100 ml of cream. Will a half-pint carton be enough?

7 A rectangular fish tank measures 300 mm by 250 mm by 500 mm. Roughly, how many gallons of water will it hold when full?

8 Petrol costs 56 p a litre. How much, roughly, will it cost to fill a tank whose capacity is 11.5 gallons?

MIXED EXERCISE

EXERCISE 15I

1 Express $3.2 \, \text{m}^3$ in **a** cm^3 **b** mm^3

2 Express $45 \, \text{cm}^2$ in **a** m^2 **b** mm^2

3 Express $3500 \, \text{cm}^3$ in litres.

4 Find the area of a square of side $2.5 \, \text{m}$.

5 Find the volume of a cube of side $4 \, \text{cm}$.

6 Find the volume of a cuboid measuring $10 \, \text{cm}$ by $5 \, \text{cm}$ by $6 \, \text{cm}$.

7 Find the area, in square centimetres, of a rectangle measuring $1.2 \, \text{m}$ by $45 \, \text{cm}$.

8 Find the volume, in cm^3, of a cuboid measuring $2 \, \text{m}$ by $25 \, \text{cm}$ by $10 \, \text{cm}$.

9 Find, roughly, the capacity in pints of a carton designed to hold 1.5 litres.

10 Which holds more water, a rectangular carton measuring $20 \, \text{cm}$ by $20 \, \text{cm}$ by $10 \, \text{cm}$ or a bottle whose capacity is $750 \, \text{ml}$?

11 Which holds more liquid, a plastic carton whose capacity is 1 pint or a plastic bottle whose capacity is $500 \, \text{ml}$?

12 These are silver pendants, drawn on a $5 \, \text{mm}$ grid. Find the perimeter and area of each.

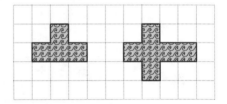

13 Find the volume of each of these solids. They are drawn on $1 \, \text{cm}$ isometric grid which are shown here reduced in size.

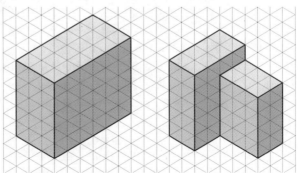

PUZZLE

The cube shown is made from 8 smaller white cubes. The outside of this cube is painted red. Is it possible to put the small cubes together to form a white cube?

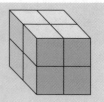

INVESTIGATION

This investigation develops the investigation given in the chapter on solids in Book 7B. A rectangular sheet of steel is used to make an open rectangular box, by removing the four squares at the corners and folding up the sides. The four vertical edges are then sealed.

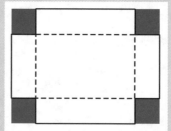

a Copy and complete the following table which gives the measurements and capacity of the box when squares of different sizes are removed from the corners.

Length of side of square (cm)	Measurement of base (cm)	Capacity of box (cm^3)
0.5	13 × 19	0.5 × 13 × 19 = 123.5
1	12 × 18	1 × 12 × 18 = 216
1.5		
2		
2.5		
3		

b What is the last number you entered in the first column of the table? Explain why you stopped there.

c What is the size of the square that should be removed to give the largest capacity recorded in the table?

d Investigate whether there is another number, not entered in the table, that gives a larger capacity than any value found so far.

Summary 4

Positive and negative numbers are collectively known as directed numbers. They can be represented on a number line.

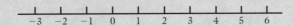

The rules for adding and subtracting directed numbers are illustrated by the following examples.

$$+(+2) = 2 \qquad +(-2) = -2$$
$$-(+2) = -2 \qquad -(-2) = 2$$

When two numbers of the same sign are multiplied together, the result is positive.
When two numbers of different signs are multiplied together, the result is negative.
For example, $(+2) \times (+3) = +6$ and $(-2) \times (-3) = +6$
$$(+2) \times (-3) = -6 \quad \text{and} \quad (-2) \times (+3) = -6$$

The same rules apply to division, for example,

$$(+8) \div (+2) = +4 \quad \text{and} \quad (-8) \div (-2) = +4$$
$$(+8) \div (-2) = -4 \quad \text{and} \quad (-8) \div (+2) = -4$$

FORMULAS

A formula is a general rule for finding one quantity in terms of other quantities,
e.g. the formula for finding the area of a rectangle is given by

$$\text{Area} = \text{length} \times \text{breadth}$$

When letters are used for unknown numbers, the formula can be written more concisely,
i.e. the area, A cm^2, of a rectangle measuring l cm by b cm, is given by the formula

$$A = l \times b$$

Multiplication signs between letters, or between a number and a letter can be left out,
e.g. $2p$ means $2 \times p$ and $l \times b$ can be written lb.

Divisions are usually written as fractions,
e.g. $2 \div s$ is written as $\dfrac{2}{s}$

IMPERIAL UNITS

Imperial units of length in common use are the mile, the yard, the foot and the inch, where

$$1 \text{ mile} = 1760 \text{ yards}, \quad 1 \text{ yard} = 3 \text{ feet}, \quad 1 \text{ foot} = 12 \text{ inches}$$

Imperial units of mass still in common use are the ton, the hundredweight (cwt), the stone (st), the pound and the ounce, where

$$1 \text{ ton} = 2240 \text{ lb}, \quad 1 \text{ ton} = 20 \text{ cwt}, \quad 1 \text{ st} = 14 \text{ lb}, \quad 1 \text{ lb} = 16 \text{ ounces}$$

For a rough conversion between metric and Imperial units, use

$$1 \text{ mile} \approx \tfrac{1}{2} \text{ km}, \quad 1 \text{ yard} \approx 1 \text{ m}, \quad 1 \text{ kg} \approx 2 \text{ lb}, \quad 1 \text{ tonne} \approx 1 \text{ ton}$$

For a better approximation use

$$5 \text{ miles} \approx 8 \text{ km}, \quad 1 \text{ inch} \approx 2.5 \text{ cm}, \quad 1 \text{ kg} \approx 2.2 \text{ lb}$$

CHANGING UNITS

To change to a smaller unit we multiply,
e.g. to express 2 metres in centimetres, we multiply 2 by 100,
i.e. $2 \text{ m} = 2 \times 100 \text{ cm} = 200 \text{ cm}$

To change to a larger unit we divide,
e.g. to express 20 m in km, we divide 20 by 1000,
i.e. $20 \text{ m} = 20 \div 1000 \text{ km} = 0.02 \text{ km}$

AREA

Area is measured by standard sized squares.

$$1 \text{ cm}^2 = 10 \times 10 \text{ mm}^2 = 100 \text{ mm}^2$$
$$1 \text{ m}^2 = 100 \times 100 \text{ cm}^2 = 10\,000 \text{ cm}^2$$
$$1 \text{ km}^2 = 1000 \times 1000 \text{ m}^2 = 1\,000\,000 \text{ m}^2$$

The area of a square = (length of a side)^2.

The area of a rectangle = length × breadth.

VOLUME AND CAPACITY

Volume is measured by standard sized cubes.

$$1 \text{ cm}^3 = 10 \times 10 \times 10 \text{ mm}^3 = 1000 \text{ mm}^3$$
$$1 \text{ m}^3 = 100 \times 100 \times 100 \text{ cm}^3 = 1\,000\,000 \text{ cm}^3$$

The volume of a cuboid = length × breadth × height.

The capacity of a container is the volume of liquid it could hold.
The main metric units of capacity are the litre (l) and the millilitre (ml), where

$$1 \text{ litre} = 1000 \text{ ml} \quad \text{and} \quad 1 \text{ litre} = 1000 \text{ cm}^3$$

Note: $1 \text{ ml} = 1 \text{ cm}^3$

The main Imperial units of capacity are the gallon and the pint, where

$$1 \text{ gallon} = 8 \text{ pints}$$

Rough conversions between metric and Imperial units of capacity are given by

$$1 \text{ litre} \approx 1.75 \text{ pints} \quad \text{and} \quad 1 \text{ gallon} \approx 4.5 \text{ litres}$$

SUMMARISING DATA

For a list of values,

- the *range* is the difference between the largest value and the smallest value,

- the *mean* is the sum of all the values divided by the number of values,

- the *median* is the middle value when they have been arranged in order of size, (when the middle of the list is half way between two values, the median is the average of these two values),

- the *mode* is the value that occurs most frequently.

The mean, median and mode are together known as *measures of central tendency*.

REVISION EXERCISE 4.1 (Chapters 11 and 12)

1 Write either < or > between the two numbers

a 4   −6   **c** −4   −5   **e** 8   −5
b −5   6   **d** −8   −3   **f** −4   −2

2 Write down the next two numbers in each sequence.

a 5, 2, −1, −4, ...   **b** 11, 5, −1, −7, ...

3 Copy each statement and fill in the missing numbers

a $12 - 8 = \square$ **c** $\square - 7 = -4$
b $-3 - 4 = \square$ **d** $-3 - (\square) = 12$

4 Find

a $8 - 2 - 4$ **d** $-3 - (-4)$
b $-3 - 5 + 2$ **e** $8 + (-3) - (-5)$
c $5 + (-3)$ **f** $(5 - 8) - (8 - 12)$

5 a Add +8 to −6   **c** From −3 take away −5
   b Subtract 7 from −3   **d** Subtract positive 4 from −3

6 Write, in a mixture of words and symbols, the rule that tells you how to get the bottom number from the top number

6	8	10	14	21
11	13	15	19	26

7 The formula for P in terms of n is $P = 4n - 1$. Copy the table and complete it.

n	1	3	5	7	10
P					

8 Find the value of   **a** $4 \times (-3)$ **b** $(-5) \times 4$ **c** $\dfrac{-21}{7}$

9 Hank is 24 years older than his son George.

  a Write down a formula that expresses Hank's age (p years) in terms of George's age (q years).

  b Use your formula to find Hank's age when George is 21.

10 The formula connecting p, q and r is $r = 3p - 2q$. Find the value of r when

  a $p = 4$ and $q = 5$ **b** $p = -3$ and $q = 4$

REVISION EXERCISE 4.2 (Chapters 13, 14 and 15)

1 Express each quantity in the unit in brackets.

  a 400 mm (cm)   **c** 2048 ml (litres)
  b 3490 mg (g)   **d** 5320 m (km)

2 Express the given quantity in the unit given in brackets.

  a 83 m (km)   **c** 76 g (kg)
  b 53 kg (t)   **d** 54 mm (cm)

3 Find, expressing your answer in the unit in brackets

  a 63 mm + 42 cm (m)   **d** 6 ft 4 in (in)
  b 42 kg − 8430 g (kg)   **e** 5 yd 2 ft (ft)
  c 0.4 m + 63 cm (cm)   **f** 10 stone 3 lb (lb)

4 a Arrange these weights in order of size with the lightest first.

$$0.3\,\text{kg}, \quad 3\,\text{oz}, \quad 30\,\text{g}, \quad \tfrac{1}{4}\,\text{lb}$$

b Arrange these lengths in order of size with the longest first.

$$30\,\text{cm}, \quad 10\,\text{in}, \quad 45\,\text{mm}, \quad 2\,\text{ft}$$

5 In three different bookshops a particular book costs £11.99, £12.99 and £13.99.

a What is the mean price?   **b** What is the range of prices?

6 Seven pupils tried to estimate when 1 minute has passed. Their times, in seconds, were actually

$$58, \ 52, \ 68, \ 63, \ 61, \ 58, \ 67$$

Find

a the mode   **c** the mean

b the median   **d** the range

7 The sums of money donated to a charity by the members of a club are given in the table.

Amount (£)	Frequency
1	7
2	11
3	5
4	4
5	3

a How many members donated money to the charity?

b Guess the mean amount donated per member.

c Find the mean amount donated per member.

8 The table gives some measurements of two rectangles.
Copy the table and fill in the missing values.

Rectangle	Length	Breadth	Perimeter	Area
A	6 cm		18 cm	
B		5 cm		50 cm^2

9

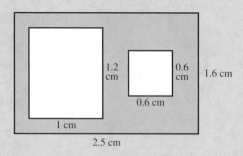

Find the area of the cork (shown shaded) in this gasket.

10 A rectangular box measures 4.78 cm by 3.23 cm by 1.88 cm. Estimate its capacity. Use a calculator to find the capacity of the box correct to 2 decimal places. How near is your estimate?

REVISION
EXERCISE 4.3
(Chapters 11
to 15)

1 a Write either < or > between each pair of numbers.

    i −5 9   **ii** −7 −8   **iii** −4 −6   **iv** −4 4

  b Find **i** −4 − 5 − 6 + 10   **ii** −4 − (−6) + 8

2 a Copy each statement and fill in the missing numbers.

    i 4 − 9 = □ **ii** −7 − □ = −16 **iii** 4 − (□) = −7

  b Subtract **i** 4 from −7   **ii** −5 from 10   **iii** −3 from −12

3 A number y is always 9 less than a number x.

  a Write down the formula connecting x and y.

  b Find y when x is **i** 20   **ii** 5   **iii** −5

4 Use the formula $f = \dfrac{9c}{5} + 32$ to find the value of f when

  a $c = 40$ **b** $c = 0$ **c** $c = -10$

5 Express the given quantity in the unit in brackets.

  a 5000 m (km)   **e** 34 cm (m)

  b 9000 kg (t)   **f** 53 mm (cm)

  c 450 cm (m)   **g** 350 ml (litres)

  d 8493 g (kg)   **h** 30 mg (g)

6 Write the first unit very roughly in terms of the unit in brackets.

  a 5 kg (lb)   **c** 20 miles (km)

  b 3 m (ft)   **d** 500 g (oz)

7 Find the range, mode and median of the following set of numbers.

4.1, 3.8, 4.2, 4.3, 3.9, 3.8, 4.5, 3.7

8 Esther carried out a survey of the number of people per car, including the driver, passing her home. Her results are given in the table.

Number of people	Frequency
1	24
2	12
3	8
4	5
5	1

Find   **a** the mode   **b** the median   **c** the mean.

9 Five squares, each of side 4 cm, are arranged to form a cross as shown in the diagram.

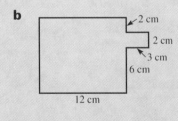

   a Find   **i** its perimeter   **ii** its area.

   b Suppose the squares are now rearranged in a row.
   How does the perimeter of this shape compare with the perimeter of the cross in part **a**?

10 Find the area of each shape.

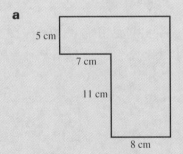

a

5 cm
7 cm
11 cm
8 cm

b

2 cm
2 cm
3 cm
6 cm
12 cm

REVISION EXERCISE 4.4 (Chapters 1 to 15)

1 a In an election there were three candidates. 1456 voted for Barstow, 1033 for Waite and 394 for Peters.

   i How many people voted?

   ii If 4392 people were entitled to vote, how many failed to do so?

   b Find $18 \div 6 \times 3 + 15 \times 2 - 42 \div 7$

2 a Find the largest whole number that will divide exactly into 50, 75 and 125.

b Express as the sum of three odd prime numbers

   i 23   **ii** 53

c Express each number in prime factors in index form

   i 189   **ii** 432

d Is 4422 exactly divisible by 12?

3 Copy the diagram onto squared paper.

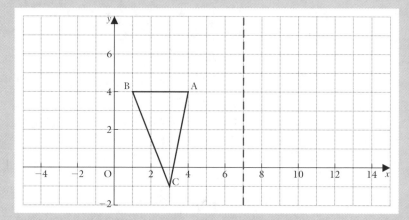

Draw the image of the triangle when it is

a reflected in the broken line

b rotated through 90° clockwise about the point A

c translated 6 units to the left followed by 3 units up.

4 First find a rough value, then use a calculator to find the value, correct to the number of decimal places shown in brackets, of

a 3.85×0.86 (1)   **c** $52.92 \div 11.67$ (2)

b 0.834×13.2 (1)   **d** $48.77 \div 10.66$ (3)

5 Find the size of each of the marked angles.

a
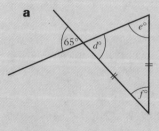

b
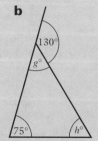

c
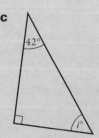

6 a Write either < or > between each pair of numbers.

    i 8 −4   **ii** −7 9   **iii** −5 −3

  b Find

     i $-5 + 6 - 7$

    ii $6 + (-4) - (-3)$

   iii $-7 - (-5) + 10$

7 Use the formula $R = p \times q$ to find the value of R when

  a $p = 3.5$ and $q = 3$ **c** $p = 4$ and $q = -1.5$

  b $p = 2.4$ and $q = 5.5$ **d** $p = -3$ and $q = -2.5$

8 Express

  a $842\,\text{kg} + 1.04\,\text{t}$ in kilograms   **c** 3 ft 9 inches in inches

  b 8 stone 4 lb in pounds   **d** $560\,\text{cm} + 850\,\text{mm}$ in metres

9 The heights (correct to the nearest centimetre) of a group of girls are

      152, 157, 156, 152, 154, 150, 148, 149, 147, 155

  Find

  a their mean height   **c** their median height

  b their modal height   **d** the range of their heights.

10 a Find the volume of a solid wooden cube of side 2 cm.

   b How many cubes of side 2 cm will fit inside a cubical box of side 10 cm ?

REVISION
EXERCISE 4.5
(Chapters 1 to 15)

1 Estimate the size, in degrees, of each of the following angles

a   **b**   **c**   **d**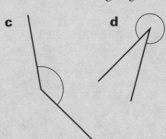

2 **a** Change into a mixed number

    i $\frac{23}{6}$ **ii** $\frac{45}{7}$ **iii** $\frac{69}{12}$

 b Change into an improper fraction

    i $3\frac{3}{4}$ **ii** $5\frac{4}{7}$ **iii** $12\frac{8}{9}$

 c Find **i** $3\frac{7}{12}+1\frac{1}{4}$ **ii** $5\frac{1}{4}-2\frac{5}{8}$

3 **a** Find, without using a calculator

    i 300×0.4 **iii** $0.42 \div 300$

    ii 0.0018×900 **iv** $4.5 \div 0.005$

 b Find the cost of 8 magazines at £2.95 each.

 c The cost of 0.6 kg of tomatoes is 63 p. What is the cost of 1 kilogram?

4 **a** Find **i** $\frac{2}{3}$ of £96   **ii** $\frac{3}{4}$ of 48 cm   **iii** $\frac{5}{9}$ of 36 kg

 b Which is the smaller: $\frac{5}{12}$ of 9 or $\frac{3}{4}$ of 7?

 c Which is the larger: $\frac{2}{3}$ of $\frac{4}{9}$ or $\frac{4}{7}$ of $\frac{3}{4}$?

 d Anne bought a £1.20 magazine out of her £5 pocket money. What fraction of her pocket money did she spend on the magazine?

5 **a** Express $\frac{13}{20}$ as **i** a decimal   **ii** a percentage.

 b Express 1.45 as **i** a percentage **ii** a fraction in its lowest terms.

 c In a department store 84% of the 325 staff are women.

    i How many women are there on the staff?

    ii How many men are there?

6 **a** Add -6 to **i** 5   **ii** -4 **iii** -8

 b Take -8 from the sum of 5 and -3.

 c Find $-5+(-4)-(-7)$

7 The formula for finding the profit £p when n boxes of chocolates are sold is $p = 2.5n - 30$. Find p when $n = 10$.

8 a Put these weights in order of size with the lightest first.

$$530 \,\text{kg}, \ 2.5 \,\text{t}, \ 94.5 \,\text{kg}, \ 85\,000 \,\text{g}, \ 0.4 \,\text{t}$$

b Which is the heavier:

a bag of potatoes weighing 5 kg or
a bag of swedes weighing 10 lb?

9 The marks out of 50 in a science test for the pupils in a class are

$$32, \ 25, \ 18, \ 42, \ 26, \ 24, \ 36, \ 15, \ 37, \ 25, \ 18, \ 22, \ 27, \ 24,$$
$$16, \ 26, \ 26, \ 24, \ 36, \ 26, \ 28, \ 24, \ 41, \ 23, \ 26, \ 40, \ 23$$

Find

a the mean mark   **c** the median mark

b the modal mark   **d** the range of marks.

10 The diagram shows a rectangular plot of ground measuring 30 m by 20 m. It is laid out as a rectangular lawn surrounded by a path that is 1 m wide.

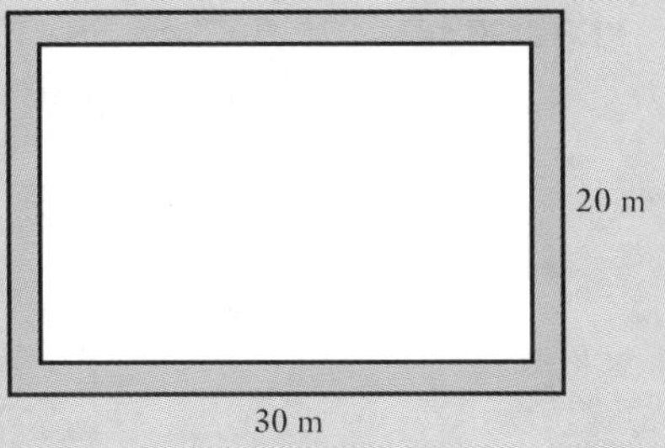

Find

a the measurements of the lawn

b the area of the lawn

c the area of the whole plot

d the area of the path.

INFORMATION FROM CHARTS

16

READING BAR
CHARTS

Numerical information is often easier to understand when it is presented visually; this is why the news media often give statistical information in the form of charts or diagrams.

It is important that we can understand these diagrams and that we can extract information from them.

EXERCISE 16A

1 This bar chart shows the sums of money spent by the Brown family on various categories of expenditure in one half-term holiday.

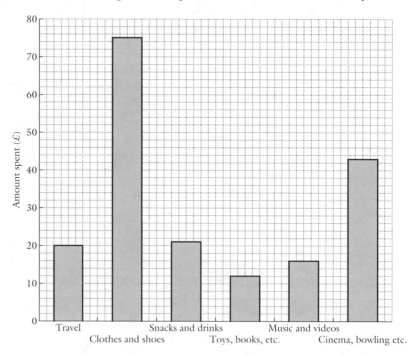

Use the bar chart to find

a the amount spent on drinks and snacks

b the total amount spent

c the amount spent on drinks and snacks as a decimal of the total sum spent. Give your answer correct to 1 decimal place.

2

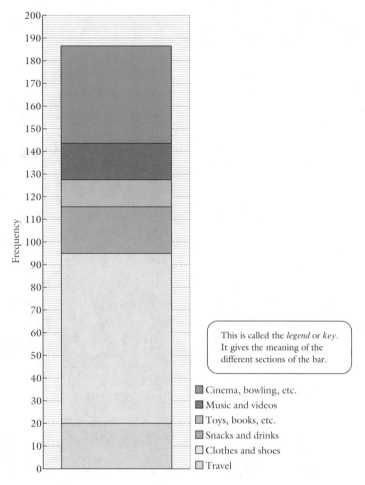

This is called the *legend* or *key*. It gives the meaning of the different sections of the bar.

■ Cinema, bowling, etc.
■ Music and videos
☐ Toys, books, etc.
■ Snacks and drinks
☐ Clothes and shoes
☐ Travel

This chart shows the same information as the bar chart on the previous page. It is called a stacked bar chart.

Use this chart to find

a the amount spent on toys, books etc.

b the total amount spent

c the amount spent on toys, etc. as a decimal fraction of the total amount spent. Give your answer correct to 1 decimal place.

3 From which of these two charts is it easier to see

a the total sum of money spent

b the sum of money spent on an individual category

c the money spent on each individual category as a fraction of the total sum spent?

Give reasons for your answers.

**DIAGRAMS
COMPARING
TWO SETS OF
INFORMATION**

These two bar charts (from Chapter 14) illustrate the results of the same test given to two sets of pupils: Group A and Group B.

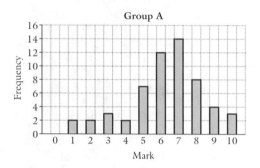

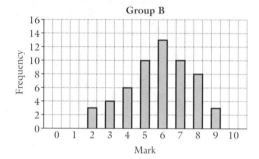

The two sets of marks can be compared from the separate bar charts, but comparisons can be easier to see when the information is given in a single chart. These diagrams give some examples of combined charts.

This is a parallel bar chart; for each mark the bars are drawn next to each other. Notice that this chart needs a *legend* or *key*.
(This chart is also called a compound or multiple bar chart.)

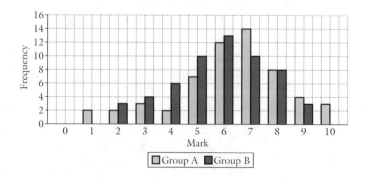

This is a stacked bar chart; this time the bars are drawn one on top of the other.

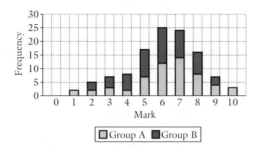

This chart shows the two sets drawn horizontally and separately, but 'back to back'.

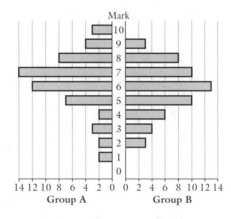

EXERCISE 16B

Use the charts given opposite and above to answer questions **1** to **6**. For each question, use the chart which you think gives the answer most clearly and say why you chose it.

1 In Group A how many more pupils scored 9 marks than in Group B?

2 How many pupils altogether scored less than 5?

3 One mark was obtained by the same number of children from each group. What is this mark?

4 For which group was the range of marks greatest?

5 For which group was the modal mark highest?

6 Can you say which group, taken as a whole, performed better on the test? Give a reason for your answer.

7 A group of Year 8 pupils went on a school outing. The diagram shows the distribution of spending money that the pupils had at the start of the trip.

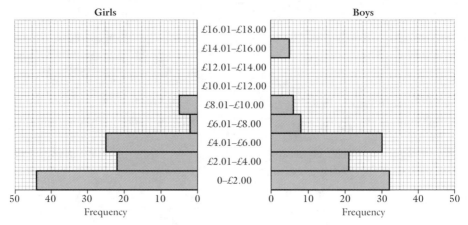

a How many girls went on this trip?

b How many boys went on the trip?

c Do you think that, on average, the boys had more spending money than the girls? Give a reason for your answer.

d What fraction of the boys had more than £10 to spend?

e What fraction of the girls had more than £10 to spend?

f Find the percentage of the boys who had more than £6 to spend.

g Repeat part **f** for the girls.

h Give two ways in which this diagram shows differences between the girls' and the boys' spending money.

8 A survey of the amount spent on one day in the school canteen by pupils in Year 8 produced the results shown in this table.

Sum spent	£0.00–£0.99	£1.00–£1.99	£2.00–£2.99	£3.00–£3.99
Boys	4	15	39	17
Girls	8	16	15	4

a How many pupils took part in the survey?

b How many of these pupils were **i** boys **ii** girls?

c What kind of diagram would you suggest for comparing the boys' and girls' spending patterns? Give, with reasons, one advantage and one disadvantage of your choice.

9 A survey was carried out in which some pupils were asked which they thought was the most important subject to do well in: Mathematics, English or Science. This stacked bar chart illustrates the results of the survey.

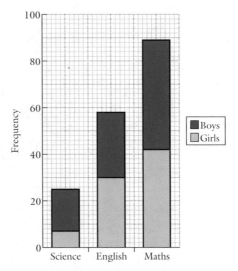

a Which subject was considered most important by more boys than girls?

b Which subject was considered most important by the largest number of boys?

c Did the largest number of girls choose a different subject?

d What differences does the graph show between the subject considered most important by the boys and the one chosen by the girls?

e Are the numbers of boys and girls represented in the diagram the same?

PIE CHARTS

This frequency table shows the sums of money spent by 30 pupils in Class 8A during one day in the school canteen.

Amount in pence	0–49	50–99	100–149	150–199	200–249	Total
Frequency	3	7	10	8	2	30

The number of pupils who spent 0 to 49 p can be given as a fraction of the 30 pupils,   i.e. $\frac{3}{30}$ of the group spent 0 to 49 p,

The same calculation can be done for each of the other categories of expenditure,   e.g. $\frac{7}{30}$ of the group spent 50 p to 99 p, and so on.

These fractions, which show the proportions of pupils expenditure in the chosen groups, can be illustrated with a *pie chart*. A pie chart is a circle that is divided into 'slices'. The size of each slice represents the fraction that one category is of the whole.

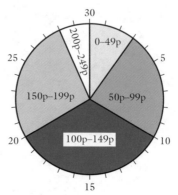

This information is being collected on each of several days so that the catering manager can look at the spending pattern.

On different days, the total number of pupils in Class 8A that are in school will vary, so comparing the numbers each day who spend 0 to 49 pence, say, will not have much meaning. Comparing the proportions that spend 0 to 49 pence each day will give more useful information.

Pie charts do not usually come with the circumference of the circle divided into a convenient number of parts. Each slice is usually labelled with the category which it represents and its percentage of the whole quantity.

This pie chart was drawn by a chart-drawing program on a computer, using the information given in Question **1**, Exercise 16A. It shows the percentages of the total money spent by the Brown family on various categories in one half-term holiday.

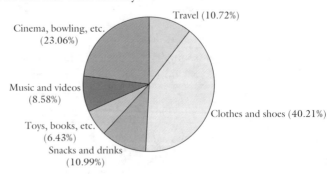

Even without looking at the percentages, we can see that the proportions spent on travel and on snacks, etc., are about the same. We can also see that the proportion spent on cinema, bowling, etc., is just under one quarter of the total.

EXERCISE 16C

1 This pie chart shows the various purposes for which personal computers are used.

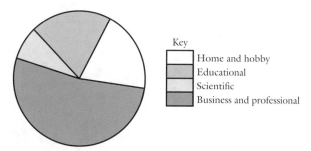

Key

☐ Home and hobby
▨ Educational
▨ Scientific
▓ Business and professional

a For which purpose were computers used most?

b Estimate the fraction of the total numbers used for

   i scientific purposes   **ii** home and hobbies.

2 The pie chart below shows how fuel is used for different purposes in the average house.

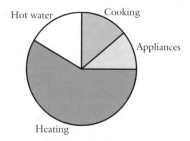

a For which purpose is most fuel used?

b How does the amount of fuel used for cooking compare with the amount used for hot water?

3 The age distribution of the population in years, in 1988, is shown in this pie chart.

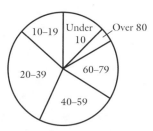

a Estimate the size of the fraction of the population in the age groups   **i** under 10 years   **ii** 60–79 years.

b State which groups are of roughly the same size.

4 This pie chart, taken from *Social Trends 22*, shows average household water use.

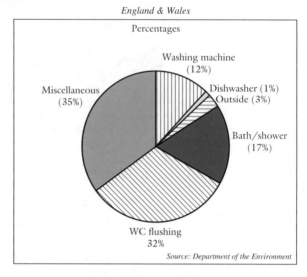

England & Wales

Percentages

Washing machine (12%)

Dishwasher (1%)
Outside (3%)

Miscellaneous (35%)

Bath/shower (17%)

WC flushing
32%

Source: Department of the Environment

Without looking at the percentages estimate

a the proportion of water used for WC flushing as a fraction of the total used

b the proportion of water used for washing machines as a fraction of that used for WC flushing.

5 Sometimes proportions are shown as a stacked bar chart.
This bar chart shows the proportion by weight of different nutrients in a brand of tortellini.

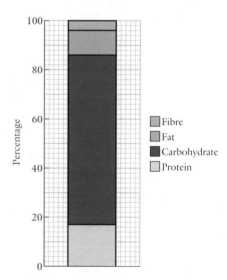

Percentage

Fibre
Fat
Carbohydrate
Protein

a Estimate the carbohydrate content as a percentage of the nutrients.

b Estimate what fraction of the nutrients is fat.

c Is it easier to estimate the size of one category as a fraction of the whole from a pie chart or from a stacked percentage bar chart?

This diagram is taken from *the Observer*. Use it to answer questions **6** to **8**.

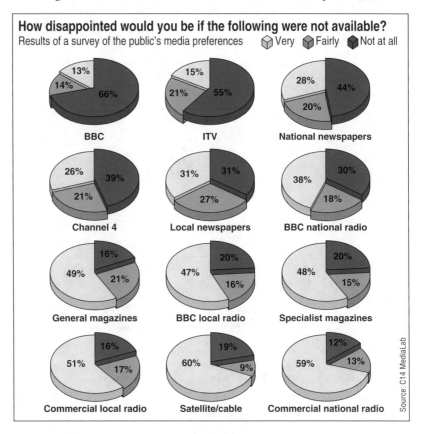

How disappointed would you be if the following were not available?
Results of a survey of the public's media preferences   Very   Fairly   Not at all

6 If it were not available, which of the media shown would

a cause most people to be very disappointed

b leave most people not at all disappointed?

7 Look at the pie chart referring to general magazines.

a What percentage would not be at all disappointed if these were not available?
Is this more or less than a half?

b Without looking at the percentage on the chart, what fraction of the pie does the slice representing the percentage in part **a** appear to be?

c What is the total of the percentages shown on this pie? Is this what you expected?

8 Look carefully at the other pie charts in this diagram. What do you notice? Can you give any explanation for what you notice?

**PRACTICAL
WORK**

This chart, from *Social Trends 22*, illustrates the changes in population of the regions of the UK in the 1980s.

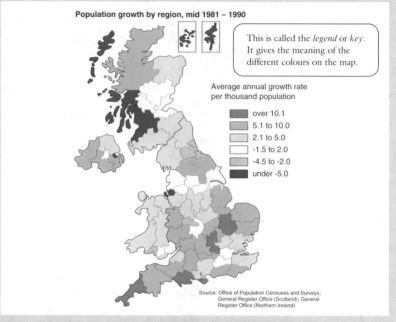

Population growth by region, mid 1981 – 1990

This is called the *legend* or *key*.
It gives the meaning of the different colours on the map.

Average annual growth rate
per thousand population

over 10.1
5.1 to 10.0
2.1 to 5.0
-1.5 to 2.0
-4.5 to -2.0
under -5.0

Source: Office of Population Censuses and Surveys;
General Register Office (Scotland); General
Register Office (Northern Ireland)

a What do the negative numbers in the legend represent?

b Name one region of the UK where the population grew by more than 10 people per 1000.

c Name one region of the UK where the population fell by more than 5 people per 1000.

d If, in 1981, the population of a town in Cornwall was 15 000, give a rough value for what you think the population would have been in 1990. What assumption have you made to give your answer? Do you think that your assumption gives a reasonably reliable answer?

e Discuss the problems that you would meet if you tried to show this information in a bar chart.

INVESTIGATION

Find some statistical diagrams from newspapers or magazines.
Write a short report on them.
Include in your report

a whether you consider the diagram to be useful

b whether it is misleading and why.

EQUATIONS

Jo went into a shop and bought some chocolate for Karl and some boiled sweets for herself. Together they cost £1.13. When Karl asked Jo how much he owed her for his chocolate all she could remember was that it cost 15 p more than her boiled sweets. They could find out how much each had to pay by

- guessing until they found two amounts that have a total of 113 p and a difference of 15 p, or
- writing down the information using mathematical symbols.

To do this we can write

$$(\text{amount Karl owed}) + (\text{amount Jo owed}) = 113\,\text{p}$$

but (amount Jo owed) = (amount Karl owed − 15 p)

so (amount Karl owed) + (amount Karl owed − 15 p) = 113 p

This is called an *equation*.
Now we can see that twice the amount Karl owed = 128 p
so Karl owed Jo 64 p.

EXERCISE 17A   Discuss how you might solve the problems that arise in the following situations.

1 Chris and Joy have been given £10 between them and must divide it so that Chris has £1 more than Joy.

2 Rod and Daniel go for a meal. The total cost comes to £34.60. Daniel's meal costs £1.70 more than Rod's and Rod is unwilling to split the bill down the middle. He wants each of them to pay the cost of his own meal.

3 A teacher had a full box of 100 drawing pins. She gave 4 to each pupil to pin a painting on the wall. She came across 3 faulty pins and still had 5 pins left over when all the pupils had taken the pins they needed. She wondered how many pupils had come to her to put their paintings up.

4 Can you think of other situations where it should be easier to form an equation and use it, rather than guess and then have to check to see if the chosen solution works?

THE IDEA OF
EQUATIONS

I think of a number, add seven and get twenty-one.
This sentence could be rewritten using symbols i.e.

the number I think of $+ 7 = 21$

from which we can see that the number I think of is 14.
If we use a letter (we shall use x) to stand for 'the number' I think of,
the sentence could be rewritten more briefly

$$x + 7 = 21$$

Then, if we take away 7 from each side

$$x = 21 - 7$$
$$= 14$$

so the number I first thought of was 14.

The next exercise is concerned more with forming an equation than in
solving one.

EXERCISE 17B

> I think of a number, add 4, and the result is 10.
> If x stands for the unknown number, form an equation in x and
> hence find the number I thought of.
>
> The equation is $x + 4 = 10$
> The number is 6

In each question from **1** to **15** let the letter x stand for the unknown
number.
Use the given statement to form an equation in x. Hence find the
unknown number.

1 I think of a number, subtract 3 and get 4.

2 I think of a number, add 1 and the result is 3.

3 If a number is added to 3 we get 9.

4 If 5 is subtracted from a number we get 2.

5 I think of a number, add 8 and get 21.

6 If 7 is subtracted from a number we get 19.

I think of a number, multiply it by 3 and the result is 12.
What is the number?

$$x \times 3 = 12$$

The equation is $3x = 12$

The number is 4.

WHEN TWO NUMBERS ARE MULTIPLIED, IT DOES NOT MATTER IN WHICH ORDER THEY ARE WRITTEN,
i.e. $x \times 3 = 3 \times x$
ALSO $3 \times x = 3x$

7 I think of a number, double it and get 8.

8 If a number is multiplied by 7 the result is 14.

9 When we multiply a number by 3 we get 15.

10 6 times an unknown number gives 24.

11 I think of a number, multiply it by 4 and get 24.

12 I think of a number, divide it by 6 and get 5.

13 When a number is divided by 3 we get 7.

14 If a number is divided by 7 the answer is 7.

15 I think of a number, divide it by 8 and get 32.

Write a sentence to show the meaning of the equation $4x = 20$.

$4x = 20$ means '4 times an unknown number gives 20', or, 'I think of a number, multiply it by 4 and the result is 20'.

Write sentences to show the meaning of the following equations.

16 $3x = 18$

17 $x + 6 = 7$

18 $x - 2 = 9$

19 $5x = 20$

20 $5 + x = 7$

21 $x - 4 = 1$

22 $4x = 8$

23 $x + 1 = 4$

SOLVING EQUATIONS

Some equations need an organised approach, rather than guesswork.

Imagine a balance:

On this side there is a bag containing an unknown number of marbles, say x marbles, and 4 loose marbles.

On this side there are 9 separate marbles, balancing the marbles on the other side.

$$x + 4 = 9$$

Take 4 loose marbles from each side, so that the two sides still balance.

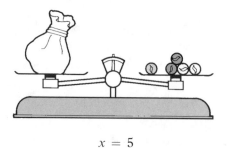

$$x = 5$$

We write: $x + 4 = 9$

Take 4 from both sides $x = 5$

When we have found the value of x we have *solved the equation*.

As a second example suppose that:

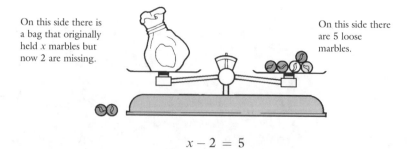

On this side there is a bag that originally held x marbles but now 2 are missing.

On this side there are 5 loose marbles.

$$x - 2 = 5$$

We can make the bag complete by putting back 2 marbles but, to keep the balance, we must add 2 marbles to the right-hand side also.

So we write $\qquad\qquad x - 2 = 5$

Add 2 to each side $\qquad\qquad x = 7$

> Whatever you do to one side of an equation
> you must also do to the other side.

Use the equations in the following exercise to practise this idea. It is easy enough to 'see' the solutions, so you should have no difficulty in checking your answers.

EXERCISE 17C

> Solve the equation $y + 4 = 6$
>
> $$y + 4 = 6$$
> Take 4 from both sides $\qquad y = 2$

Solve

1 $x + 7 = 15$	**5** $a + 3 = 7$	**9** $a + 1 = 6$
2 $x + 9 = 18$	**6** $x + 4 = 9$	**10** $a + 8 = 15$
3 $10 + y = 12$	**7** $a + 5 = 11$	**11** $7 + c = 10$
4 $2 + c = 9$	**8** $9 + a = 15$	**12** $c + 2 = 3$

13 Kim is n years old and Toni is 2 years older than Kim. If Toni is 14 we can form the equation

$$n + 2 = 14$$

How old is Kim?

14 A cup of coffee costs 15 pence more than a cup of tea. If a cup of tea costs x pence and a cup of coffee costs 75 pence we can form the equation

$$x + 15 = 75$$

How much is a cup of tea?

15 Adam has c cassettes and Peg has 8. Altogether they have 21 cassettes between them.
Use this information to form an equation.
How many cassettes does Adam have?

16 A concert hall has two car-parks and 364 cars are parked in them. There are 193 cars in the east car-park and n cars in the north car-park.

Use this information to form an equation in n.

How many cars are parked in the north car-park?

NEGATIVE ANSWERS

Some equations may have negative answers.

For example, if we know the temperature fell last night by 3 °C to −9 °C, we could find the temperature before it got colder by forming the equation

$$x - 3 = -9$$

where x °C was the temperature before it fell.

Then adding 3 to both sides gives

$$x = -9 + 3 = -6$$

EXERCISE 17D

Solve $x + 8 = 6$

$$x + 8 = 6$$

Take 8 from both sides $x = -2$

Solve

1 $x + 4 = 2$ **3** $3 + a = 2$ **5** $4 + w = 2$

2 $x + 6 = 1$ **4** $s + 3 = 2$ **6** $c + 6 = 2$

Solve $x - 6 = 2$

$$x - 6 = 2$$

Add 6 to both sides $x = 8$

Solve

7 $x - 6 = 4$ **11** $c - 8 = 1$ **15** $a - 4 = 8$

8 $a - 2 = 1$ **12** $x - 5 = 7$ **16** $x - 3 = 0$

9 $y - 3 = 5$ **13** $s - 4 = 1$ **17** $c - 1 = 1$

10 $x - 4 = 6$ **14** $x - 9 = 3$ **18** $y - 7 = 2$

19 A chelsea bun costs 16 pence less than a jam doughnut. If a jam doughnut costs n pence and a chelsea bun 32 pence we can form the equation

$$n - 16 = 32.$$

What is the cost of a jam doughnut?

20 A small loaf weighs 450 grams less than a large loaf. If a large loaf weighs x grams and a small loaf weighs 500 grams, we can form the equation

$$x - 450 = 500$$

How heavy is a large loaf?

21 A cup of tea cost 80 p less than a sandwich. A sandwich costs 150 p and a cup of tea costs x p.
Use this information to form an equation.
How much is a cup of tea?

22 The temperature early this morning was $t\,°$C. Since then it has increased by 3° and is now 2 °C. From this information we can form the equation

$$t + 3 = 2$$

Solve this equation and so find the temperature early this morning.

23 Jean Pearce paid her gas bill for £80 by writing a cheque. Before it was presented at the bank she had a credit of £55. After it had been cleared she was £x overdrawn.
Form an equation in x and use it to find out how much she was overdrawn after the gas bill had been paid.

24 Simon Mann lives just outside Jerusalem. His house is 510 m above sea level. He also has a weekend flat near the Dead Sea which is 220 m below sea level. The vertical distance through which he descends when he travels from his Jerusalem home to his flat is x m.
Form an equation in x.
By what vertical distance does he descend when he goes from Jerusalem to his flat for the weekend?

EXERCISE 17E   Sometimes the letter term is on the right-hand side instead of the left.

Solve $3 = x - 4$

$$3 = x - 4$$
Add 4 to both sides $7 = x$ $\boxed{7 = x \text{ is the same} \\ \text{as } x = 7}$
$$x = 7$$

Solve

1 $4 = x + 2$ **3** $7 = a + 4$ **5** $1 = c - 2$

2 $6 = x - 3$ **4** $6 = x - 7$ **6** $5 = s + 2$

7 $x + 3 = 10$ **11** $6 + c = 10$ **15** $x - 6 = 5$

8 $9 + x = 4$ **12** $d + 4 = 1$ **16** $x + 3 = 15$

9 $c + 4 = 4$ **13** $7 = x + 3$ **17** $y - 6 = 4$

10 $3 = b + 2$ **14** $x + 1 = 9$ **18** $x - 7 = 4$

Solve $7.5 = x - 2.8$

$$7.5 = x - 2.8$$
Add 2.8 to both sides $7.5 + 2.8 = x$
i.e.
$$10.3 = x$$
$$x = 10.3$$

Solve the equations.

19 $x - 1.5 = 6$ **22** $x - 3.2 = 5.6$ **25** $x - 4.1 = 7.8$

20 $6 = x - 4$ **23** $10 = a - 1$ **26** $x - 3 = 6$

21 $x - \frac{1}{2} = 5$ **24** $x + \frac{1}{2} = 4$ **27** $\frac{2}{3} = x - 1\frac{2}{3}$

28 $x - 4 = 2$ **31** $9 = x - 7$ **34** $c - 7 = 10$

29 $3 = x - 5.6$ **32** $x + 4.7 = 11.2$ **35** $6.6 = x - 3.9$

30 $4 + x = 5\frac{1}{4}$ **33** $\frac{3}{4} + x = 1\frac{1}{2}$ **36** $x - 1\frac{3}{4} = \frac{1}{2}$

37 $y - 9 = 14$ **40** $x + 1 = 8$ <u>**43**</u> $x + 8 = 1$

38 $2 = z - 2$ **41** $x - 1 = 8$ <u>**44**</u> $x - 8 = 1$

39 $d - 3 = 1$ **42** $1 = c + 3$ <u>**45**</u> $z + 3 = 5$

46 Terry cuts a piece of wood 1.75 m long from a piece that is 2.64 m long.
The piece he has left is x m long.

   a Form an equation in x.

   b How long was the piece Terry had left?

47 A lorry weighs $5\frac{1}{4}$ tons and is loaded with $5\frac{3}{4}$ tons of steel.
The total weight of the loaded lorry is N tons.

   a Form an equation in N.

   b Find the weight of the loaded lorry.

MULTIPLES OF x   Imagine that on this side of the scales there are 3 bags each containing the same unknown number of marbles, say x in each.   On this side there are 12 loose marbles

$$3 \times x = 12$$

$$3x = 12$$

We can keep the balance if we divide the contents of each scale pan by 3.

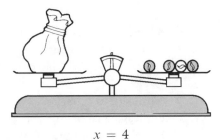

$$x = 4$$

EXERCISE 17F

Solve $6x = 12$

$$6x = 12$$
Divide both sides by 6 $\quad x = 2$

Solve $3x = 7$

$$3x = 7$$
Divide both sides by 3 $\quad x = \frac{7}{3}$
$$x = 2\frac{1}{3}$$

Solve the following equations.

1 $5x = 10$ **5** $4b = 16$ **9** $5p = 7$

2 $3x = 9$ **6** $4c = 9$ **10** $2x = 40$

3 $2x = 5$ **7** $3a = 1$ **11** $7y = 14$

4 $7x = 21$ **8** $6z = 18$ **12** $6a = 3$

13 $6x = 36$ **17** $5z = 9$ **21** $4y = 3$

14 $6x = 6$ **18** $2y = 7$ **22** $5x = 6$

15 $6x = 1$ **19** $3x = 27$ **23** $2z = 10$

16 $5z = 10$ **20** $8x = 16$ **24** $7x = 1$

25 Danny is n years old now. His father is 48 years old and is four times as old as Danny. From this information we get the equation $4 \times n = 48$ or more simply $4n = 48$.
How old is Danny?

26 A light bulb costs x pence and a pack of 6 light bulbs costs 360 pence.
We can form the equation $6x = 360$.
How much does 1 bulb cost?

27 A plank of wood 3.4 m long is cut into 4 equal pieces, each x m long.
Form an equation in x and solve it.
How long is each piece?

28 Salman has $3.5\,\mathrm{lb}$ of potatoes. They are divided equally among 7 diners.
If each diner receives $x\,\mathrm{lb}$ form an equation in x and solve it.
What weight of potatoes does each diner receive?

**MIXED
OPERATIONS**

EXERCISE 17G   Solve the following equations.

1 $x + 4 = 8$ **4** $5y = 6$ **7** $2x = 11$

2 $x - 4 = 8$ **5** $4x = 12$ **8** $x - 2 = 11$

3 $4x = 8$ **6** $x - 4 = 12$ **9** $x - 12 = 4$

10 $8 = c + 2$ **13** $7y = 2$ **16** $3 = a - 4$

11 $20 = 4x$ **14** $3x = 8$ **17** $3x = 5$

12 $2 + x = 4$ **15** $x + 6 = 1$ **18** $z - 5 = 6$

19 The temperature at midday was $T\,°\mathrm{C}$. By $6\,\mathrm{p.m.}$ it had fallen by $6\,°\mathrm{C}$ to $12.5\,°\mathrm{C}$.
From this information we can form the equation $T - 6 = 12.5$.
Solve this equation.
What was the temperature at midday?
Now that you think you know what the temperature was, read through the given information again to see that it fits.

20 A glass of squash costs $65\,\mathrm{p}$ and a chocolate eclair costs x pence more than a glass of squash. Together they cost 150 pence. As a chocolate eclair costs $(65 + x)$ pence we can form the equation $65 + 65 + x = 150$.
Solve this equation.
How much does an eclair cost?

21 Helen is x years old now. Her mother, who is 35 years old, is five times as old as Helen.

a Write down Helen's mother's age in terms of x.

b Form an equation in x and solve it.

c How old is Helen now?

TWO OPERATIONS

One of the problems in the discussion exercise on page 311 concerned Rod and Daniel sharing the cost of a meal. If we suppose that Rod's meal cost £x then the cost of Daniel's meal was £$x + £1.70$. The total cost of the two meals was £34.60, so we can form the equation

$$x + x + 1.70 = 34.60$$

i.e. $\qquad 2x + 1.70 = 34.60$

To solve this equation requires two operations.

First, subtract 1.70 from both sides

$$2x = 34.60 - 1.70$$

$$2x = 32.90$$

Secondly, divide both sides by 2

$$x = 16.45$$

The cost of Rod's meal was £16.45
and the cost of Daniel's meal was £16.45 + £1.70 = £18.15.

(*Check*: cost of Rod's meal + cost of Daniel's meal
$\qquad = £16.45 + £18.15 = £34.60,$
$\qquad$ which agrees with the information given in the question.)

EXERCISE 17H

Solve the equations $\quad$ **a** $7 = 3x - 5 \qquad$ **b** $2x + 3 = 5$

a $\qquad\qquad\qquad\qquad\qquad\qquad 7 = 3x - 5$
Add 5 to both sides $\qquad\qquad\quad 12 = 3x$
Divide both sides by 3 $\qquad\qquad 4 = x \qquad$ To solve an equation
i.e. $\qquad\qquad\qquad\qquad\qquad\qquad x = 4 \qquad\quad$ our aim is to get the
$\qquad\qquad\qquad\qquad\qquad\qquad\qquad\qquad\qquad\qquad$ letter on its own.

b $\qquad\qquad\qquad\qquad\qquad\qquad 2x + 3 = 5$
Take 3 from both sides $\qquad\qquad 2x = 2$
Divide both sides by 2 $\qquad\qquad\quad x = 1$

It is possible to check whether your answer is correct. We can put $x = 1$ in the left-hand side of the equation and see if we get the same value as on the right-hand side.

Check: If $x = 1$, left-hand side $= 2 \times 1 + 3 = 5$
Right-hand side $= 5$, so $x = 1$ fits the equation.

Solve the following equations.

1 $6x + 2 = 26$ **7** $6 = 2x - 4$ **13** $20 = 12x - 4$

2 $4x + 7 = 19$ **8** $5z + 9 = 4$ **14** $9x + 1 = 28$

3 $17 = 7x + 3$ **9** $3x - 4 = 4$ **15** $9 = 8x - 15$

4 $4x - 5 = 19$ **10** $3x + 4 = 25$ **16** $8 = 8 + 3z$

5 $3a + 12 = 12$ **11** $13 = 3x + 4$ **17** $5x - 4 = 5$

6 $10 = 10x - 50$ **12** $5z - 9 = 16$ **18** $15 = 1 + 7x$

19 $9x - 4 = 14$ **25** $3a + 4 = 1$ **31** $10x - 6 = 24$

20 $3x - 2 = 3$ **26** $2x + 6 = 6$ **32** $5x - 7 = 4$

21 $7 = 2z + 6$ **27** $3x + 1 = 11$ **33** $9 = 6a - 27$

22 $6x + 1 = -5$ **28** $2x + 4 = 14$ **34** $7 = 1 - 2x$

23 $5 = 7x - 23$ **29** $16 = 7x - 1$ **35** $10 + 2x = -2$

24 $5x + 1 = 4.5$ **30** $2.4 = 3x - 1.2$ **36** $2 + 3x = 7.4$

I think of a number, double it and add 3. The result is 15. What is the number?

IF THE NUMBER IS x, THEN DOUBLING IT GIVES 2x.

Let the number be x $2x + 3 = 15$
Take 3 from both sides $2x = 12$
Divide both sides by 2 $x = 6$
The number is 6.

In the remaining problems in this exercise form an equation and solve it.

37 I think of a number, multiply it by 4 and subtract 8.
The result is 20.
What was the number?

38 I think of a number, multiply it by 3 and add 6. The result is 21.
What is the number?

39 I think of a number, multiply it by 3 and add the result to 7. The total is 28.
What is the number?

40 The sides of a rectangle are x cm and 3 cm.
The perimeter is 24 cm.
Find x.

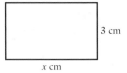

3 cm

x cm

41 The lengths of the three sides of a triangle are x cm, x cm and 6 cm. The perimeter is 20 cm.
Find x.

42 Mary and Jean each have x sweets and Susan has 10 sweets. They have 24 sweets altogether.
What is x?

43 Three boys had x sweets each. They gave 9 sweets to a fourth boy and then found that they were left with 18 sweets among the three of them.
Find x.

44 I have two pieces of ribbon each x cm long and a third piece 9 cm long. Altogether there are 31 cm of ribbon.
What is the length of each of the first two pieces?

45 Jen is y years old and her mother is 27 years older. Together their ages total 45 years.

a In terms of Jen's age, how old is her mother now?

b Form an equation in y and solve it to find Jen's age and her mother's age now.

46 A fishing rod is 27 ft long and consists of three parts. The first part is x ft long, the second part is 1 ft longer than the first and the third part is 1 ft longer than the second part.
Form an equation in x and solve it to find the length of each part.

47 Sonia is n years old now and Cynthia, her sister, is 2 years older. In 5 years time the sum of their ages will be 20.
How old is Sonia now?
How old will Cynthia be in 5 years time?

SIMPLIFYING
EXPRESSIONS

We can shorten, i.e. *simplify*, $2x + x$ to $3x$
because $2x$ means $x + x$,

i.e. $\qquad 2x + x = x + x + x$
$\qquad\qquad\qquad = 3x$

Like Terms

Consider $3x + 5x - 4x + 2x$.

This is called an *expression* and can be simplified to $6x$.

$3x$, $5x$, $4x$ and $2x$ are all *terms* in this expression. Each term contains x. They are of the same type and are called *like terms*.

Like terms can be simplified using the ordinary rules of addition and subtraction.

EXERCISE 17I

Simplify $4h - 6h + 8h - h$

Remember the sign in front of a term tells you what to do with just that term, so
$$4h - 6h + 8h - h = 4h + 8h - 6h - h$$
$$= 12h - 7h$$
$$= 5h$$

$4h - 6h + 8h - h = 5h$

Simplify

1 $3x + x + 4x + 2x$

2 $3x - x + 4x - 2x$

3 $-6x + 8x$

4 $6x - 1 + 4 - 7$

5 $-8x + 6x$

6 $9y - 3y + 2y$

7 $2 - 3 + 9 - 1$

8 $-16 - 3 - 4$

9 $-3x + 5x - 1$

10 $-2x - x + 3x$

Unlike Terms

$3x + 2x - 7$ can be simplified to $5x - 7$,
and $5x - 2y + 4x - 3y$ can be simplified to $9x - 5y$.

Terms containing x are different from terms without an x.
They are called *unlike terms* and cannot be collected to make one term.

Similarly $9x$ and $5y$ are unlike terms; therefore $9x - 5y$ cannot be simplified.

EXERCISE 17J

Simplify **a** $3x + 4 - 7 - 2x + 4x$ **b** $2x + 4y - x - 5y$

a $3x + 4 - 7 - 2x + 4x$
$= 5x - 3$

$3x - 2x + 4x$ is a group of like terms.
$+4 - 7$ is a different group of like terms.
$3x + 4 - 7 - 2x + 4x = 3x - 2x + 4x + 4 - 7$
$= 5x - 3$
$5x$ and 3 are unlike terms,
so $5x - 3$ cannot be simplified.

b $2x + 4y - x - 5y$
$= x - y$

$2x + 4y - x - 5y = 2x - x + 4y - 5y$
$= x - y$
x and y are unlike terms
so $x - y$ cannot be simplified.

Simplify

1 $2x + 4 + 3 + 5x$

2 $2x - 4 + 3x + 9$

3 $5x - 2 - 3 - x$

4 $4a + 5c - 6a$

5 $6x - 5y + 2x + 3y$

6 $6x + 5y + 2x + 3y$

7 $5a - 3b - 2a - 2b$

8 $7x + 3y - 5x - 6y$

9 $6x + 5y + 2x - 3y$

10 $6x + 5y - 2x + 3y$

11 $4x + 1 + 3x + 2 + x$

12 $6x - 9 + 2x + 1$

13 $7x - 3 - 9 - 4x$

14 $9x + 3y - 10x$

15 $2x - 6y - 8x$

16 $7 - x - 6 - 3x$

17 $8 - 1 - 7x + 2x$

18 $9x - 1 + 4 - 11x$

19 $6x - 5y + 2x + 3y + 2x$

20 $6x - 5y - 2x - 3y + 7x - y$

21 $30x + 2 - 15x - 6 + 4$

22 $-2z + 3x - 4y + 6z + x - 3y$

23 $4x + 3y - 4 + 6x - 2y - 7 - x$

24 $7x + 3 - 9 - 9x + 2x - 6 + 11$

25 $3x + 2y - 3z - x - 4y - 5z$

26 $5x - 2y - 6 - 8x + 2y + 3x + 9$

EQUATIONS WITH LETTER TERMS ON BOTH SIDES

Some equations have letter terms on both sides. Consider the equation

$$5x + 1 = 2x + 9$$

We want to have a letter term on one side only so we need to take $2x$ from both sides. This gives

$$3x + 1 = 9$$

and we can go on to solve the equation as before.

Notice that we want the letter term on the side which has the greater number of xs to start with.

If we look at the equation

$$9 - 4x = 2x + 4$$

we can see that xs have been taken away on the left-hand side, so there are more xs on the right-hand side.
Add $4x$ to both sides and then the equation becomes

$$9 = 6x + 4$$

and we can go on as before.

EXERCISE 17K

Deal with the letters first, then the numbers.

Solve $5x + 2 = 2x + 9$

DEAL WITH THE x TERMS FIRST.

$5x + 2 = 2x + 9$

Take $2x$ from both sides $3x + 2 = 9$
Take 2 from both sides $3x = 7$
Divide both sides by 3 $x = \frac{7}{3} = 2\frac{1}{3}$

Solve the equations.

1 $3x + 4 = 2x + 8$

2 $x + 7 = 4x + 4$

3 $2x + 5 = 5x - 4$

4 $3x - 1 = 5x - 11$

5 $7x + 3 = 3x + 31$

6 $6z + 4 = 2z + 1$

7 $7x - 25 = 3x - 1$

8 $11x - 6 = 8x + 9$

Solve $9 + x = 4 - 4x$

$$9 + x = 4 - 4x$$

> x is greater than $-4x$, so the left-hand side contains the greater number of xs. Therefore we add $4x$ to both sides to remove the xs from the right-hand side.

Add $4x$ to both sides $9 + 5x = 4$

Take 9 from both sides $5x = -5$

Divide both sides by 5 $x = -1$

Check: If $x = -1$, left-hand side $= 9 + (-1)$
$= 8$

right-hand side $= 4 - (-4)$
$= 8$

So $x = -1$ is the solution.

Solve the equations.

9 $4x - 3 = 39 - 2x$ **13** $5x - 6 = 3 - 4x$

10 $5 + x = 17 - 5x$ **14** $12 + 2x = 24 - 4x$

11 $7 - 2x = 4 + x$ **15** $32 - 6x = 8 + 2x$

12 $24 - 2x = 5x + 3$ **16** $9 - 3x = -5 + 4x$

EQUATIONS CONTAINING LIKE TERMS

If there are a lot of terms in an equation, first collect the like terms on each side separately.

EXERCISE 17L

Solve $2x + 3 - x + 5 = 3x + 4x - 6$

$$2x + 3 - x + 5 = 3x + 4x - 6$$

> Simplify each side.

$$x + 8 = 7x - 6$$

Take x from both sides $8 = 6x - 6$

Add 6 to both sides $14 = 6x$

Divide both sides by 6 $\frac{14}{6} = x$

$$x = \frac{7}{3} = 2\frac{1}{3}$$

Solve the following equations.

1 $3x + 2 + 2x = 7$ <u>**6**</u> $3x + 2x - 4x = 6$

2 $7 + 3x - 6 = 4$ <u>**7**</u> $7 = 2 - 3 + 4x$

3 $6 = 5x + 2 - 4x$ <u>**8**</u> $5x + x - 6x + 2x = 9$

4 $9 + 4 = 3x + 4x$ <u>**9**</u> $5 + x - 4x + x = 1$

5 $3x + 8 - 5x = 2$ <u>**10**</u> $6x = x + 2 - 7 - 1$

11 $5x + 6 + 3x = 10$ <u>**14**</u> $1 - 4 - 3 + 2x = 3x$

12 $8 = 7 - 11 + 6x$ <u>**15**</u> $3x - 4x - x = x - 6$

13 $7 + 2x = 12x - 7x + 2$ <u>**16**</u> $2 - 4x - x = x + 8$

Solve $9 - 3x = 15 - 4x$

$$9 - 3x = 15 - 4x$$

It is easier to work with a positive number of xs, so we add $4x$ to both sides.

Add $4x$ to both sides $9 + x = 15$

Take 9 from both sides $x = 6$

---

17 $5 - 3x = 1 - x$ <u>**21**</u> $16 - 6x = 1 - x$

18 $16 - 2x = 19 - 5x$ <u>**22**</u> $4 - 3x = 1 - 4x$

19 $6 - x = 12 - 2x$ <u>**23**</u> $4 - 2x = 8 - 5x$

20 $-2 - 4x = 6 - 2x$ <u>**24**</u> $3 - x = 5 - 3x$

25 $6 - 3x = 4x - 1$ <u>**29**</u> $13 - 4x = 4x - 3$

26 $4x + 1 = 6x - 3$ <u>**30**</u> $7x + 6 = x - 6$

27 $3 - 6x = 6x - 3$ <u>**31**</u> $6 - 2x = 9 - 5x$

28 $8 - 4x = 14 - 7x$ <u>**32**</u> $3 - 2x = 3 + x$

Solve $3 - 2x = 5$

$$3 - 2x = 5$$

It is easier to work with a positive number of xs, so we collect them on the right-hand side.

Add $2x$ to both sides $\quad 3 = 5 + 2x$
Take 5 from both sides $\quad -2 = 2x$
Divide both sides by 2 $\quad x = -1$

33 $13 - 4x = 5$ **35** $6 = 8 - 3x$

34 $6 = 2 - 2x$ **36** $0 = 6 - 2x$

37 $9x + 4 = 3x + 1$ **42** $5 - 3x = 2$

38 $2x + 3 = 12x$ **43** $6 + 3x = 7 - x$

39 $7 - 2x = 3 - 6x$ **44** $5 - 2x = 4x - 7$

40 $3x - 6 = 6 - x$ **45** $5x + 3 = -7 - x$

41 $-4x - 5 = -2x - 10$ **46** $4 - 3x = 0$

47 $-2x + x = 3x - 12$ **54** $4 - x - 2 - x = x$

48 $-4 + x - 2 - x = x$ **55** $4 - x - 2 + x = x$

49 $3x + 1 + 2x = 6$ **56** $2x + 7 - 4x + 1 = 4$

50 $4x - 2 + 6x - 4 = 64$ **57** $6 - 3x - 5x - 1 = 10$

51 $2x + 7 - x + 3 = 6x$ **58** $6x + 3 + 6 = x - 4 - 2$

52 $6 - 2x - 4 + 5x = 17$ **59** $x - 3 + 7x + 9 = 10$

53 $9x - 6 - x - 2 = 0$ **60** $15x + 2x - 6x - 9x = 20$

61 Nia weighs 4 kg less than Madge who weighs 3 kg less than Penny. Altogether they weigh 137 kg.
If Madge weighs x kg, what is the weight of each of Penny and Nia in terms of x?
How much does Madge weigh?

62 Laura goes to a shop that sells two models of radio. One cost three times as much as the other and the two together cost £72. Laura's mother wants to know the cost of the cheaper one.
If the cheaper radio costs £x form an equation in x.
What should Laura's answer be?

63 Keith and Sheila go into a cafe because they want a hot drink. Keith has a cup of tea and a cake, while Sheila has a cup of coffee and 2 cakes. Coffee costs 15 p more than tea, and each cake is 35 p more than a cup of coffee.

    a If a cup of tea costs x pence write down, in terms of x, the cost of

        i a cup of coffee   **ii** a cake   **iii** 2 cakes.

    b The total cost of the tea, coffee and cakes is £4.15.
    Form an equation in x and solve it.
    Hence write down the cost of

        i a cup of tea   **ii** a cup of coffee   **iii** a cake.

64 Four brothers play in a cricket team. In their last match Jim scored 15 more runs than Norman, Dennis scored five times as many as Norman and 16 more than Pete. In total they scored 107 runs. How many did each brother score?

65 Two sisters, Janet and Nora, each have a box holding 20 chocolates. Janet eats 5 and gives some away to her friends. Nora gives 1 away and eats three times as many as Janet has given away. When they compare boxes, the sisters still have the same number of chocolates left. If Janet gave x chocolates away, form an equation in x and solve it.
How many chocolates did Nora eat?

66 Divide 45 into two parts so that if 4 is subtracted from the larger number the result is 7 more than the smaller number.

MIXED EXERCISES

EXERCISE 17M

    1 A cola costs 10 p more than an orange squash.
    If the orange squash costs x pence and the cola costs 75 pence, form an equation in x. How much does an orange squash cost?

    2 Solve $5y = 45$

3 Solve the equation   **a** $5x - 0.7 = 2.8$ **b** $3x + 2 = 4$

4 I think of a number, add 4 and the result is 10.
Form an equation and solve it to find the number I thought of.

5 Solve the equation   **a** $6x + 2 = 3x + 8$ **b** $4x - 2 = -6$

6 Simplify $4x - 3y + 5x + 2y$

7 Solve the equation   **a** $4x + 2 - x = 6$ **b** $14 - 3x = 5$

EXERCISE 17N

1 An iced slice costs 14 pence less than a cream doughnut.
If a cream doughnut costs n pence and an iced slice costs 27 pence,
form an equation in n. How much does a cream doughnut cost?

2 Solve $5x = 1$

3 Solve the equation   **a** $4x = 0.5$ **b** $4x - 5 = 3$

4 Simplify   **a** $3c - 5c + 9c$ **b** $2a + 4 - 3 + 5a - a$

5 Solve the equation $3x - 2 = 4 - x$

6 When I think of a number, double it and add three, I get 11.
What number did I think of?

7 Solve the equation   **a** $x + 2x - 4 = 9$ **b** $12 - x = 6 - 2x$

INVESTIGATION

Meg wanted to find out Malcolm's age without asking him directly
what it was. The following conversation took place.
Meg: Think of your age but don't tell me what it is
Malcolm: Right
Meg: Multiply it by 5, add 4 and take away your age.
Malcolm: Yes
Meg: Divide the result by 4 and tell me your answer.
Malcolm: 15
Meg: That means you are 14.
Malcolm: Correct. How do you know that?
However many times Meg tried this on her friends and relations she
found their age by taking 1 away from the number they gave.
Does it always work?
Can you use simple algebra to prove that it always gives the correct
answer?

PROBABILITY

Probability measures the chance that something will happen in the future. We can use words based on experience to describe the chances that some events will happen. If we toss a coin, for example, we can say that the chances that it will land head up are even.

Not all situations are this obvious.
Consider this situation.
Lloyd wants to book a concert and
has a choice of an open-air venue in
each of two different cities.
To help in making the decision, he wants to
know what the chances are of rain in each city.
For one venue he is told that it is very likely
to be dry, and for the other venue he is told
it is highly likely to be dry.

- Lloyd finds it difficult to decide whether 'very likely' or 'highly likely' gives the greater chance of dry weather.
  This means that the information he is given about the likelihood of rain does not help with the decision he has to make.
- Lloyd also needs to consider what else the weather is capable of being, for example, what about wind, ice, and so on? He might hope to get better descriptions of the likelihood of these weather conditions occurring.

EXERCISE 18A For each question, discuss how you would describe the probability that the given events will happen. Discuss also whether you can decide which of the events is the more likely to happen.

1 An ordinary six-sided dice is thrown.

  a It will score more than 4.   **b** It will score less than 3.

2 A sweet is taken out of a bag containing 3 chocolates and 4 toffees.

  a The sweet is a chocolate.   **b** The sweet is a toffee.

3 Your group is being given a mathematics test next week.

  a All your group will fail.   **b** All your group will get over 90%.

EQUALLY LIKELY EVENTS

From talking about the events described in the exercise above, it is clear that sometimes we need a more precise description of probability than words can provide. This is particularly true when we want to compare the likelihoods of different events happening.

Another aspect that is important when working with probabilities is to know what else might happen, that is, what all the possible outcomes are. We also have to judge if these outcomes are equally likely or not.

If a coin is tossed, it can land head up or tail up. If the coin has not been damaged, these two events are equally likely.

EXERCISE 18B

1 If a dice is tossed, what are the possible scores that you can get? Are all these scores equally likely?

2 If Rebecca decides to pick out one card from an ordinary pack of playing cards, how many possible choices does she have? Is each of these possibilities equally likely?

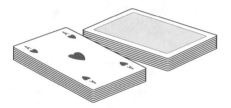

3 A bag contains one red disc and one blue disc. Is the chance of taking out a red disc the same as the chance of taking out a blue one?

4 If a bag contains two red discs and one blue disc, is it equally likely that a blue disc or a red disc is taken out?
What are the equally likely events in this situation?

PROBABILITY

If you throw an ordinary dice, it is reasonable to assume that you are as likely to throw any one score as any other, that is, all outcomes are equally likely.

As throwing a four is only 1 of the 6 equally likely outcomes you have a 1 in 6 chance of throwing a four.

We can use these numbers to 'measure' the chance of throwing a four: we say that the probability of throwing a four is $\frac{1}{6}$.

This can be written more briefly as

$$P(\text{throwing a four}) = \frac{1}{6}$$

We will now define exactly what we mean by 'the probability that something happens'.

If A stands for a particular event, the probability of A happening is given by

$$P(A \text{ happens}) = \frac{\text{the number of ways in which } A \text{ can occur}}{\text{the total number of equally likely outcomes}}$$

We can use this definition to work out, for example, the probability that if one card is drawn at random from a full pack of ordinary playing cards, it is the ace of spades.
(The phrase '*at random*' means that any one card is as likely to be picked as any other.)

There are 52 cards in a full pack, so there are 52 equally likely outcomes. There is only one ace of spades, so there is only one way of drawing that card,

i.e. $$P(\text{ace of spades}) = \tfrac{1}{52}$$

EXERCISE 18C

In the following questions, assume that all possible outcomes are equally likely.

1 What is the probability of throwing a two with a dice?

2 One letter is chosen at random from the letters in the word SALE. What is the probability that it is A?

3 A box contains 10 different coloured pencils including one red one. If one pencil is taken from this box, what is the probability that it is the red one?

4 What is the probability of throwing a three with a dice?

5 What is the probability of picking a prime number from the numbers 6, 7, 8, 9, 10?

6 What is the probability of choosing a multiple of 3 from the numbers 4, 5, 6, 7, 8?

7 A number is chosen at random from the whole numbers from 24 to 30 inclusive. What is the probability that it is a prime number?

8 What is the probability of taking the bruised apple from a bag containing six apples, only one of which is bruised?

9 What is the probability of picking an integer that is exactly divisible by 5 from the list 6, 7, 8, 9, 10, 11, 12?

10 In a raffle 200 tickets are sold. If you have bought one ticket, what is the probability that you will win first prize?

11 One card is taken at random from a pack of 52 ordinary playing cards. What is the probability that it is the ace of hearts?

12 What is the probability of choosing the colour red from the colours of the rainbow?

13 A whole number is picked at random from the first 15 positive whole numbers. What is the probability that it is exactly divisible both by 3 and by 4?

EVENTS THAT CAN HAPPEN MORE THAN ONCE

If a card is taken at random from an ordinary pack of 52 playing cards, what is the probability that it is a 'five'?

There are 4 fives in the pack, the five of spades, the five of hearts, the five of diamonds and the five of clubs.

So there are 4 ways in which a five can be picked.
Altogether there are 52 cards that are equally likely to be picked,

therefore $\qquad$ P (picking a five) $= \frac{4}{52} = \frac{1}{13}$

Now consider a bag containing 3 white discs and 2 black discs.

If one disc is taken from the bag it can be black or white. But these are not equally likely events: there are three ways of choosing a white disc and two ways of choosing a black disc, so

$$P (\text{choosing a white disc}) = \frac{3}{5}$$

and

$$P (\text{choosing a black disc}) = \frac{2}{5}$$

EXERCISE 18D

THIS MEANS THAT EACH LETTER IS EQUALLY LIKELY TO BE CHOSEN.

A letter is taken at random from the letters of the word DIFFICULT.
How many ways are there of taking the letter I?
What is the probability that the letter I will be taken?

There are 2 ways of taking the letter I and there are 9 letters in DIFFICULT, so I can be chosen in 2 out of 9 equally likely choices.

There are 2 ways of taking the letter I.

$P(\text{choosing I}) = \frac{2}{9}$

1 How many ways are there of taking an even number from the first 10 positive whole numbers?

2 A prime number is picked at random from the list

4, 5, 6, 7, 8, 9, 10, 11.

How many ways are there of doing this?

3 A card is taken at random from an ordinary pack of 52 playing cards. How many ways are there of taking a black card?

4 An ordinary six-sided dice is thrown. How many ways are there of getting a score that is greater than 4?

5 A lucky dip contains 50 boxes, only 10 of which contain a prize, the rest being empty. What is the probability of choosing a box that contains a prize?

6 A bag contains 4 white counters and 6 red counters. What is the probability of taking out a red counter?

7 A number is chosen at random from the first 10 positive integers. What is the probability that it is

a an even number   **c** a prime number

b an odd number   **d** exactly divisible by 3?

8 One card is drawn at random from an ordinary pack of 52 playing cards. What is the probability that it is

a an ace

b a red card

c a heart

d a picture card (include the aces)?

9 One letter is chosen at random from the word INNINGS. What is the probability that it is

a the letter N   **c** a vowel

b the letter I   **d** one of the first five letters of the alphabet?

10 An ordinary six-sided dice is thrown. What is the probability that the score is

a greater than 3   **b** at least 5   **c** less than 3?

11 A book of 150 pages has a picture on each of 20 pages. If one page is chosen at random, what is the probability that it has a picture on it?

12 One counter is picked at random from a bag containing 15 red counters, 5 white counters and 5 yellow counters. What is the probability that the counter removed is

a red   **b** yellow   **c** not red?

13 If you bought 10 raffle tickets and a total of 400 were sold, what is the probability that you win first prize?

14 A roulette wheel is spun. What is the probability that when it stops the ball is resting in

a an even number

b an odd number

c a number less than 10 excluding zero?

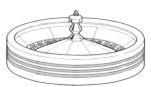

(The numbers on a roulette wheel go from 0 to 35, and zero is neither an even number nor an odd number.)

15 One letter is chosen at random from the letters of the alphabet. What is the probability that it is a consonant?

16 A number is chosen at random from the set of two-digit numbers (i.e. the numbers from 10 to 99).
What is the probability that it is exactly divisible by both 3 and 4 ?

17 A bag of sweets contains 4 caramels, 3 fruit centres, 5 mints and 4 cola bottles. If one sweet is taken out, what is the probability that it is

a a mint **b** a caramel **c** not a fruit centre ?

CERTAINTY AND IMPOSSIBILITY

Some events are certain and some are impossible. It is certain, for example, that if you take a sweet from a tube that only has Smarties in it, the sweet will be a Smartie. It is impossible that the sweet will be a wine gum.

EXERCISE 18E

This bag contains five black discs.

1 What fraction of the discs in the bag are black ?

2 If a disc is taken from the bag what are the chances that it is a black disc ?

3 If a disc is taken from the bag what is the probability that it is a black disc ?

4 A disc is taken from the bag. What are the chances that it is a red disc ? Write this as a probability.

THE PROBABILITY SCALE

From the last exercise we see that, if an event is certain to happen, the probability that is happens is 1.
If an event is impossible, the probability that it happens is 0.

Most events fall somewhere between impossible and certain. So probabilities lie on a scale from 0 to 1.

EXERCISE 18F

1 A bag holds 2 red counters, 3 blue counters and 1 yellow counter. One counter is drawn from the bag. What is the probability that it is

a a red counter **c** a black counter

b a yellow counter **d** not a black counter ?

2 An ordinary dice is thrown. What is the probability of scoring

 a 1 or more   **b** 3 or more   **c** 7 or more?

3 A bag holds twenty tickets numbered 1 to 20. One ticket is drawn from the bag.
What is the probability that the number on it is

 a a multiple of 5   **b** an even number?

4 A card is drawn from an ordinary pack of 52 playing cards. What is the probability that it is

 a a joker   **c** a black card

 b the two of clubs   **d** a red or a black card?

5 One letter is chosen at random from the letters in the word MATHEMATICS. What is the probability that it is

 a the letter B   **c** a vowel

 b the letter T   **d** a consonant?

RELATIVE FREQUENCY

We have assumed that if you toss a coin it is as equally likely to land head up as tail up so $P(\text{a head}) = \frac{1}{2}$.
Coins like this are called 'fair' or 'unbiased'.

Most coins are likely to be unbiased but it is not necessarily true of all coins. A particular coin may be slightly bent or even deliberately biased so that there is not an equal chance of getting a head or a tail.

The only way to find out if a particular coin is unbiased is to collect some information about how it behaves when it is tossed. We can do this by tossing it several times and recording the results.

Tossing a bent coin gave these results.

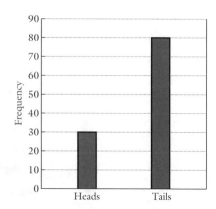

For this coin we have 30 heads out of 110 tosses.

We say that the *relative frequency* of heads with this coin is $\frac{30}{110}$.

We can use the relative frequency of heads as an estimate for the probability of a head with this coin, i.e.

$$P\,(\,\text{a head}\,) \approx \frac{\text{number of heads}}{\text{total number of tosses}} = \frac{30}{110} = \frac{3}{11}$$

The approximation gets more reliable as the number of tosses gets larger, but on this evidence it looks as though this coin is more likely to give a tail than a head.

EXERCISE 18G   **1**

To answer this question, Matt looked at the following information from a survey carried out into the faults that developed in some makes of television set.

Make	Number that developed a fault in the first five years	Total number of sets in the survey	Relative frequency of faults	
			Fraction	Decimal
Cony	25	100		
Hitchi	5	50		
Thorson	60	120		
Elite	63	90		

a Copy and complete the table.

b What is the probability of a Cony television failing in the first five years?

c If you decide to buy a Hitchi set, will you take out the extra five-year guarantee? Write one sentence giving reasons for your answer.

d An Elite set is much cheaper than the other sets. Would you buy one of these sets? Write one sentence giving reasons for your answer.

e Which of the four makes seems to be the most reliable?

2 This bar chart illustrates the results of a survey to test the water resistances of watches.

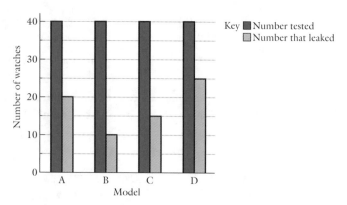

Each of these models claimed to be water resistant. They were tested by putting them at the bottom of the deep end (3 m) of a swimming pool and leaving them there for two hours.

a For each model, work out the fraction of the number tested that leaked.

b Express these relative frequencies as decimals, correct to two decimal places if necessary.

c If you go swimming wearing a Model A watch, what is the probability that it will leak?

PRACTICAL WORK

Work with a partner or collect information from the whole class.

1 Use an ordinary six-sided dice.

a Toss it 25 times and keep a tally of the number of times that you get a six.
Use your results to find the relative frequency of sixes.

b Now toss the dice another 25 times and add the results to the last set. Use these to find again the relative frequency of sixes.
Now do another 25 tosses and add the results to the last two sets to find another value for the relative frequency.

c Carry on doing this in groups of 25 tosses until you have done 200 tosses altogether.
You know that the probability of getting a six is $\frac{1}{6}$. Now look at the sequence of results obtained from your experiment.
What do you notice? (It is easier to compare your results if you change the fractions into decimals to 2 d.p.)

2 a A dice is to be thrown 60 times and the numbers that appear are to be recorded. Roughly how many times do you expect each of the numbers 1 to 6 to appear?

b Now throw a dice 60 times. Record the results on a tally chart and draw a bar chart.
Has it come out as you expected?

c Combine your information with that of several other people, so that you have the results of, say, 180 or 240 throws.
Draw a bar chart. Comment on its shape.

d Throw the dice 10 times and record the numbers.
Would it make sense to make a judgement about the fairness of this dice using the relative frequencies of each score from these results alone?

e Throw the dice again 10 times. Has the same set of numbers been thrown as in part **d**?

f Imagine that the dice is thrown 10 more times.
Can you rely on getting the same numbers again as in parts **d** and **e**? What extreme case might you get?

3 a A coin is to be tossed 100 times and the number of heads and tails is to be recorded. Roughly how many heads would you expect to get?

b Imagine that you are now tossing the coin 1000 times. What is likely to happen? What, though very unlikely, might happen?

c If the coin is tossed only 10 times, what might happen?

d If the coin is tossed again 10 times, will the same number of heads appear as before?

e How many tosses of a bent coin do you think you need to find a reasonably reliable estimate for the probability of tossing a head with that coin?

f Find a damaged coin and use it to estimate the chances of tossing a head with that coin.

COORDINATES AND STRAIGHT LINES

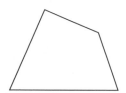

In Book 7B, Chapter 11, we considered how we can locate a point on a grid by giving its coordinates. These coordinates can be positive or negative. We begin this chapter by using coordinates to classify quadrilaterals.

QUADRILATERALS

A quadrilateral has four sides.
No two of the sides need be equal and
no two of the sides need be parallel.

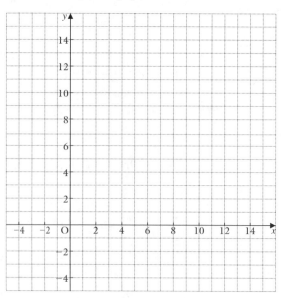

There are, however, some special quadrilaterals, such as a square, which have some sides parallel and/or some sides equal.

The questions in the next exercise investigate the properties of these special quadrilaterals.

EXERCISE 19A

For each question in this exercise you will need a set of axes, like the one below, drawn on 2 mm squared paper and scaled from −4 to 15.

If you are not sure whether two lines are equal, *measure them*.

1 The Square
A($3, 2$), B($11, 2$), C($11, 10$) and D($3, 10$) are the four corners
of a square.
Draw a diagram like the one given above. Mark these points on your
diagram and then draw the square ABCD.

a Write down, as a number of sides of squares, the lengths of the
sides AB, BC, CD and DA.

b Which side is parallel to AB?
Are BC and AD parallel?

c What is the size of each angle of the square?

2 The Rectangle
A($-1, -1$), B($-1, 4$), C($11, 4$) and D($11, -1$) are the vertices
of a rectangle ABCD.
Draw the rectangle ABCD on your own set of axes.

a Write down the sides which are equal in length.

b Write down the pairs of sides which are parallel.

c What is the size of each angle of the rectangle?

3 The Rhombus
A($8, 1$), B($11, 7$), C($8, 13$) and D($5, 7$) are the vertices of a
rhombus ABCD.
Draw the rhombus on your own set of axes.

a Write down the sides which are equal in length.

b Write down the pairs of sides which are parallel.

c Measure the angles of the rhombus.
Are any of the angles equal?

4 The Parallelogram
A($-1, -1$), B($11, -1$), C($14, 4$) and D($2, 4$) are the vertices of
a parallelogram.
Draw the parallelogram on your own set of axes.

a Write down which sides are equal in length.

b Write down which sides are parallel.

c Measure the angles of the parallelogram.
Write down which, if any, of the angles are equal.

5 The Trapezium
A($1, 1$), B($12, 1$), C($10, 5$) and D($5, 5$) are the vertices of a
trapezium.
Draw the trapezium on your own set of axes.

a Write down which, if any, of the sides are the same length.

b Write down which, if any, of the sides are parallel.

c Write down which, if any, of the angles are equal.

PROPERTIES OF THE SIDES AND ANGLES OF THE SPECIAL QUADRILATERALS

We can summarise our investigations in the last exercise as follows:

In a square
- all four sides are the same length
- both pairs of opposite sides are parallel
- all four angles are right angles.

In a rectangle
- both pairs of opposite sides are the same length
- both pairs of opposite sides are parallel
- all four angles are right angles.

In a rhombus
- all four sides are the same length
- both pairs of opposite sides are parallel
- the opposite angles are equal.

In a parallelogram
- both pairs of opposite sides are the same length
- both pairs of opposite sides are parallel
- the opposite angles are equal.

In a trapezium
- just one pair of opposite sides are parallel.

EXERCISE 19B

For each question in this exercise you need a set of axes like those given below but drawn on 2 mm squared paper. The points A, B, C and D are the vertices of a quadrilateral.

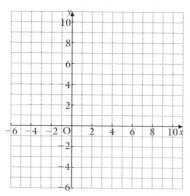

Draw the figure ABCD on your own set of axes. Write down the type of quadrilateral you have drawn.

1 A$(2, 4)$ B$(7, 4)$ C$(8, 7)$ D$(3, 7)$

2 A$(2, 1)$ B$(6, -1)$ C$(7, 1)$ D$(3, 3)$

3 A$(2, 2)$ B$(7, 2)$ C$(5, 5)$ D$(3, 5)$

4 A$(2, 0)$ B$(6, 0)$ C$(6, 4)$ D$(2, 4)$

5 A$(-1, -1)$ B$(2, -2)$ C$(2, 4)$ D$(-1, 1)$

6 A($3, 1$) B($6, 3$) C($3, 5$) D($0, 3$)

<u>**7**</u> A($-3, 0$) B($0, -2$) C($2, 1$) D($-1, 3$)

<u>**8**</u> A($2, 4$) B($3, 7$) C($9, 5$) D($8, 2$)

<u>**9**</u> A($3, 1$) B($5, 1$) C($3, 5$) D($1, 5$)

<u>**10**</u> A($-4, -2$) B($1, -2$) C($4, 2$) D($-1, 2$)

STRAIGHT LINE GRAPHS

The diagram shows a straight line drawn on x- and y-axes.

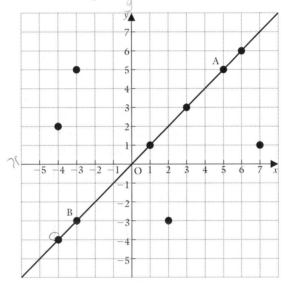

The points A and B are on the line and, for A, the x-coordinate is 5 and the y-coordinate is also 5.

For B, we see that the x-coordinate is -3 and the y-coordinate is also -3.

Looking at other points on the line, we can see that the y-coordinate is always equal to the x-coordinate.

However, if we take any point that is *not* on this line, we find that the y-coordinate is *not* equal to the x-coordinate.

- From this we can deduce that for any point on this line the x-coordinate is equal to the y-coordinate,
  i.e. for points on this line we can give a formula for y, in terms of x
  namely $y = x$

- We can also see that, for points not on the line, $y \neq x$.

  (The symbol $\neq$ means 'is not equal to'.)

EXERCISE 19C

1 The diagram shows some points on a line drawn through the origin.

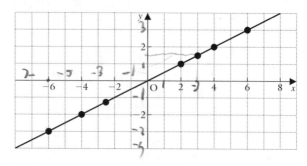

a Copy and complete the table for the *x*- and *y*-coordinates of the points marked.

x	−6	−4	−2.5	2	3	4	6
y			−1.25				

b Give an instruction in words for finding the *y*-coordinate of a point on this line from its *x*-coordinate.

c Find a formula for *y*.

d Does this formula apply to the coordinates of any point on the line? Discuss the reasons for your answer.

e Does this formula apply to the coordinates of any point *not* on the line? Discuss the reasons for your answer.

2 Repeat question **1** for the line and table given below.

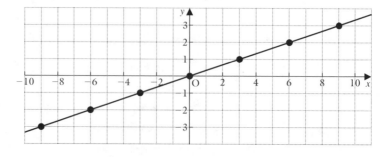

x	−9	−6	−3	0	3	6	9
y					1		

3 The diagram shows some points on a line drawn through the origin.

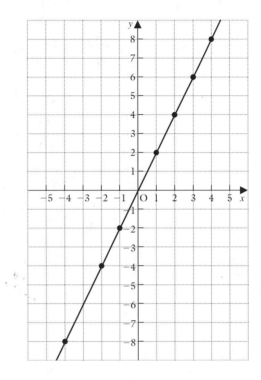

a Copy and complete the table for the x- and y-coordinates of the points marked.

x	-4	-2	-1	1	2	3	4
y		-4					

b Give an instruction in words for finding the y-coordinate of a point on this line from its x-coordinate.

c Find a formula for y.

d Does this formula apply to the coordinates of any point on the line?
Discuss the reasons for your answer.

e Does this formula apply to the coordinates of any point *not* on the line?
Discuss the reasons for your answer.

4 a The diagram shows some points on a line drawn through the origin.

 b Make a table, like the one in question **1**, showing the *x*- and *y*-coordinates of six points on this line.

 c Use your completed table to find a formula for *y*.

 d Discuss which points on the graph your formula applies to, and to which points it does not.

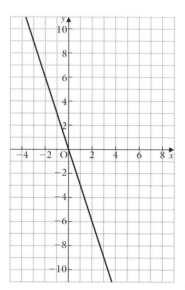

5 The diagram shows three straight lines. For each straight line write down, in a table similar to the one used in question **1**, the *x*- and *y*-coordinates of five points on that line. If the formulas of these three lines are: $y = x + 1$, $y = 2x + 1$ and $y = x - 2$, use the information in the tables to decide which formula goes with which straight line.

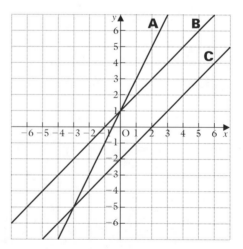

**THE EQUATION
OF A LINE**

The examples in the previous exercise show that

- it is possible to give an instruction which you can use to find the
  y-coordinate from the x-coordinate of any point on a line.
- this instruction can be given as a formula in the form $y = \ldots$

> The formula that gives the y-coordinate of a point on the line
> in terms of the x-coordinate is called the *equation of the line.*

In the example above **Exercise 19C**, the equation of the line is $y = x$.
We often refer to this line briefly as 'the line $y = x$'.

EXERCISE 19D

Find the y-coordinate of the point on the line $y = 3x$ whose
x-coordinate is **a** 3 **b** −5

> The equation $y = 3x$ is a formula for finding the y-coordinate from the x-coordinate.

a When $x = 3$, $y = 3x$ gives

$$y = 3 \times 3 = 9$$

b When $x = -5$, $y = 3x$ gives

$$y = 3 \times (-5) = -15$$

> This means that the points $(3, 9)$ and $(-5, -15)$ are points on the line $y = 3x$.

1 Find the y-coordinate of the point on the line $y = x$ which has an
x-coordinate of

a 2 **c** 7 **e** −1 **g** −8

b 3 **d** 12 **f** −6 **h** −20

2 Find the y-coordinate of the point on the line $y = 4x$ which has
an x-coordinate of

a 3 **c** 1 **e** −2 **g** 15

b 5 **d** −4 **f** −10 **h** $\frac{1}{2}$

Find the y-coordinate of the point on the line $y = -5x$ whose x-coordinate is   **a** 4   **b** -3

a When $x = 4$, $y = -5x$ gives

$$y = -5 \times 4 = -20$$

b When $x = -3$, $y = -5x$ gives

$$y = -5 \times (-3) = 15$$

> A negative number times a negative number gives a positive number.

3 Find the y-coordinate of the point on the line $y = -x$ which has an x-coordinate of

   a 4   **b** 2   **c** $3\frac{1}{2}$ **d** $-4\frac{1}{2}$ **e** -6 **f** $8\frac{1}{4}$

4 Find the y-coordinate of the point on the line $y = -3x$ which has an x-coordinate of

   a 3   **b** -6 **c** -4 **d** $2\frac{1}{2}$ **e** 3.4   **f** -4.7

Find the y-coordinate of the point on the line $y = 2x + 1$ whose x-coordinate is

a 5   **b** -9.

a When $x = 5$, $y = 2x + 1$ gives

$$y = 2 \times 5 + 1$$
$$= 10 + 1$$
$$= 11$$

> Remember to do multiplication before addition.

i.e. when $x = 5$, $y = 11$

b When $x = -9$, $y = 2x + 1$ gives

$$y = 2 \times (-9) + 1$$
$$= -18 + 1$$
$$= -17$$

i.e. when $x = -9$, $y = -17$

5 Find the y-coordinate of a point on the line $y = x + 5$ which has an x-coordinate of

   a 7   **b** -2 **c** $5\frac{1}{2}$ **d** -8 **e** -6.4

6 Find the y-coordinate of a point on the line $y = x - 4$ which has an x-coordinate of

    a 3   **b** -9 **c** 6   **d** -4 **e** $-1\frac{1}{2}$

7 Find the y-coordinates of a point on the line $y = 2x - 3$ which has an x-coordinate of

    a 5   **b** 8   **c** -4 **d** $3\frac{1}{2}$ **e** -2.5

Find the x-coordinate of a point on the line $y = 5x$ whose y-coordinate is   **a** 15   **b** -30

a When $y = 15$, $y = 5x$ gives

$$15 = 5x$$

$$3 = x$$

THIS IS AN EQUATION WE CAN SOLVE BY DIVIDING BOTH SIDES OF THE EQUATION BY 5.

i.e. when $y = 15$, $x = 3$

b When $y = -30$, $y = 5x$ gives

$$-30 = 5x$$

$$-6 = x$$

DIVIDING A NEGATIVE NUMBER BY A POSITIVE NUMBER GIVES A NEGATIVE NUMBER.

i.e. when $y = -30$, $x = -6$

---

8 Find the x-coordinate of the point on the line $y = 3x$ which has a y-coordinate of

    a 3   **b** 9   **c** -6 **d** -24 **e** 2

9 Find the x-coordinate of the point on the line $y = 2x + 3$ which has a y-coordinate of

    a 5   **b** 11   **c** -7 **d** -1 **e** 6

10 Find the x-coordinate of the point on the line $y = 2x - 1$ which has a y-coordinate of

    a 5   **b** -19 **c** 13   **d** -3 **e** -1

11 If the points $(-1, a)$, $(b, 15)$ and $(c, -20)$ lie on the straight line with equation $y = 5x$, find the values of a, b and c.

12 If the points $(3, a)$, $(-12, b)$ and $(c, -12)$ lie on the straight line with equation $y = -2x$, find the values of a, b and c.

13 Using squared paper and 1 square to 1 unit on each axis, plot the points $(-2, -6)$, $(1, 3)$, $(3, 9)$ and $(4, 12)$. What is the equation of the straight line which passes through these points?

14 Using squared paper and 1 square to 1 unit on each axis, plot the points $(-3, 6)$, $(-2, 4)$, $(1, -2)$ and $(3, -6)$. What is the equation of the straight line which passes through these points?

15 Using the same scale on each axis, plot the points $(-4, -11)$, $(2, 1)$, $(6, 9)$ and $(9, 15)$. What is the equation of the straight line which passes through these points?

16 Which of the points $(-2, -4)$, $(2.5, 4)$, $(6, 12)$ and $(7.5, 10)$ lie on the line $y = 2x$?

17 Which of the points $(-5, -15)$, $(-2, 6)$, $(1, -3)$ and $(8, -24)$ lie on the line $y = -3x$?

18 Which of the points

$$(2, 6), \ (-2, -1), \ (3, 0), \ (-4, 2), \ (6, -3.2), \ (-3.4, 4.6)$$

a lie above the line $y = x + 3$ **b** lie below the line $y = x + 3$?

PLOTTING A LINE FROM ITS EQUATION

If we want to draw the graph of $y = 3x$ for values of x from -3 to $+3$, then we need to find the coordinates of some points on the line.

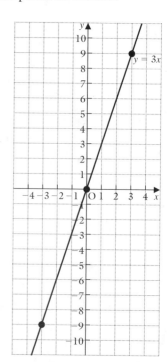

As we know that it is a straight line, two points are enough. However, it is sensible to find three points and use the third point as a check on our working. It does not matter which three points we find, so we will choose easy values for x, well spread over the range -3 to 3.

If $x = -3$, $y = 3 \times (-3) = -9$

If $x = 0$, $y = 3 \times 0 = 0$

If $x = 3$, $y = 3 \times 3 = 9$

These are easier to use if we write them in a table,

i.e.

x	-3	0	3
y	-9	0	9

We can plot these points and draw a straight line through them.

Notice that we label the line with its equation.

EXERCISE 19E You will need a copy of the diagram given below for each question from **1** to **6**. A further copy is needed for questions **7** to **12**.

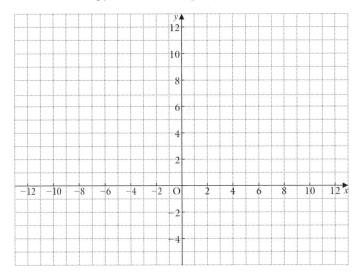

For each equation, copy the table and fill in the blanks. Draw the graph of each equation on a diagram. Write the equation of each line somewhere on the line. Keep your graphs: you will need them for the next exercise.

1 $y = x$

x	−3	1	8
y			

4 $y = \frac{1}{4}x$

x	−4	2	12
y			

2 $y = 2x$

x	−3	2	5
y			

5 $y = \frac{1}{2}x$

x	−12	6	12
y			

3 $y = 4x$

x	−2	1	3
y			

6 $y = \frac{2}{3}x$

x	−9	3	12
y			

In questions **7** to **12**, draw the graphs of the given equations all on the same axes.

7 $y = -x$ **9** $y = -\frac{1}{2}x$ **11** $y = -\frac{1}{3}x$

8 $y = -2x$ **10** $y = -\frac{1}{4}x$ **12** $y = -\frac{2}{3}x$

13 In questions **1** to **12**, the equation of the line is of the form
$y = mx$ that is, y is equal to a number multiplied by x. Discuss the
effect that the value of m and whether m is positive or negative, has
on the position of the line.

Discussion from question **13** shows that

> the graph of an equation of the form $y = mx$, is a straight line that
>
> - passes through the origin
> - gets steeper as m increases
> - slopes 'uphill' to the right if m is positive
> - slopes 'downhill' to the right if m is negative.

14

x	-4	0	1	5
y				

Copy and complete this table for each of the equations

a: $y = x + 1$,   **b**: $y = x + 2$,   **c**: $y = x - 1$

Hence draw the graphs of the three equations on the same diagram.
Are the graphs of these three straight lines related in a special way?
If your answer is 'yes', state the relationship.

15 Repeat question **14** for the equations

    a: $y = 2x + 1$,   **b**: $y = 2x - 3$ **c**: $y = 2x + 4$

**CONVERSION
GRAPHS**

Straight line graphs are useful in many practical situations where the
coordinates of points represent real quantities.

For example, if you go to Spain on holiday, it is useful to be able to
convert prices given in pesetas quickly to the equivalent price in sterling
and vice versa. (The £s we use in the UK are called pounds sterling to
distinguish them from the pounds used in other countries in the world.)

Suppose the exchange rate is 210 pesetas (pta) to £1

then if n pta is equivalent to £N,

we see that $n = 210N$.

Comparing this formula with $y = mx$ shows that plotting values of n
against values of N will give a straight line through the origin.

To draw the graph we need points on the line which goes through the
origin. We can get these direct from the exchange rate,
i.e. as £1 = 210 pta, £50 = 10 500 pta, and so on.
We can put these values in a table.

£ Sterling	0	50	100
Pesetas	0	10 500	21 000

Plotting the points in the table gives this graph.

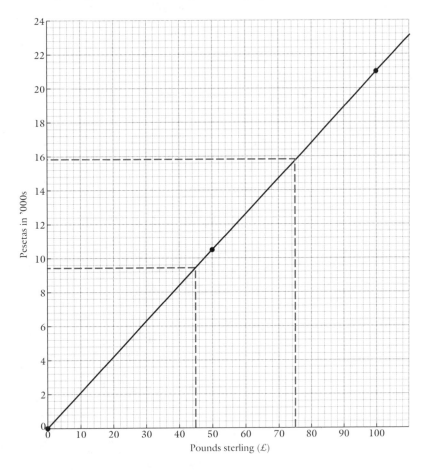

From the graph we can see that £45 ≈ 9400 pesetas

and that 15 800 pesetas ≈ £75

EXERCISE 19F

1 Use the conversion graph above for this question.

  a Why do you think this graph is drawn on graph paper not on 5 mm squared paper?

  b The scales on the axes are not equal. Why do you think that 1 cm for 10 units is not used for both scales?

  c Can you find the cost in pounds sterling of a mountain bike priced at 100 000 pta from this graph?

  d To what values would the axes need to be scaled for this graph to be used to convert prices up to £500 into pesetas?

  e Why is the conversion from one currency to the other approximate?

2 This graph can be used to convert values up to £100 into Norwegian kroner. Use the graph to find

    a the cost in pounds sterling of a pair of shoes priced at 760 kroner

    b how many kroner are equivalent to £46

    c the exchange rate on which this graph is based.

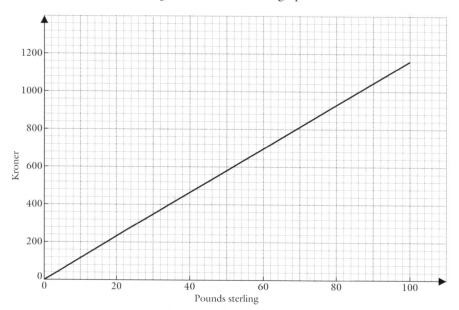

3 There are electronic gadgets that will convert from one currency into any other currency. The calculations can also be done using an ordinary calculator. Discuss the advantages and disadvantages that conversion graphs have over electronic aids.

Use 2 mm graph paper for the remaining questions in this exercise.

4 The table shows the conversion from US dollars to pounds sterling for various amounts of money.

US dollars ($)	50	100	200
Pounds sterling (£)	35	70	140

Plot these points on a graph and draw a straight line to pass through them. Let 4 cm represent 50 units on both axes.

    a Use your graph to convert

        i $160 into pounds sterling   **iii** £122 into dollars

        ii $96 into pounds sterling   **iv** £76 into dollars

    b What is the exchange rate between £s and $ that this graph is based on?

5 The table shows the conversion of various sums of money from Deutschmarks to French francs.

Deutschmarks (DM)	100	270	350
French francs (Ff)	310	837	1085

Plot these points on a graph and draw a straight line to pass through them. Take 2 cm to represent 50 units on the Deutschmarks axis and 100 units on the francs axis.
Use your graph to convert

a 16 DM into francs   **c** 440 Ff into Deutschmarks

b 330 DM into francs   **d** 980 Ff into Deutschmarks

6 The table shows the distance a girl walks in a given time.

Time walking in hours	0	1	$2\frac{1}{2}$	4	5
Distance walked in km	0	6	15	24	30

Draw a graph of these results. What do you conclude about the speed at which she walks?

How far has she walked in   **a** 2 hours   **b** $3\frac{1}{2}$ hours?
How long does she take to walk   **c** 10 km   **d** 21 km?

7 The table shows the distance an aircraft has travelled at various times from the start of a particular journey.

Time after departure in hours	0	1	$3\frac{1}{2}$	6
Distance travelled from take-off in km	0	550	1925	3300

Draw a graph using these results. What can you conclude about the speed of the aircraft?

How far does it fly in   **a** $1\frac{1}{2}$ hours   **b** $4\frac{1}{2}$ hours?
How long does it take to fly   **c** 1000 km   **d** 2500 km?

8 Marks in an examination range from 0 to 65. Draw a graph which enables you to express the marks in percentages from 0 to 100. Note that a mark of 0 is 0% while a mark of 65 is 100%.
Use your graph

a to express marks of 35 and 50 as percentages

b to find the original mark for percentages of 50% and 80%.

9 The table gives temperatures in degrees Fahrenheit ($°F$) and equivalent values in degrees Celsius ($°C$).

Temperature in $°F$	57	126	158	194
Temperature in $°C$	14	52	70	90

Plot these points on a graph for Celsius values from 0 to 100 and Fahrenheit values from 0 to 220. Let 2 cm represent 20 units on each axis.

a Use your graph to convert

    i 97 $°F$ into $°C$ **iii** 25 $°C$ into $°F$

    ii 172 $°F$ into $°C$ **iv** 80 $°C$ into $°F$

b Explain why this graph does not pass through the origin.

10 a Given that 20 mph $=$ 32 km/h, find in km/h

    i 40 mph   **ii** 60 mph

b Use the values found in part **a** to draw a graph to convert between speeds in mph and speeds in km/h.

11 Given that 1 gallon is equivalent to **4.**546 litres, draw a graph to convert from 0 to 100 litres into gallons.

Give an example of a situation where this conversion graph would be useful.

MIXED EXERCISE

EXERCISE 19G

1 Plot the points A($-4, -2$), B($-2, 6$), C($6, 4$) and D($4, -4$) on your own set of axes. If these points are the vertices of a quadrilateral ABCD what type of quadrilateral is it?

2 The equation of a straight line is $y = 4x$.

a Find the y-coordinate of the point on the line that has an x-coordinate of **i** 3   **ii** 5

b Find the x-coordinate of the point on the line that has a y-coordinate of **i** 8   **ii** -12

c Does the point ($5, -20$) lie on the line? Justify your answer.

3 Look at these equations which are equations of straight lines.

A $y = -3x$ **B** $y = \frac{1}{4}x$ **C** $y = \frac{3}{4}x$ **D** $y = 4x$ **E** $y = -x$

a Which lines slope 'upwards' with the positive x-axis?

b Which lines slope 'downwards' with the positive x-axis?

c Which line makes the steeper angle with the x-axis: line **B** or line **D**?

4 The table shows the conversion from Belgian francs to pounds sterling for various amounts of money

Belgian francs (Bf)	3000	9000	12 000
Pounds sterling (£)	50	150	200

Plot these points on a graph using 4 cm to represent £50 on the pounds axis and 2 cm to represent 2000 Bf on the francs axis.

a Use your graph to convert
  i £70 into Belgian francs   **ii** 8400 Bf into pounds.

b What is the exchange rate between pounds and Belgian francs that this graph is based on?

PRACTICAL WORK

a Starting with 6, form a number chain using this rule: multiply the units digit by 4 and add the tens digit if there is one. This means that the second number in the chain is $6 \times 4 + 0 = 24$, the third number is $4 \times 4 + 2 = 18$ and the fourth number is $8 \times 4 + 1 = 33$.
Continue to write down the numbers in the chain until you get back to the number you started with. How many numbers are there in the chain before it starts to repeat?

b Group these numbers in pairs by pairing each number with the one that follows it and then pairing that number with itself.
Applying these rules gives the pairs (6, 24), (24, 24), (24, 18), (18, 18), (18, 33) and so on.

c Draw x- and y-axes from 0 to 36 marking each axis 0, 3, 6, 9, 12, and so on. Plot, in order, the points whose coordinates are given by the pairs of numbers in part **b**. Join each point to the next one as you plot it, and join the last point to the first.

d Does your completed shape have
  i line symmetry   **ii** rotational symmetry?

If it has line symmetry, mark the mirror line; if it has rotational symmetry, state the order.

INVESTIGATION

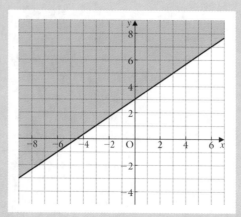

a In this chapter you have found that for any point on a given straight line there is a relationship between the two coordinates. What is the relationship between the coordinates of points on the line shown in this diagram?

b What can you say about the relationship between the coordinates of points in the shaded area?

c How can you describe the shaded area? Explain your reasoning.

USING ARITHMETIC

20

A knowledge of basic arithmetic is essential for everyday life in the modern world.

- At the Post Office we need to be able to work out how much it will cost to send some letters and parcels. If we have accurate scales we can weigh the letters and parcels and put stamps on them so that we are paying the correct postage. This way we can avoid standing in a queue.

- Before we go to the travel agent to book a holiday we need to be able to work out the different costs from brochures to see if we can afford a particular holiday.

- If we want to cook we need to know whether or not we have enough of each ingredient and, if not, we need to know how much we should buy.

- When we borrow money we want to know where we can get the best deal and how much it will cost.

This chapter gives the kind of information that allows us to answer some of the questions that are raised in these situations.

EXERCISE 20A

1 Discuss the factors that determine the value of the stamps you must put on a letter if you want to push it into a postbox rather than go to the Post Office and let the counter clerk tell you.

2 You have a holiday brochure for next summer. What costs must you remember to include to find the total cost of an intended holiday?

3 You have been asked to make ten dozen sausage rolls for a school fête. How do you decide what you need to buy to make them?

WORKING OUT THE COST OF POSTAGE

This is a list of postal charges for letters within the United Kingdom.

Letter Post

Weight not over	First Class	Second Class	Weight not over	First Class	Second Class
60 g	26 p	20 p	500 g	£1.25	98 p
100 g	38 p	29 p	600 g	£1.55	£1.20
150 g	47 p	36 p	700 g	£1.90	£1.40
200 g	57 p	43 p	750 g	£2.05	£1.45
250 g	67 p	52 p	800 g	£2.15	Not
300 g	77 p	61 p	900 g	£2.35	admissible over
350 g	88 p	70 p	1000 g	£2.50	750 g
400 g	£1.00	79 p	Each extra 250 g or part thereof 65 p		
450 g	£1.13	89 p			

EXERCISE 20B

Find the cost of posting 2 letters, each weighing 50 g, and one letter weighing 220 g: all to be sent first class.

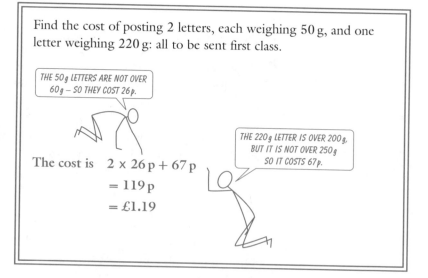

THE 50 g LETTERS ARE NOT OVER 60 g – SO THEY COST 26 p.

THE 220 g LETTER IS OVER 200 g, BUT IT IS NOT OVER 250 g SO IT COSTS 67 p.

The cost is $\quad 2 \times 26\,p + 67\,p$

$\qquad = 119\,p$

$\qquad = £1.19$

Find the cost of posting

1 4 letters, all under 60 g, by first-class post

2 5 letters, all under 60 g, by second-class post

3 3 letters by first-class post, two of which weigh 50 g and one weighs 140 g

4 4 letters, each weighing 90 g, by second-class post

5 2 letters, each weighing 80 g, and 3 letters, each weighing 120 g, all by first-class post

6 1 letter weighing 145 g by first-class post, and 1 letter weighing 230 g by second-class post

7 2 letters weighing 155 g by first-class post and 1 letter weighing 320 g by second-class post

8 2 letters weighing 55 g by first-class post and 3 letters weighing 165 g by second-class post

9 1 packet weighing 1800 g by first-class post

10 John wants to send a packet weighing 950 g, but he does not want to send it parcel post. How else can he send it through the post? How much will it cost him?

11 How much more does it cost to send three packages, each weighing 680 g, by first-class rather than by second-class post?

12 A publicly owned company must, by law, send a copy of its annual report to every shareholder. The annual report for Brockway Plastics plc, which weighs 235 g, is to be sent to 9476 shareholders.

   a How much will this cost if they are sent

     i by first-class post   **ii** by seond-class post?

   b How much is saved by using second-class rather than first-class post?
     (In practice companies are able to negotiate lower rates for posting large amounts of mail.

PAYING FOR THE PHOTOCOPIER

Grange School rents its photocopier.
The school has to pay rent each quarter (i.e. every three months) and 2 p for each copy made.

EXERCISE 20C

> 8500 photocopies were made in the first quarter of 1996, and the rent for that quarter was £350. What was the bill for that quarter?
>
> The charge for 8500 copies is $\quad 8500 \times 2\,p = 17\,000\,p$
>
> $$= £170$$
>
> $$\text{The rent} = £350$$
>
> The bill for rent plus charge for copies $\quad = £350 + £170$
>
> $$= £520$$

Find the bill for the quarter when the rent is

1 £200 and 2500 copies are made

3 £425 and 10 000 copies are made

2 £330 and 9000 copies are made

4 £250 and 20 000 copies are made.

Hill School also rents a photocopier. The rent is £200 for each quarter in 1996. The cost of each copy is 2.3 p. Find the bill for each quarter when

5 7800 copies are made in the first quarter

6 10 250 copies are made in the second quarter

7 12 500 copies are made in the third quarter

8 19 650 copies are made in the last quarter.

9 How much does Hill School have to pay for photocopying for the whole year?

10 The governors at Hill School decide to buy a photocopier. This costs them £6000. Paper costs £4.15 for 500 sheets. They make 50 000 copies each year.

a How much does the paper cost for one year?

b If the photocopier lasts 5 years, what is the total cost for 5 years of the photocopier and paper?

c How much does this work out for each year?

HOLIDAYS

The cost of a holiday depends on where it is, when it is, how long it is, the type of travel, and so on. Holiday brochures need to be read very carefully to find all the charges for a holiday.

EXERCISE 20D

This is part of a brochure offering self-catering flats in France. The prices given are for one week's rent in £s per flat.

	MAY	JUNE	JULY	AUGUST	SEPTEMBER
FLAT A (sleeps 2)	190	220	220	300	200
FLAT B (sleeps 3)	200	240	240	330	210
FLAT C (sleeps 3) large terrace	220	260	260	370	240
FLAT D (sleeps 4) large terrace	250	300	300	400	270

Find out how much it costs to rent

1 Flat A for two weeks in August

2 Flat B for three weeks in July

3 Flat C for the last week in August and the first week in September

4 Flat A for the last two weeks in July and the first week in August

5 Flat D for the last week in May and the first week in June

6 Flat C for the last week in June and the first two weeks in July.

When a flat is booked, the travel agent asks for a deposit of 10% of the total rent.

Find the deposit to be paid on Flat A booked for two weeks in July.

The rent is $\quad$ 2 x £220 = £440

The deposit is 10% of £440 = £(0.10 x 440)

$$= £44$$

Find the deposit needed for booking

7 Flat C for two weeks in September

8 Flat D for one week in August

9 Flat B for three weeks in May

10 Flat A for the last week in July and the first two weeks in August.

Details from a holiday brochure are given below.

Prices based on	SH WC BL				
Nights	7	10	11	14	All
Adult/Child	Adult	Adult	Adult	Adult	1st Child
01 Apr-04 Apr	295	-	-	455	149
05 Apr-08 Apr	285	-	-	435	149
09 Apr-08 May	269	349	369	425	149
09 May-15 May	299	375	395	445	159
16 May-22 May	339	409	429	479	199
23 May-27 May	405	469	485	529	219
28 May-12 Jun	369	449	465	525	179
13 Jun-19 Jun	379	459	485	545	189
20 Jun-26 Jun	385	465	489	555	209
27 Jun-03 Jul	389	475	499	565	209
04 Jul-10 Jul	395	485	505	575	229
11 Jul-18 Jul	409	499	525	599	269
19 Jul-05 Aug	445	539	559	635	289
06 Aug-12 Aug	439	529	555	629	289
13 Aug-19 Aug	435	525	549	625	289
20 Aug-26 Aug	429	519	545	615	259
27 Aug-02 Sep	425	509	535	599	219
03 Sep-09 Sep	415	499	525	589	219
10 Sep-16 Sep	409	489	509	575	179
17 Sep-23 Sep	399	479	499	565	179
24 Sep-30 Sep	375	455	469	529	169
1 Oct-16 Oct	359	425	439	479	159
17 Oct-28 Oct	399	455	465	495	179

Departures on or between (left axis label)

Supplements per person per night	Sea View £1.00 Bath £1.00 Single Room £7.30

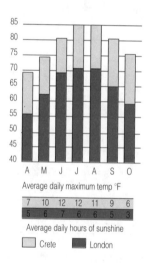

Average daily maximum temp °F

7	10	12	12	11	9	6
5	6	7	6	6	5	3

Average daily hours of sunshine

☐ Crete   ■ London

Birmingham

Flight Code	Airline Aircraft Type	No of Nts	Day/Time of Dept.	Day/Time of Return	Departure	Supplement per person departures on or between					
						31 MAR-30 APR	1 MAY-17 JUN	18 JUN-19 JUL	20 JUL-9 SEP	10 SEP-17 SEP	18 SEP-31 OCT
Crete (Heraklion Airport) - 3³/₄ hrs											
36038	BY†	7/14	MON 08.15	MON 17.20	29 APR-28 OCT	£35	£40	£25	£35	£45	£35

Tom and Enid Sneed, together with their young daughter Hannah, wish to go to Crete for a 14-night holiday leaving Birmingham airport on 16 August. Find

a the total basic brochure price for the three of them

b the total flight supplement for them to fly from Birmingham

c the average daily maximum temperature in Crete that they can expect while they are away.

a

To find the basic brochure price per adult, go down the first column until you find the period that includes their departure date (16 Aug): this is 13 Aug–19 Aug. Then go across until you reach the column headed 14 (Nights). The entry reads 625 which means that the basic price for an adult leaving on 16 August for a 14 night holiday in Crete is £625. The cost for one child appears in the same line but in the next column. It is £289.

Basic holiday cost = 2 × £625 + £289

$$= £1250 + £289$$

$$= £1539$$

b

Since 16 August is during the period 20 Jul–9 Sep we look for the figure below these dates.

The supplement to fly from Birmingham on 16 August is £35 per person.

∴ total flight supplements for all three is 3 × £35 = £105

c

Go to the bar chart and take the readings off the left-hand scale for the bar given for the month of August.

The average daily maximum temperature in Crete during August is 85 °F.

Questions **11** to **19** refer to the data given on page 368.

11 Find the brochure price for one adult to go to Crete for

    a 7 nights, leaving on 28 May

    b 7 nights, leaving on 14 September

    c 11 nights, leaving on 9 July

    d 14 nights, leaving on 1 August.

12 Find the brochure price for 2 adults to go on holiday to Crete if they go for

  a 10 nights, leaving on 18 September

  b 14 nights, leaving on 16 August

  c 7 nights, leaving on 13 July

  d 11 nights, leaving on 27 May.

13 What is the brochure price for a father, mother and 1 child to go to Crete for

  a 11 nights, leaving on 23 August

  b 14 nights, leaving on 15 June?

14 The cost for a second child is £99 more than the cost for the first child. Mr and Mrs Amey plus their two young children go to Crete for a 14-night holiday, leaving on 22 July. Find the total brochure price.

15 a What is the average maximum daily temperature

  i in Crete during the month of June

  ii in London during September

  iii in Crete during July?

  b How much higher is the average daily temperature in Crete than in London during **i** May   **ii** September?

  c During which months is the difference in the average daily temperature in Crete and in London **i** greatest   **ii** least?

16 a What is the average daily number of hours of sunshine

  i in Crete during August   **ii** in London during May?

  b How many more hours of sunshine can be expected in Crete than in London during **i** April   **ii** August?

17 What is the flight supplement per person to fly from Birmingham on

  a 10 June   **b** 20 September   **c** 15 August?

18 A family of three go to Crete for a 14-night holiday leaving on 15 June. How much extra in total must they pay if they want a room with

  a a sea view   **b** a bath instead of a shower?

19 What other expenses, apart from those listed in the questions above, would a family of four be likely to incur if they went to Crete for a 14-night holiday?

ADAPTING RECIPES

This recipe is enough for 4 people.

CRUNCHY CHICKEN

4 chicken legs
50 g salted crisps
25 g butter

Crush the crisps with a rolling pin. Melt the butter. Coat each chicken piece with butter and then roll in the crushed crisps. Place in an oven-proof dish and bake for about 40 minutes at 200 °C.

EXERCISE 20E

For Questions **1** to **3** use the recipe for crunchy chicken.

1 Write out the list of ingredients needed for two people.

2 Write out the list of ingredients needed for six people.

3 Mrs Leal uses this recipe for a party and makes enough for 10 people.

   a How many chicken legs should she buy?

   b Crisps are sold in 50 g bags. How many bags will she need?

   c How long will it take to cook this quantity, assuming that it fits into the oven?

4 The recipe below makes a cake big enough for eight portions.

FRUIT CAKE

100 g margarine	200 g mixed dried fruit
100 g soft-brown sugar	50 g candied cherries
2 eggs	50 g mixed peel
150 g self-raising flour	20 ml milk

Cream the butter and sugar. Beat in the eggs with a little flour. Mix in the rest of the flour and the milk. Stir in the remaining ingredients. Cook in a 20 cm diameter tin in a slow oven for about one hour.

---

   a Write down the list of ingredients needed to make a cake twice as heavy. How many portions will you get from a cake this size?

   b Write down the ingredients needed to make a cake half the weight. How many portions will you get from a cake this size?

   c Mr Arnold uses this recipe to make a cake big enough for 20 portions. Write down the list of the ingredients that he uses.

HOUSEHOLD BILLS

Most households have regular bills to pay for electricity, gas, water and a telephone. Samples of an electricity bill and a telephone bill are given in the next exercise.

EXERCISE 20F

 South Wales
ELECTRICITY
Trydan De Cymru

South Wales Electricity plc
Registered Office: Newport Road,
St. Mellons, Cardiff CF3 9XW.
Registered in Wales No. 2366985
VAT No. 542 6869 16

Account No. Rhif Cyfrif	83272 00128

INVOICE DATE   17 Jul 96

MR A. SAMPLE
35 GREEN STREET
LLANDOGO GWENT

Meter Readings Darlleniadau'r mesurydd				Units Consumed Unedau a losgwyd	Unit Charges Prisiau unedau			£
Previous Blaenorol	S E	Present Presennol	S E		@8.24			
DOMESTIC BASIC TARIFF								
11506′		12546′		1040	1040			85.69
STANDING CHARGE								11.25
ELECTRICITY CHARGES							£96.94	

S = Self Reading - Darlleniad y cwsmer E = Estimated - Amcangyfrif	⬆	ESTIMATED BILLS if there is a big difference between our estimate and what you have actually used please see overleaf.	Value excl. VAT Gwerth heb TAW	VAT TAW %	
Any under or over estimate will adjust itself at the next meter reading Cyweiria'r amcangyfrif el hun y tro nesaf y darlienir y mesurydd	⇨	AMCANGYFRIF Os oes gwahaniaeth mawr rhwung ein hamcangyfrif ni a'r hyn a ddefnyddiwyd mewn gwirionedd, gweler trosodd.	96.94	8	7.76
		For payment of account see overleaf. I dalu'r cyfrif gweler trosodd.			

Value including VAT Gwerth yn cynnwys TAW		104.70
Brought forward Ddygwyd ymlaen		0.00
Total Amount cyfanswm	**DUE**	104.70

Use the quarterly electricity bill given above to answer questions **1** to **6**.

1 What is the price of 1 unit of electricity?

2 What was the meter reading

    a at the beginning of the quarter   **b** at the end of the quarter

3 How many units of electricity were used during the quarter?

4 How much was the 'standing' or fixed charge?

5 a What rate of value added tax was charged?

b How much did the VAT come to?

c How much would be charged for VAT if the rate was increased to **i** $17\frac{1}{2}\%$ **ii** 20%?

6 Rework the above account if the cost of each unit of electricity was raised to **9.03** p and the rate of VAT was raised to 20%.

 BT

Personal Communications	*Your Customer No.* SW 1019 4940 Q035 EU
PP 405B Telephone House	*Date (and tax point)* 22 June 1996
Factory Head	
Sheffield	*Tel* Bill Payment/Queries
Yorks	please ring 0800 125678.
	150 for Sales Enquiries.
MR K. YOUNG	*Fax* 01222 529609
29 KING STREET	*Telex* 444781
SOUTHCROSS	
SMEDLEY	
YORKS	
SF3 2YD	

Phone bill for Burnham (01295) 227369

Your bill is	£	89.53	**Call charges**
		£ 22.038	for direct-dialled calls of less than 10 units
			See Breakdown pages 1–6
		£ 67.497	for direct dialled calls (itemised)
			Details are in the Breakdown
plus	£	28.29	**Advance charges from 1 Jun 96 to 31 Aug 96**
		£ 21.09	for the rental of your line
		£ 3.80	for the rental of your equipment
		£ 3.40	for your Customer Option
	£	117.82	Subtotal excluding VAT
plus	£	20.61	**VAT at 17.5%**
	£	**138.43**	**Total amount now due**

Use the quarterly telephone bill given above to answer questions **7** to **10**.

7 What was the cost of

a the direct-dialled calls of less than 10 units

b the itemised direct-dialled calls?

8 How much was the fixed quarterly charge, which is shown on the bill as 'Advance charges'?

9 a What is the rate of value added tax?

b By how much does the VAT increase the bill?

10 How much is the quarterly rental for

a the telephone line **b** the equipment?

11 Rework the bill given above if the charges for direct-dialled calls of less than 10 units increase to £25.309, the cost of itemised calls increases to £74.072, the rental charge for the line decreases to £20.50 and VAT is increased to 20%. Assume that any other charges remain unchanged.

SAVING

People who have money that they do not wish to spend usually invest it. The most common places where money can be invested are building societies, banks or in National Savings. Each of these usually pays interest which is given as an annual percentage rate.

EXERCISE 20G

1 Susan saves £1.80 a week.
How much will she save in

a 4 weeks **b** 12 weeks **c** a year of 52 weeks?

2 Findlay saves £15 a week in the local building society.

a How much will he save in **i** 20 weeks **ii** 35 weeks?

b How long will it take him to save

i £330 **ii** £450 **iii** at least £100?

3 William wants to save £870 to go on holiday next summer. He calculates that there are 37 weeks before he goes. What is the least whole number of pounds he must save every week to cover the cost of the holiday?
How much more than £870 will he save?

The High Interest Share Account in the Bromley Building Society pays interest of 7.25% a year, payable yearly. If Nora invests £500 in this account and the interest is not withdrawn, find the amount in the account at the end of the first year.

$$7.25\% = \tfrac{7.25}{100} = 0.0725$$

Interest on £500 for 1 year at 7.25% of £500 = 0.0725 × £500

$$= £36.25$$

Amount in the account at the end of 1 year

$$= \text{original sum} + \text{interest}$$
$$= £500 + £36.25$$
$$= £536.25$$

In questions **4** to **8** find the interest earned if

4 £300 is invested for 1 year at 2% p.a.

5 £1000 is invested for 1 year at 4% p.a.

THIS STANDS FOR 'PER ANNUM' AND IT MEANS 'EACH YEAR'.

6 £1500 is invested for 1 year at 10% p.a.

7 £3000 is invested for 1 year at 7% p.a.

8 £5500 is invested for 1 year at 5% p.a.

In questions **9** to **15** find

a the interest earned in 1 year

b the total of the original sum invested and interest earned in 1 year, if

9 £500 is invested at an annual rate of 3%

10 £1000 is invested at an annual rate of 5%

11 £400 is invested at an annual rate of 6%

12 £2000 is invested at an annual rate of 7.5%

13 £3500 is invested at an annual rate of 4.75%

14 £1500 is invested at an annual rate of 5.56%

15 £2800 is invested at an annual rate of 3.48%

TIMETABLES

Here is part of the weekday timetable for trains running between London Euston and Glasgow Central.

Mondays to Fridays

London Euston	—	—	0620	—	0740	—	0840	—	0940	—			
Watford Junction	—	—	0636	—	0741	—	—	—	0924	—			
Milton Keynes Central	—	—	0658	—	0815	—	—	—	1015	—			
Rugby	—	0548	0725	—	0844	—	—	—	—	—			
Coventry	—	0601	0715	—	—	0808	—	0903	—	1015			
Birmingham Intern'l ⊕	—	1619	—	—	—	0824	—	0915	—	1047			
Birmingham ⎰ arrive	—	—	—	—	—	—	0929	—	1100				
New Street ⎱ depart	—	0655	—	—	—	0905	—	9834	—	1105			
Wolverhampton	—	0712	—	—	—	0922	—	0952	—	1121			
Stafford	—	0726	0816	—	—	.0936	—	1008	—	1136			
Crewe	—	0751	0840	—	0942	1001	—	—	1137	1200			
Warrington Bank Quay	—	0810	0859	—	1001	1020	—	—	1156	—			
Manchester Piccadilly (d)	0616	0712	0812	0903	—	0945	1003	1125	—	1145			
Liverpool Lime Street (d)	0542	0732	0812	0850	—	0937	—	1037	—	1137			
Wigan North Western	0637	0823	0911	0928	1013	1031	1037	1113	1208	1229			
Preston	0710	0838	0928	1006	1036	1048	1107	1219	1230	1244			
Blackpool North	—	0916	1013	—	1118	1124	1213	—	1313	1324			
Lancaster	0727	0856	0946	1022	—	1106	1126	1239	—	1304			
Oxenholme: Lakes	0745	0912	1002	1041	—	1122	1143	1256	—	—			
Penrith	0815	—	1028	1106	—	—	—	1322	—	—			
Carlisle	0848	1005	1048	1126	—	1204	1230	1345	—	1358			
Dumfries	—	—	1145	—	—	—	1345	—	—	—			
Motherwell	1019	—	—	—	—	1309	1336	—	—	1505			
Glasgow Central	1039	—	1212	—	—	1330	1358	—	—	1530			

Light printed timings indicate connecting services.

EXERCISE 20H

Use the timetable in the text to answer the following questions.

1 How long does the 0620 from Euston take to get to

   a Crewe   **b** Carlisle   **c** Glasgow?

2 How long does the 0840 from Euston take to travel

   a from Preston to Glasgow   **b** from Lancaster to Carlisle?

3 Sid Gough flies into Birmingham Airport and arrives at Birmingham International railway station by 0749.

   a How long must he wait before he can begin his train journey to Lancaster?

   b Does he have to change trains? If so, where?

   c At what time should he arrive at Lancaster?

   d How long has his journey from Birmingham International railway station taken?

   e How long has he spent in a train?

4 Sheila George leaves Milton Keynes at 0815 to travel to Motherwell. She changes trains at Preston.

   a At what time does she arrive at Preston?

   b How long is the journey from Milton Keynes to Preston?

   c How long did Sheila have to wait at Preston before her connection left for Motherwell?

   d At what time did she arrive at Motherwell?

   e How long did the journey from Milton Keynes to Motherwell take?

MIXED EXERCISE

EXERCISE 20I

1 Use the table of postage charges given on page 364 to find the cost of sending

    a 7 letters weighing 35 g by first class post

    b 4 letters weighing 125 g by second class post

    c a package weighing 840 g by first class letter post.

2 a Use the holiday details given on page 368 to find the basic brochure cost for three adults to go on an 11-night holiday in Crete if they leave on 7 September.

    b Find the flight supplement per person to fly from Birmingham?

    c They decide that they each want a sea view and a room with a bath. How much extra, in total, must they pay?

    d How much higher should the maximum daily temperature be in Crete than in London?

    e They spend 10 days at the resort. How much sunshine, in total, should they have?

3 Use the train timetable on page 376 to find

    a how long the 1047 from Birmingham International Airport waits at Birmingham New Street

    b the time at which this train arrives at Glasgow Central

    c the time this train takes to travel from Stafford to Lancaster

    d the time taken by the fastest train travelling between Wigan and Carlisle

PRACTICAL WORK

Jim and Marion Pane live near you and plan to take their young son to Turkey on holiday next summer. Their son finishes school on 23 July and starts the new term on 1 September and they have decided that they must go during the school holidays. Their total budget for the holiday is £1800 including spending money.

Obtain some brochures from a travel agent and investigate some of the possible holidays they can consider. You have to decide how long they should go for, whether they should stay in an hotel or go self-catering, how much spending money they need, which company they should go with, which airport they should use, and so on.

When you have decided, write a plan and a route for the holiday. (This is called an itinerary.)

SUMMARY 5

ALGEBRAIC
EXPRESSIONS

Terms such as $5n$ mean $5 \times n = n + n + n + n + n$
Similarly ab means $a \times b$.
$2x + 5x$ can be simplified to $7x$.

SOLVING
EQUATIONS

An equation is a relationship between an unknown number, represented
by a letter, and other numbers, e.g. $2x - 3 = 5$
Solving the equation means finding the unknown number.
Provided that we do the same to both sides of an equation, we keep the
equality; this can be used to solve the equation,

e.g.   to solve $2x - 3 = 5,$

first add 3 to both sides: $2x - 3 + 3 = 5 + 3$

this gives $2x = 8$

Now divide each side by 2: $x = 4$

SPECIAL
QUADRILATERALS

In a square

- all four sides are the same length
- both pairs of opposite sides are parallel
- all four angles are right angles.

In a rectangle

- both pairs of opposite sides are the same length
- both pairs of opposite sides are parallel
- all four angles are right angles.

In a rhombus

- all four sides are the same length
- both pairs of opposite sides are parallel
- the opposite angles are equal.

In a parallelogram

- the opposite sides are the same length
- the opposite sides are parallel
- the opposite angles are equal.

In a trapezium

- just one pair of opposite sides are parallel.

COORDINATES

Coordinates give the position of a point as an ordered pair of numbers,

e.g.   (2, 4)

The first number is called the x-coordinate and gives the distance from the y-axis in the direction of the x-axis.

The second number is called the y-coordinate and gives the distance from the x-axis in the direction of the y-axis.

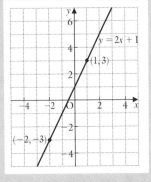

The *equation of a straight line* can be thought of as a formula that gives the y-coordinate of a point on the line in terms of its x-coordinate.

For example, for the line in the diagram, the y-coordinate of any point on the line is twice its x-coordinate plus 1.

The equation of this line is $y = 2x + 1$

PROBABILITY

The probability that an event A happens

$$= \frac{\text{the number of ways in which } A \text{ can occur}}{\text{the total number of equally likely outcomes}}$$

When we perform experiments to find out how often an event occurs, the *relative frequency* of the event is given by

$$\frac{\text{the number of times the event occurs}}{\text{the number of times the experiment is performed}}$$

Relative frequency is used to give an approximate value for probability.

**REVISION
EXERCISE 5.1
(Chapters 16
to 18)**

1 The pie chart shows the choice of juices taken for breakfast by the 60 guests in a hotel one morning.

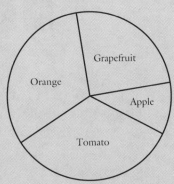

Estimate the sizes of the angles and hence find, approximately, the number who preferred

a orange juice   **b** tomato juice   **c** apple juice.

2 This pie chart shows how some chocolates are shared among three sisters.

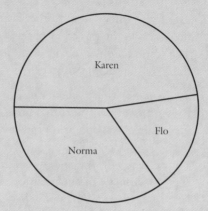

Estimate the percentage of the chocolates that

a Karen receives

b Norma gets

c Flo is given.

3

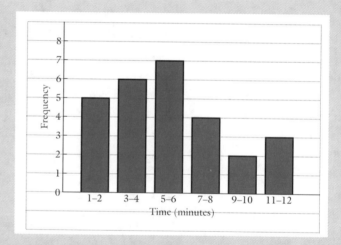

Some pupils were asked to time to the nearest half-minute, how long they spent in the bathroom one morning. The bar chart shows the results.

a How many pupils are there ?

b Where does the first group start and where does it end ?

c Make a frequency table showing this information.

d What is the range of the times shown here ?

e What is the modal group ?

4 Solve the equations

   a $a + 5 = 12$ **c** $4.5 + x = 10$

   b $b - 5 = 12$ **d** $y - 2.5 = 6$

5 Solve the equations

   a $4z = 24$ **c** $5x - 3 = 12$

   b $3x + 4 = 19$ **d** $6x - 1 = 3.2$

6 Simplify

   a $5x - 3x - 8x$ **c** $6a - 3b - 3a + 2b$

   b $5 - x - 8 - 3x$ **d** $3x - 5y - 6x + 2y$

7 Solve the equations

   a $7x - 4x = x + 8$ **c** $8x - 5 - 3x - 15 = 0$

   b $6x + 11 = 3x + 2$ **d** $6 + x = 18 - 5x$

8 What is the probability of choosing

   a a prime number from the numbers 14, 15, 16, 17, 18

   b a multiple of 3 from the numbers 20, 21, 22, 23, 24, 25

   c a square number from the numbers 4, 9, 16, 49, 121?

   d a rectangular number from the numbers 10, 11, 12, 13, 14, 15?

9 One letter is chosen at random from the word APPLAUSE. What is the probability that it is

   a the letter P

   b the letter S

   c a vowel

   d one of the first five letters of the alphabet?

10 Paul bought three strips of tickets for the club's Christmas Raffle. Each strip contains 5 tickets. In all 125 strips were sold. What probability does Paul have of winn ng the first prize?

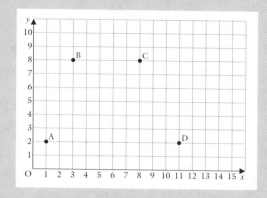

Copy this diagram and use it to answer questions **1** to **3**.

1 Write down the coordinates of **a** A   **b** D

2 a Join the points ABCDA in order. What name do you give to this shape ?

b Mark the point E so that ABED is a parallelogram. Write down the coordinates of E.

3 Write down the coordinates of M, the middle point of AD. Join M and C. How is CM related to ED ?

Questions **4** and **5** refer to the diagram below.

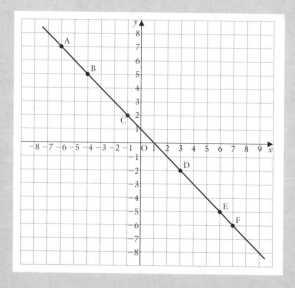

4 The points A, B, C, D, E and F are all on the same straight line. Write down the coordinates of each point.

5 G, H, I, J, K and L are further points on the line. Find the missing coordinates.

G(-2,), H(5,), I(,6), J(,-1), K(-5,), L(,-7)

6 Harry saves £12.50 a week in the Hillsborough Building Society.

a How much will he save in 20 weeks?

b How long will it take him to save £300?

An extract from a brochure detailing holidays in the Los Arcos apartments, Gran Canaria, is given below. Use this extract to answer questions **7** and **8**.

Name & Board	LOS ARCOS APTS				
	Self Catering				
Flights	All Gran Canaria Flights				
Code	TQS				
Prices based on	2 Bed Apt up to 5 persons				
Nights	7	10	11	14	All
Adult/Child	Adult	Adult	Adult	Adult	Child
02 May-08 May	195	205	225	235	59
09 May-15 May	209	219	239	255	59
16 May-22 May	239	255	275	295	99
23 May-27 May	279	285	305	309	129
28 May-12 Jun	249	259	285	299	109
13 Jun-19 Jun	255	269	295	309	119
20 Jun-26 Jun	269	289	329	339	129
27 Jun-03 Jul	279	299	339	349	129
04 Jul-10 Jul	305	325	355	375	149
11 Jul-18 Jul	325	349	389	419	159
19 Jul-05 Aug	355	385	425	459	179
06 Aug-12 Aug	349	375	415	449	179
13 Aug-19 Aug	339	369	409	439	179
20 Aug-26 Aug	315	335	369	395	149
27 Aug-02 Sep	309	325	359	379	139
03 Sep-09 Sep	299	315	349	369	139
10 Sep-16 Sep	279	299	325	345	119
17 Sep-23 Sep	275	295	319	335	119

Departures on or between

7 What is the brochure price for Paul Drake to go to the Los Arcos apartments for

a a 7-night holiday if he leaves on 27 June

b a 14-night holiday if he leaves on 19 August?

8 Mr and Mrs Peters who have three children, aged 7, 9 and 11, wish to book a 14-night holiday at the Los Arcos apartments.

a What is the brochure price if they leave on 16 June?

b How much more would it cost them if they went on 8 August instead of on 16 June?

Use the following extract from a train timetable to answer questions **9** and **10**.

Saturdays

Sheffield	—	—	0622	—	0740	0750	0838	—	0954	—
Chesterfield	—	—	0635	—	0753	0803	0851	—	1007	—
Derby	0505	—	0659	—	0817	—	0915	—	1031	—
Alfreton	—	—	—	—	—	0815	—	—	—	1003
Nottingham	—	0558	0617	0729	—	0846	—	0947	—	1124
Loughborough	—	0612	0716	0746	0813	0903	—	1001	1048	1101
Leicester	0530	0630	0730	0800	0845	0915	0945	1015	1100	1145
Market Harborough	—	0645	—	0814	—	0931	—	1031	—	1201
Kettering for Corby	0553	0656	0752	0824	0907	0943	—	1041	1124	1212
Wellingborough	0600	0704	0759	0832	0914	—	1011	1049	1132	1219
Bedford	0615	—	—	0846	—	—	1025	—	—	1234
Luton ♦→	0632	0730	—	0904	—	1013	1102	1115	1158	1317
London St Pancras	0659	0757	0848	0931	1003	1040	1105	1142	1225	1314

Saturdays

Sheffield	1124	—	1254	—	1424	—	1554	—	1724	—
Chesterfield	1137	—	1307	—	1437	—	1607	—	1737	—
Derby	1201	—	1331	—	1502	—	1631	—	1801	—
Alfreton	—	1203	—	1312	1404	1504	—	1603	—	1812
Nottingham	—	1254	—	1424	1453	1552	—	1724	—	1903
Loughborough	1218	—	1348	—	1518	—	1648	1704	1818	1917
Leicester	1230	1315	1400	1445	1530	1615	1700	1745	1830	1930
Market Harborough	—	1332	—	1459	—	1631	—	1801	—	1945
Kettering for Corby	1254	1343	1424	1511	1555	1642	1723	1812	1855	1956
Wellingborough	—	1352	—	1519	—	1649	1732	1820	—	2004
Bedford	1313	—	—	1534	1614	—	—	1835	—	2018
Luton ♦→	1347	1418	1454	1617	1647	1715	1758	1917	1927	2036
London St Pancras	1353	1445	1521	1614	1654	1742	1825	1915	1954	2103

9 How long does the 1254 from Sheffield take to get to London, St Pancras?

10 Terry gets to the railway station at Nottingham at 0832.

a How long does he have to wait to get a train to Luton?

b At what time is he due to arrive at Luton?

REVISION EXERCISE 5.3 (Chapters 16 to 20)

1 A Year 8 pupil spent 2 hours one evening revising for the end-of-term examinations. The pie chart shows how she divided up her time.

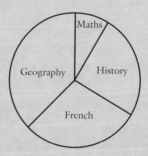

Which of the following statements are obviously not true?

a She spent more than half the time revising geography.

b She spent half an hour revising history.

c She spent twice as much time revising French as revising maths.

2

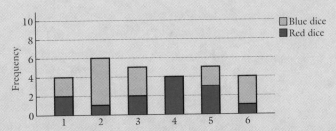

This stacked bar chart shows the scores when two dice were rolled, one red and one blue.

a How many times was the red dice rolled?

b How many times was the blue dice rolled?

c How many sixes were scored?

3 Solve the equations

  a $p + 7 = 10$ **b** $q - 7 = 8$ **c** $2x + 6 = 5x - 15$

4 Simplify

  a $5x - 4 + 6x - 1$ **b** $3a + 5b - 2a + 4b$

5 A card is chosen at random from an ordinary pack of 52 playing cards. How many different ways are there of choosing

  a a black card   **b** a heart   **c** an ace?

6 A bag contains 3 yellow discs and 7 black discs. Nia selects a disc at random from the bag.
What is the probability that the colour of the disc is

  a black   **b** blue   **c** black or yellow?

7 The equation of a straight line is $y = 5x$.

  a Find the y-coordinate of the point on the line that has an x-coordinate of

    i 3   **ii** -5

  b Find the x-coordinate of the point on the line that has a y-coordinate of

    i 25   **ii** -20

  c Does the point $(4, -20)$ lie on the line? Justify your answer.

8 The table shows the conversion from French francs to pounds sterling for various amounts of money.

French francs (Ff)	100	200	300
Pounds sterling (£)	12	24	36

Plot these points on a graph and draw a straight line to pass through them. Let 2 cm represent Ff 50 on the horizontal axis and £5 on the vertical axis.

Use your graph to convert

i £28 into francs   **iii** Ff 116 into pounds

ii Ff 260 into pounds   **iv** £16 into francs

9 Use the extract from a holiday brochure which is given on page 383 to answer this question.

What is the brochure price for a father, mother and one child to go to the Los Arcos apartments for 11 days if they fly out on 10 July?

10 A recipe to make 40 raisin cakes includes the following ingredients.

2 oz margarine, 6 oz sugar, 1 egg, 6 oz plain flour, $\frac{1}{4}$ teaspoon nutmeg.

Harriett wants to make 120 raisin cakes.

a How much sugar does she need?

b How many eggs will she use?

c How much margarine should she weigh out?

d Why would there be a problem if she wanted to make 100 cakes?

REVISION EXERCISE 5.4 (Chapters 1 to 20)

1 a Find, without using a calculator

     i 45×63 **iii** 243×505

     ii $14460 \div 60$ **iv** $36 \div 9 - 2 + 15 \times 7 \div 3$

 b What is the remainder when 659 is divided by 56?

2 a Write $2 \times 3 \times 2 \times 3 \times 3 \times 2$ in index form.

 b Find the value of

     i 2^5 **ii** 6^3 **iii** eight squared   **iv** $2^2 \times 5^3$

 c Find the smallest whole number that 12, 16 and 56 will divide into exactly.

 d Share 228 p equally among four brothers.

3 Find, simplifying where you can

a $\frac{2}{5} + \frac{3}{8}$ **b** $\frac{7}{10} + \frac{7}{100}$ **c** $3\frac{11}{12} + 4\frac{1}{3}$ **d** $5\frac{2}{3} - 3\frac{11}{15}$

4 a Copy the drawing onto squared paper and complete it so that the broken line is the axis of symmetry.

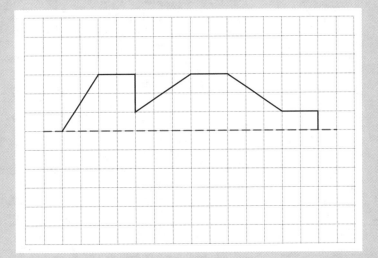

Copy the following drawings onto squared paper and complete them so that the broken lines are axes of symmetry.

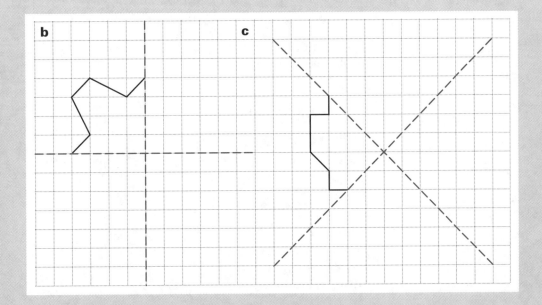

5 a Find

   i $\frac{3}{4} \times \frac{8}{9}$ **iii** $\frac{5}{7}$ of 63 cm

   ii $\frac{2}{5}$ of 45 km   **iv** $\frac{3}{8}$ of 88 litres

b Which is the larger and by how much: $\frac{8}{9}$ of $\frac{9}{16}$ or $\frac{7}{12} + \frac{3}{4}$?

6 a In the eighth year of Thornley School 52% of the 250 pupils study French.
How many pupils **i** study French   **ii** do not study French?

b Express $\frac{29}{25}$ as   **i** a decimal   **ii** a percentage.

c Find   **i** $\frac{4}{7}$ of £164.29   **iii** 40 p as a fraction of £1.20

         ii $9\frac{3}{4}$% of 2340 g   **iv** $\frac{3}{5}$ of 1 hour in minutes.

7 a State whether each of the following inequalities is true or false.

   i $-4 > -6$ **ii** $6 < -3$ **iii** $-8 > 4$ **iv** $-5 < -3$

b Copy each statement and fill in the missing numbers

   i $-8 + 4 - 7 - \square = -16$ **ii** $-6 - 8 - 3 + \square = 4$

8 The ages (in years) of 20 children attending a swimming class are

$$9,\ 9,\ 10,\ 10,\ 10,\ 10,\ 10,\ 10,\ 10,\ 11,$$
$$11,\ 11,\ 11,\ 11,\ 11,\ 11,\ 11,\ 11,\ 12,\ 12$$

The ages (in years) of a different group of 20 children in a trampoline class are

$$6,\ 7,\ 7,\ 8,\ 8,\ 8,\ 9,\ 9,\ 9,\ 9,\ 9,$$
$$10,\ 10,\ 11,\ 11,\ 11,\ 12,\ 13,\ 13,\ 14$$

a Find the mean and the range of the ages of each group.

b Use your answers to part **a** to compare the ages of the two groups.

9 a Simplify **i** $4x - 5x - 2x$ **ii** $5x - 6y + 2x - 4y$

b I think of a number, multiply it by 6 and subtract 4.
The answer is 44.
What is the number?

10

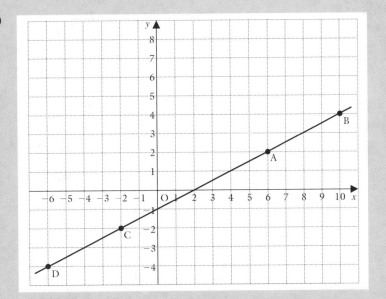

The points A, B, C and D are all on the same straight line.

a Write down the coordinates of these four points.

b F is another point on this line. The x-coordinate of F is 4. Write down the y-coordinate of F.

c G is another point on this line. The y-coordinate of G is −1. What is the x-coordinate of G?

REVISION EXERCISE 5.5
(Chapters 1 to 20)

1 Find the size of each marked angle.

a

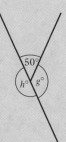

c

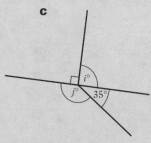

b

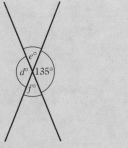

d

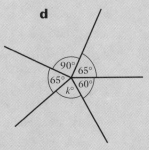

2 Find, without using a calculator

   a 5.62×100 **c** $14.6 \div 1000$ **e** $63 \div 0.09$

   b $0.34 \div 100$ **d** 0.09×0.6 **f** 0.4×0.037

3 Use a calculator to find, correct to 2 decimal places

   a $6.49 \div 8.26$ **c** $0.84^2 \div 0.67$

   b 5.07^3 **d** $43.66 \times (13.32 - 11.42)$

4 Construct a triangle XYZ in which $XY = 10.5$ cm, $X = 65°$ and $Y = 60°$. Measure XZ.

5 a If each side of an equilateral triangle is l units in length, find a formula for the perimeter, P units, of the triangle.

   b The formula for changing $x°C$ to $y°F$ is $y = \dfrac{9x}{5} + 32$.

      Find the temperature in $°F$ when a thermometer reads $20°C$.

6 a Express the given quantity in the unit in brackets.

    i 490 m (km)   **iii** 1420 mm (m)

    ii 3400 kg (t)   **iv** 750 ml (litres)

   b Write the first unit very roughly in terms of the unit in brackets.

    i 2.5 kg (lb)   **iii** 20 oz (g)

    ii 50 km (miles)   **iv** 13 ft (m)

7 A rectangular box measures 8.88 cm by 7.23 cm by 5.76 cm.
Estimate the capacity of the box. Use a calculator to find the capacity
of the box correct to 2 decimal places. How near is your estimate ?

8 Find the value of x.

   a   **b**   **c**

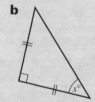
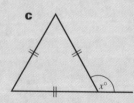

9 Sim is p years old now and his sister Kate is 4 years older. In
10 years time the sum of their ages will be 36. How old is Sim
now? How old will Kate be in 10 years time ?

10 The Bradshot Building Society pays interest of 5.65% a year, payable
yearly. Sim invests £300 in this account and the interest is not
withdrawn. Find the amount in the account after 1 year.

INDEX